THE HILARIOUS STORY OF YACHT
CHARTERING AND RUNNING A RESTAURANT IN THE
CARIBBEAN

By
JAMES DALBY

(A GREAT BOOK TO TAKE ON HOLIDAY)

Signed by

JAMES DALBY
For: Susie ~ Gabriel.

SAILING ON SILVER
AND BEYOND
ISBN 978-1-9163372-3-7

By James Dalby

This is based on a true story.

The story is based on sailing and subsequently the running of a large sailing charter yacht and a restaurant in the Caribbean during the early 1980's.

To save embarrassment most individual names have been disguised as have the yacht charter companies. There never has been a Sunshine Yacht Charter Company or a Marine Charter Company. The yachts mentioned are described correctly, but their names have been altered. Names of the islands, the bays as well as the hotels and restaurants are correct; the incidents are based on fact.

The book includes some interesting stories regarding famous figures such as MICHAEL CAINE and BILLY CONNOLLY and their wives who ate at our restaurant. See the Chapter 'THE U BOAT AFFAIR'. The two actors were filming WATER in the south of the island of Saint Lucia. Other stories figure KOO STARK and THE DUKE OF YORK who were in Mustique and CHRISTINE KEELER and the Minster of War JOHN PROFUMO both true stories told to us by a close friend, John Golds MBE. In an earlier print I protected his name, but sadly John died in 2020, so I have now used his real name.

This is the story of my lifetime partner Liz and me during the early 1980's. We both decided to sell our shares in a large public company that I had headed for several years, thus quitting the 'rat race' to change our previous very busy and stressful life.

Liz was a senior buyer, and keen to have a change and a new challenge. My idea was to write a best-selling financial novel and make a living as an author. To do this we took a sabbatical to the West Indies and chartered a yacht to get away from the world, relax and create an environment conducive to creativity. It didn't quite work the way we planned, and we initially struggled with learning to sail a yacht, something neither of us had done before. The first craft we sailed was not designed for Caribbean waters and we had to deal with various unforeseen challenges, one life threatening.

Some amusing chapters highlight the changes experienced, from us being high-flying executives to dealing with a Caribbean lifestyle. Subsequently we fell into the charter business rather by mistake. We found ourselves sailing a large luxury yacht around the Leeward and the Windward Islands pandering to wealthy and sometimes unreasonable charter guests. As a skipper and host we experienced what it was like to deal with the rich set, a group that we'd recently been part of, and often having to deal with bizarre situations. Then we met Laurie.

The yacht we sailed during the first year of chartering was called Silver Star a 63-foot Nautilus ketch. This book only deals with the first year out of 2 years chartering in the Caribbean.

After chartering on a luxury yacht for two years, Liz decided to buy a restaurant in the West Indies to acquire an easier lifestyle.

It did not quite work out as planned either. From an alcoholic chef who loved women, any woman, to the vagaries of provisioning in an area that constantly ran out of staple foods, such as potatoes, onions and fish, Liz had her hands full.

Dealing with storms that sometimes left the restaurant without water or electricity for days on end, was another factor that tried the sanity of the new owners.

COMPLETE WITH MAPS & DRAWINGS

***

To my first mate and cook

and my life time partner

Elizabeth

Learn more about James Dalby

http://www.goodnessmepublishing.co.uk

Books written by JAMES DALBY

The Crowley Affair – Romantic/Historical
The Morning Mists - Historical
I Am Who I Am - Psychological

*** The Gorazde Incident – The Bosnian Conflict
Espionage & Political Thriller
*** The Shanghai Incident – Espionage & Political
Thriller
*** Moscow Assassination – Espionage Thriller ***
*** The Castrators – Political/Military Thriller
*** The Scottish Prerogative –Political thriller

Don't Stop the Eating - Based on a true story
A Shitty Day in Paradise Based on a true story

Sailing on Silver Based on a true story.
This book is a compilation of A Shitty Day in Paradise
and Don't Stop the Eating

Short Stories

***Behind the News Series

TABLE OF CONTENTS

4

SAILING ON SILVER

AND BEYOND

1 - THE BEGINNING

"Don't cry because it's over
smile because it happened."
— Dr. Seuss

It all began one Friday several months back when I'd had a terrible day at the office and was late for my train back from London. I hadn't time to get a newspaper before just managing to catch the 19:10 from Paddington, so I had an hour and a half to do some thinking.

"I need to change my life, the last ten years have been great, but I've had enough," I said as my wife drove me home from the train station.

Liz looked at me with some surprise, "I guess you're tired, that's all, you'll feel better after the weekend," she said patting my leg with one hand and swerving the car due to her sudden lack of concentration. I didn't reply, and we drove home in silence, both with our separate thoughts.

It was two days later when we sat down and talked about our future. After ten years at the head of a large public company, I suggested that I leave my highly stressed job and take a long break to assess what we should do with the remainder of our lives. Liz who was a senior buyer for a small supermarket chain indicated that she wouldn't mind a change either but was concerned because at the age of forty neither of us was able to throw in the towel financially. We were still educating three of our children at expensive public schools.

"Well let's look at our position," I said. "I've now organised a merger with a much larger company and the present chief executive of that company is nearing retiring age. This means that within a few months I'd almost certainly take over his job. The problem is I no longer enjoy the commercial environment." I paused, "we own about two percent of the present company and at this stage we could sell our shares if I resigned without affecting the deal. If I stay involved in the merger, our cash will be tied up for some years and will trap us; now is our chance to break away."

Liz nodded, "well, I must say it would be nice to see you occasionally, you've been so busy that the children hardly know you." Liz was referring to our three children aged 12, 16 and 19. "But what would you do? You're not the sort of person that would be able to sit at home watching television," and she added, "as a lot of my work is done at home, the last thing I need is you prowling around the house like a 'bear with a sore head.'"

I grinned, "you're right of course, but the thing I have in mind is to write a novel based on my experience with the financial vagaries of the city of London, a sort of financial drama. I've always wanted to write, and this could be my opportunity."

Liz looked doubtful, "the problem with the publishing industry is that they tend to look for well-known personalities, whatever trash they write, but because the authors are well known, their books sell. Very few publishers nowadays will take a chance on an unknown author." Liz continued, "I don't doubt your ability or your capacity for imaginative stories but getting a first book published is rather like winning the pools." She smiled.

"You always were the practical one," I smiled back at her, "but if we don't try, we'll never know, will we?"

"Hmmm, well I do know that if you've a 'bee in your bonnet' you'll persevere, and if this is what you want, then I'll support you, at least I can edit the book, and correct your atrocious spelling," she said as an afterthought.

A flurry of decisions and actions that untied us both from our entrenched lives was necessary but before committing ourselves irrevocably, we decided to take a long holiday to free our minds and plan our future.

Some years before we'd lived and worked in Jamaica but had seen little of the lower Caribbean, so we decided on an island called Saint Lucia in the Windward Islands where we'd recently spent a week's vacation. I didn't particularly want to stay on one island, but to use the opportunity to see some of the lower Caribbean, particularly the Grenadines that we'd both heard so much about.

"Why don't we charter a sailing boat, and then we can sail around all the islands?"

Liz, thinking of a restful two-month sunning on the beach, wasn't happy with the idea. She looked at me quizzically as she'd never really enjoyed being on a boat unless it stayed in the harbour. "Are you sure that they'll let you charter a sailing yacht, if you've never sailed before?" she asked, secretly hoping to put me off the idea.

I thought about her comment and nodded, "you're probably right, I can't see anyone letting us take out a boat worth some fifty thousand pounds or so without some form of proven nautical experience, but I guess we may be able to bluff our way through. We've not had high flying careers without some experience of getting what we wanted." I paused, "I know, we'll tell the charter company that we're experienced sailors, and have regularly sailed between the United Kingdom and Jersey," I said truthfully, "they may not question what sort of boat we sailed."

Earlier in our careers when our children were younger and we'd more leisure time, we'd owned a 32-foot motor cruiser, and we used to sail it from the south of England to the Channel Islands.

Liz frowned. "But we've never actually sailed a sailing boat, and we don't know that part of the Caribbean, and I for one am not happy about drowning in the Caribbean Sea, even though the water may be warm," Her lips compressed.

"I tell you what," I said, in a conciliatory manner, "I'll telephone Saint Lucia and speak to a yacht charter company, and see if they do some sort of preliminary sailing course, how's that?"

Liz shrugged, and the subject was left until the next morning when I phoned what I understood to be the principal yacht charter company based on the island.

"John Peachcombe of Sunshine Yacht Charters here, can I help you?"

I was surprised to hear a West Country accent at the end of the line.

"Good morning, John," I answered. "My name is James Dalby; my wife and I are looking to charter a yacht for a couple of months to sail around the islands."

"Have you sailed before?" He asked.

"Oh, yes, we used to own a boat and...,"

John Peachcombe interrupted. "What sort of boat?"

"Er, it was a 32-footer."

There was a pause at the end of the line. "Was it a sail boat or a motor boat?"

"A motor launch," I replied, "but we used to sail it to the Channel Islands, and" I added hastily, "I also fly a helicopter, so my radio and navigation techniques are good."

"Have you ever sailed in these waters before?" John Peachcombe asked,

"Well, we did have a small boat in Jamaica, when I worked there..."

My voice trailed off, "Also a motor boat?" John Peachcombe queried.

"Yes, but..." John interrupted me again.

"I'm afraid that unless you've a professional certificate for sailing or can produce some evidence of sailing a large sailing yacht, our insurance company wouldn't accept the liability." It was obvious that John Peachcombe was quite firm on the matter.

I tried my last throw of the dice.

"Do you do short courses for sailing?" I asked.

"No," was the reply, "although in the past we've thought of setting up a flotilla system where several boats go out with an experienced leader, everyone being in a different boat, but we haven't yet got around to organising that type of service." There was another pause on the line.

"I tell you what Mr Dalby, you might like to try your luck with Marine Charters, I'll give you their number and I know they work the flotilla system from time to time. Their boats are much smaller, and you may find a small yacht would be easier for you to start with," he continued. "If you spend a month sailing one of their 35 footer's, and providing you're still alive after that experience, and the boat is still in one piece when you've finished with it, we could then consider you taking out one of our 44's."

I thanked him, asking if I was successful with Marine Charters, could I provisionally book a boat from Sunshine for one month's hence. He agreed, and having got his assent, I finished the call.

I telephoned Marine Charters with a slightly sinking feeling in my stomach. This time a smooth English accent answered the phone, "Commander Fisher here."

I enquired if he'd any yachts to charter. "All O'Day 35 footers my dear boy, all brand new, beautiful boats that's why they're available at the height of the season," he added quickly. "Have you sailed here before?" Commander Fisher asked enquiringly. "Negative," I answered, "but we've done quite a lot of sailing in the UK."

"Splendid dear boy, when would you like to come?" My heart pounded.

"Er, do you've anything within the next week?" I asked. There was a brief silence at the end of the line.

"Hmmm, well, that may be difficult," Fisher's voice trailed off, "How long do you want a boat for?"

"A month," I answered.

I felt that there was a sudden increase in interest in the Commander's voice.

"Hmmm, well, I suppose we could just squeeze you in, let me see now."

My ears reverberated as the phone clattered onto some hard object at the other end, and I heard what appeared to be a flipping of papers in the background. Several minutes later, he returned. "Just managed to reorganise things, and you can have a boat from the 15th November, dear boy." I looked at my watch that would give us eight days to pack and fly out there.

I realised that I hadn't asked the price and it was with some trepidation I then did so. "For four weeks the cost is £1,000, plus a cash deposit on arrival of £400." I could hear his heavy breathing down the line and for some reason I felt a twinge of unease but put it down to the fact that I was neither familiar with the boat in question or Marine Charters. It did seem however to be a reasonable price for the high season.

Fisher was speaking again. "Of course, that's for a bare-boat," he explained, "if you need a Captain that'll be extra."

"No thank you Commander we don't require a Captain or crew," I shot back quickly. "I'm also a helicopter pilot, so I'm conversant with navigation and radio." I hoped that explanation would give Fisher some comfort.

There was a pause at the end of the line. "Well, dear boy, if you haven't sailed in this part of the world before, it can be very dangerous, reefs, sunken rocks, don't you know."

I made it very clear that if having a crew member was mandatory, the deal was off. Fisher, realising that he might lose a sale, quickly climbed down.

"Noo problem," he slipped into the Caribbean vernacular. "Noo problem, my dear boy, the boat is yours from 15th. Do you want us to provision it for you?" Fisher explained that, if we were sailing 'down' island, it would be better if Marine Charters bought basic supplies for us at a local store.

I agreed, but forgot to ask the cost of this service, something I was to regret later.

After receiving the bank details of Marine Charters, I ended the call and phoned our bank to arrange for a money transfer. The next day I telephoned Sunshine Yacht Charters again and booked a larger yacht for one month from the 15th of December.

Because of the high season rates the charter was much more expensive, costing more than double that of Marine Charters, but so confident was I that I'd have publishers vying to purchase my novel that we would easily recover the cost. I

11

should have remembered the adage 'fools and their money are soon parted'.

Two of our children, Jessica 16 and Robert 12 were at boarding school and Liz telephoned them with news of our plans. When she told them that we'd be flying them out for Christmas, they were both excited.

She then telephoned our elder daughter, Anne, who phoned back after an hour, and said she'd like to come too. Anne was nineteen, an exceptionally pretty girl, but because of dyslexia, a problem that not identified until nearly the end of her school life, she'd experienced a rather inglorious academic career. This, no doubt, accounted for her sometimes-poor attitude and moodiness. Leaving school prematurely, she'd worked at several jobs, but not enjoyed any of them.

"There's nothing for me here in the UK," she said.

It took a quick call to the travel agent to arrange the tickets, and on the 14th November, we drove up to Heathrow Airport, put our car in the long-term car park, and caught a pre-booked flight to St. Lucia.

The flight took eight hours, with a stop in Barbados on the way, finally arriving at 7 p.m. at Hewannora Airport, at the south end of the island. People have often asked why St. Lucia has its International Airport at the southern end when the capital Castries and almost all the hotels are in the north. The fact is that the Americans built a large air base there during the Second World War. True to their generous nature, they handed it over intact to the St. Lucian government after hostilities ceased.

The British turned it into an International airport and when independence came to St. Lucia in 1978, it became part of the acquired assets.

It was already dark when we landed, but the night was close and hot. It seemed to take an eternity to get through immigration and customs but by 8 p.m., we were standing outside the airport. It took only seconds before a taxi driver accosted us. . .

"Taxi to Castries?" I nodded.

The taxi driver grabbed the luggage and we battled through the throng of sweaty bodies that always seem to congregate in a mass around tropical airports. If we were expecting a luxurious air-conditioned limousine, we were to be disappointed. The car was an old Austin A55, at least the part that was recognisable. It was obvious that some creativity had gone into securing the rust-sodden body, and the welded repairs were very much apparent even in the moonlight.

"Ma name is Sully," the taxi driver grinned, "welcome to St. Lucia man."

"Thank you, Sully," I answered tiredly. I knew 'man' was a generic West Indian term for people of any gender over about the age of twelve.

Sully threw the bags into the trunk, and for a split second, I thought they'd go straight through. I then noticed a plywood board straddling the trunk area, but the rudimentary repair held our luggage in place. I took the front passenger seat. Liz and Anne went in the rear.

Sully switched on the radio, and the West Indian music battered our ears. I asked him to turn down the volume a little.

Sully grinned, reduced the sound ever so slightly, and turned the ignition key.

A low moaning sound suggested the battery had seen better days. After Sully had tried several times, to my surprise, the engine eventually spluttered to life.

Sully wound down his window, and a breath of welcome breeze floated through, cooling our extremely sweaty bodies. This was the air-conditioning.

The road between Hewannora and Castries winds its way from the south, through the rain forest, over the hills in the centre of the island, and then drops down to the capital Castries, which is on the north-west.

The total distance is only about 38 miles but after approximately two hours of driving, visitors are aware they've arrived in the Third World.

There are some West Indian drivers, who like the lemming appear bent on suicide. No doubt, ganja (*marijuana*) is part of the cause, but this suicidal driving is not due to drugs alone. The technique though, is simple. The driver gets behind the wheel of a vehicle, any vehicle, points the wheels in roughly the direction he wants to go, presses the accelerator flat to the floor and keeps it there. The steering wheel is useful for trying to avoid potholes a foot deep, which are numerous, and pedestrians, usually women carrying heavy loads, plus vehicles coming from the opposite direction and driven in a like manner.

The gear lever is only used out of sheer necessity, for instance, when the engine is about to stall. Corners, they treat with contempt. The driver's right foot is transferred to the brake pedal at the last moment, and like force applied. Because the engine is in the front, and the front of the car is therefore heavier, the unevenness of the road surface ensures that the rear wheels of the car frequently leave the road during braking. At the precise second of lift-off, the driver spins the wheel, and, by some magical method and confounding all the laws of physics, the vehicle somehow points in the new direction. To finish this marvel of dexterity, it needs some wild adjustments to persuade the vehicle to remain on its new course. This no doubt is the principal reason why the hotel trade at the north end of the island, offer a strong welcoming drink to all guests who have newly arrived.

After ten miles, we urged Sully to stop and let Anne out to be violently sick by the roadside. From this experience, we learned how to persuade him to drive in relative safety by pointing out that at the slightest hint of excess speed, we'd all throw up all over the inside of his taxi. Despite the death-defying driving, Sully was immensely proud of his wreck even in its dilapidated condition. The thought of it becoming unusable for a period due to European puke had a most sobering effect on him.

We eventually arrived at Vigie Marina very tired and with one very cross and debilitated daughter. Because of the frequent stops on the way, the total trip had taken about two and a half hours.

Sully, eager to rid himself of the rather sickly, smelly, European girl, quickly took his money and left to return to the airport for more unsuspecting travellers.

Vigie Marina is very small and forms a narrow waterway cul-de-sac. The quay is cut away from an inlet that runs into the main entrance to Castries harbour itself. As we walked through an archway under the marina buildings and out onto the dock, we saw lights on the other side only about 100 feet away. All the boats were tied bow to the wooden walkway on our side of the dock, the first six all being 35 footers. I looked at the one nearest to us and saw the O'Day insignia on the top of the bow, just above was the name Shady Lady. I was surprised to see so many craft. Apart from the O'Day's there were several other boats, large and small.

Obviously, Marine Charters weren't quite as busy as had been indicated.

The arrangement with Commander Fisher was that we could sleep on the boat overnight before officially taking it over the following morning, but the problem was, I didn't know the name of the boat allocated to us. I noticed padlocks glinting in the moonlight on all the cabin doors, but the man who was supposed to meet us was nowhere in sight. Liz and Anne suggested we look for a hotel, but as it was now approaching 11 p.m., the thought of trying to get another taxi wasn't an attractive one. Anne grumbled sulkily while we sat dismally on our bags. Half an hour went by and, to stretch my legs, I took a walk along the dock looking at the various boats moored there. I was faintly aware of it getting even darker and could feel an increase in humidity.

The breeze had dropped, but I didn't realise the significance of what was to happen next. It was just as if someone above us had turned on a tap. There was no warning, no slight spitting of rain; water simply fell out of the sky in a deluge. It took us less than thirty seconds to get ourselves and our luggage under the archway we'd originally come through, but by then we were all soaked, as were our bags. We'd encountered our first Windward Island squall.

"I want to go home," said Liz, miserably.

"Ditto," said Anne. "Daddy, didn't you arrange for someone to meet us?" she asked reproachfully.

She knew I had of course, but I assumed that because we were late, whoever had been waiting had given up and gone home. The rain stopped just as suddenly as it had started, and a stiff breeze began to blow. We now shivered in our wet clothes.

It was past midnight when I decided to give up and go to look for a taxi with the idea of finding a hotel. As I stood up, I noticed a light in one of the O'Day boats moored to the quay. There was some movement on board, so I walked from under the archway towards the light. A stocky, rather swarthy man climbed out of the cabin and walked unsteadily towards the bow of the boat.

"Hi," he called, cheerily, "you Dalby?" "Yes" I called back. "Do you know where we're sleeping tonight?" "Yea, man," his accent was thick Caribbean, "you're on Shady Lady," he pointed at the boat in front of him. "Ah waited for you man, an' then when you didn't come, ah fell asleep." He jumped on to the wooden sidewalk, and I could plainly smell rum on his breath. The man grinned, his white teeth glowing in the dark. It gave the impression of speaking to a set of teeth suspended in the ether. "You'se all wet, man" he observed rather unnecessarily.

He must have good night vision, I thought, still peering into the darkness, blinded by the flashlight he was now shining at me.

Anne swore and suggested in a way not designed to encourage Anglo-Caribbean relations, that he unlocks the boat so we could get on board.

The man ignored Anne's impatience. "Ma name is Josh," he held out a large paw. I grasped it, waiting for a bone–crushing result, only to experience a limp handshake, which I remembered from our days living in Jamaica, is quite normal for the indigenous Islander.

Josh then peered at Anne, as though he hadn't been previously aware of her.

"Soon 'ave you aboard man," he breathed rum fumes directly at her, and she snapped her head away. Josh turned back to me.

"It's not locked" he added, looking at the three of us in surprise.

True enough, while there was a padlock on the boat, it was unlocked. I cursed under my breath, realizing that we could have climbed aboard over an hour ago.

Josh quickly showed us around the small cabin, and with a cheery "'ave a good 'un", he swayed off back to his own boat.

Liz and I took the rear cabin and Anne headed wearily towards one of the berths in the main cabin. We'd no choice but to unpack our bags immediately, as seventy-five percent of the contents were damp. Liz did the best she could to hang the clothes up to dry, but it wasn't an easy task in the small area available. This done, Liz and I quickly undressed and fell on our berths naked. The cabin was hot, stuffy, and so, before going to sleep, I got up and opened the overhead hatch to let in some cool breeze. At 4 a.m., I awoke with the feeling that water was pouring in from above, I felt mild panic setting in and when I opened my eyes, I saw it was.

It took me some seconds to become fully conscious, by that time I realised that the boat wasn't in fact sinking.

I raised myself from the wet patch that had formed on my berth, but Liz had reacted more quickly and was already up and struggling to close the overhead hatch, through which another tropical downpour had unleashed its fury. The mattresses were soaked.

"Jesus! Whose idea was this?" I yelled, unwisely.

"YOURS," growled Liz. "Now help me turn these bloody mattresses over, so we can get some bloody sleep." I wisely complied. We dried ourselves off with a damp towel and fell back on to the bed, exhausted. With the hatch now firmly closed, it was hot and stuffy, but we slept.

The next morning, I awoke with a start to the roar of an aircraft VERY close, in fact so close that I became convinced that it must crash straight into the vessel we were in. I leapt out of bed, momentarily forgetting I was on a boat, and rushed for the opening where the cabin door had been. I then remembered that we'd left it open the night before, as this was the only method of letting air into the cabin without more lashings of rainwater. What I forgot was, the top of the deck above the door slid back to make a larger opening, we'd closed this hatch to avoid the rain flooding the interior. As a result, my head came into a rapid and crunching contact with the unopened hatch. "Ahhh," I yelled in pain and fell back into the cabin holding my head with both hands. I didn't receive too much sympathy, neither Liz nor Anne had slept well, and they were in no mood to pander to me, the instigator of their woes.

17

Liz sat up in the berth. "Oh, before you go out there, I should get some clothes on if I were you, I don't think you can compete with the natives." I'd forgotten that I was still naked, and I groped around and found my least damp T-shirt, a pair of slacks that looked like a creased dish cloth and put them on. My watch showed that it was 7:30 a.m.

I found out later that the aircraft noise was due to the proximity of Vigie Airport, used by small to medium planes.

We'd all heard the first LIAT (Leave luggage in any airport) flight landing and reversing its engines. I made a mental note not to sleep in Vigie Marina again.

Standing in the boat's cockpit, I noticed a medium-sized man standing on the quay.

"Morning," the man called out, "you must be Dalby."

"Good morning," I tried to smile, but felt a twinge of pain as I did so.

"Caught your head, eh," the man smiled. "You'll soon get used to it." My eyes slowly became accustomed to the light, although I was still squinting in the brightness of the Caribbean morning. I took stock of the man on the dock. He was obviously white, although deeply sun-tanned, and he sported a King George V beard, which was very white, except for the area immediately below the lower lip, which was gingerish. Probably due to the fact he was a smoker, I thought. He wore smart blue slacks and a white shirt with short sleeves, perched on his head was what appeared to be a naval officer's cap. I guessed his age to be somewhere around fifty.

"I'm Commander Fisher, Fishy, to my friends. Come into the office when you're ready," he swung round and pointed to a door next to the archway. He turned back towards me.

"I expect you'll want to get provisioned and away ASAP, dear boy," he smiled. "Well, once you've completed the formalities, you can be off," with that he turned again sauntering towards his office.

I inhaled the fresh morning air. The sun was up, the sky was the bluest of blues, and the heat of the day was at least an hour away. It felt good to be alive. How quickly the human spirit revives in sunshine and fresh air, I thought, and winced as I felt the swelling lump on my forehead.

Reality returned with the sound of Liz and Anne hauling out the damp mattresses and spreading various bits of damp clothing around the outside of the boat. When they'd finished, Liz noticed that the little store on the opposite side of the archway had opened.

Having established that there were no provisions on the boat, she grabbed her purse, and went off with Anne to forage for breakfast. While they were away, I decided to look around the boat. It was blue and cream in colour, with the aft cabin taking up about a quarter of the rear of the small vessel.

The cockpit was aft centre, with the wheel in the middle. Around the sides a raised area, with cushions running the full length of the cockpit, as I sat on them, they oozed with grimy water. In front of the wheel down some steps was the main cabin, which was quite roomy, the seats on both sides doubled as berths. I noticed that Anne had slept on the one opposite the let-down table, on the left side (port) of the boat looking towards the bow. I also noticed, true to character that side of the interior looked like a rubbish tip.

Inside the cabin, and before the berths, there was a small sink and an oven on gimbals, on the right side (starboard), a small chart table with a VHF radio fixed above.

At the forward end of the cabin was a small hatch that led into a tiny sail locker that stored the fore sails (Jibs). It all seemed very compact and neatly designed. The steps that led down from the cockpit into the main cabin hid the entrance to the small engine compartment, which housed the diesel engine.

Soon the smell of frying bacon filled the air and I realised just how hungry I was. The three of us had a very full breakfast; the table-talk was cheerful and optimistic, in accord with the expanding day outside.

Afterwards, I slipped on some shoes, climbed up onto the quay and walked across to Fisher's office. The utter muddle I saw inside surprised me. There were papers piled high, dusty bits of old boat parts, and a typewriter that any self-respecting museum would have given its eye-teeth for. The untidy spectacle so shocked me that I didn't notice that there was another person in the same confined space.

Fisher was sitting behind his desk, his face just visible

19

above the stacks of paper. He stood up as I entered.

"Ah, dear boy, good to see you," Fisher smiled. "Let me introduce you to Major Pittam-Bagshaw, the chap who owns all the charter yachts here. I'm just the booking agent."

I saw Pittam-Bagshaw for the first time. He was holding out his hand. He was an older man than Fisher; I guessed correctly that he was an ex–Indian Army type. He was also taller than Fisher, thick–set, sporting a bushy moustache and he had a thick crop of grey hair.

There the likeness to a military man stopped. Pittam-Bagshaw had a marked stoop and bloodshot eyes like a bloodhound might have envied.

In fact, his whole face wasn't dissimilar from the breed. As he shook my hand, the handshake was limp, and I noticed the grey pallor of his skin, possibly caused by over indulgence in alcohol.

"Good to know you," Pittam-Bagshaw said gruffly, "call me Pittam," he added as he straightened up somewhat, as though he'd just remembered how to stand erect. "I hope you found Shady Lady comfortable?"

I said we'd been perfectly comfortable, until it rained, and I recounted our experience of the previous evening, from the taxi drive to our belated meeting with Josh.

Some sixth sense warned me not to mention that our welcoming party had been rather worse for wear. Pittam's next remark showed me the wisdom of my discretion.

"Ah, that would have been my son who met you," he saw my look of surprise. Josh, even in the midnight darkness, had been very black indeed.

"Josh is my adopted son," explained Pittam, a trifle hastily, and quickly changed the subject.

We talked about the Windward Island chain, and Pittam was quite adamant that we should spend the first week or so around the lee of St. Lucia. I told him that we wanted to go further south to the celebrated Grenadines, but it was obvious that the old man didn't approve of the plan I outlined. He refrained from saying more, but simply gave Fisher a long, penetrating look.

Pittam made his excuses saying that he must get on and after exchanging another limp handshake, he quickly left the office.

Fisher rummaged around the inside of his desk and eventually found a coffee-stained file, this was the charter agreement; he handed it to me.

"Just a formality dear boy, sign here," his tobacco-stained forefinger indicated where I should sign.

Having once before found myself in hot water for signing a document without reading the terms properly, I wasn't about to make the same mistake again, so I sat on the empty chair opposite Fisher's desk and started to read.

At that moment, Liz opened the door and came in to the office and I introduced her.

She gave him a rather frigid and fleeting smile.

"I thought James had arranged for the boat to be provisioned. I can't find anything on board, I managed to get enough for our breakfast at the little shop on the quay but," Her voice trailed off.

"Ah, yes," Fisher said slowly, his whiskers twitching, "it's all in that container over there," he pointed to a small cardboard box in the corner of the office. Liz went over and examined the contents. During her inspection of the so-called provisions, Fisher opened an over filled filing cabinet and extracted a bill, which he tried to hand to me, but it was quickly intercepted by Liz.

"WHAT," she yelled, "£50.00 for this," she pointed to the box.

Fisher looked embarrassed. "Er, 'fraid so my dear, you see all our goods are imported here and, well with tax and everything." Liz sniffed, picked up the box, scowled at me, and left to convey the small collection of provisions to the boat.

We suspected afterwards, and were to receive confirmation later, that the 'tax' was a somewhat nebulous figure with no discernible ceiling. It equated to about 50% of the basic price. Provisioning vessels in advance also suited Mrs. Anderson, a petite St Lucian Lady who ran a small shop near Castries. Not only were her prices almost double that of the supermarkets in the city, but it was a marvellous way of getting rid of old stock.

Surprisingly, the charter document appeared to be in

order, in that it required the charterer not to beetle off to South America or some other far off shore, but simply stay within the Leeward and Windward Island chains that are between Anguilla in the north and Grenada in the south. I signed the document, handed it back to Fisher, and reluctantly parted with £50 to pay for the provisioning and a further £400 for the deposit.

"Good, good, dear boy," said Fisher, feeling with relish the paper on which the sterling travellers' cheques were printed.

"I'll get Josh straight away, so that he can show you the ropes, and after that you can be off," he emphasised his words with a sweep of the hand and wished me good sailing.

I returned to the boat and to keep my distance from both a grumpy Anne and Liz, I busied myself checking the rigging, although I hadn't the slightest idea what I was looking at. About half an hour or so later, which is the nearest you get to straight away in the Caribbean, Josh appeared on the quay, and dropped down onto the bow of Shady Lady.

I noticed that he looked a very different person from the night before and didn't appear to have suffered any after affects from the excess of alcohol.

Josh was a muscular young man particularly in the arms and shoulders, and he was wearing a T-shirt emblazoned with SEX RELIEVES TENSION. Anne looked at it and sniffed contemptuously.

It quickly became apparent that Josh knew his stuff; he showed me how to start the engine from the console in the cockpit. While that was running, he gave me a lesson on the workings of the water pumps and indicated the whereabouts of the water tanks. Next the diesel tank and more importantly, where to fill it. After that, he showed how the bilge pump operated and how to work it manually if the electrics failed, then the intricacies of boat heads, or toilets, of which there was only one on board. I was thankful that it was next to the aft cabin, which gave both Liz and me a sporting chance of getting in there before Anne commandeered it for what seemed to be an eternity.

Josh showed Liz and Anne how to light the oven and grill then he went over the engine procedures with me. He counselled me never to turn the engine ignition off without first stopping the engine with the traditional pull switch.

"Do dat the other way around, man, an' you'll strip your magnetos," he grinned. "We 'ad a charterer last week who did dat," he shook his head sagely "It cost 'im more than the fare 'ome to fix it."

I listened carefully. I could just imagine the 'tax' that would be added to anything going wrong that could be termed 'charterers negligence.' I recalled that there was just such a clause in the charter agreement.

Josh was speaking again. "Ahm jus' goin' to take you all fer a quick sail, jus' so you'se be happy with everything," he explained.

I felt distinctly uneasy. I'd hoped to get the boat away from the marina on our own, so that I could investigate thoroughly and determine exactly what each line pulled. In that way, any mistakes I made wouldn't be subject to critical examination. I'd no choice though and had to go along with Josh's suggestion.

"Fine with me," I said nonchalantly. Shrugging my shoulders and sitting on the least squishy of part of the cockpit seating, pretending to be totally unconcerned. While waiting for Josh to take the boat out, Liz sat down opposite me, but Anne went below to read in case anyone asked her to lend a hand.

"Right man cast off," Josh was looking directly at me.

I frowned but got up, climbed onto the top of the main cabin, and moved towards the bow of Shady Lady.

There was a man on the quay, and he expertly threw me both lines that had been holding the boat to the dock. I missed one of them and was slightly embarrassed to have to pull the dropped end from the water. Once collected, I looped them carelessly in what I hoped looked like a professional manner. There's really no difference between a motor boat and a sailing yacht, I thought to myself as I turned and beamed confidently at Liz.

Because Shady Lady was tied bow to the quay, a stern anchor had been put in place, to keep the boat in position. Josh reversed smoothly while at the same time reeling in the rear anchor line to avoid it catching the propeller. When I'd finished stowing the bow lines, I went back to help him. It was then I realized just how little manoeuvring space there was. This was mainly because a large galleon type vessel had tied up on the other side of the quay and was taking up almost half the waterway.

After hauling in the last of the rear anchor line, Josh pulled up the rear anchor himself. He handled it as though the fifty-pound chunk of metal was a light piece of driftwood, slipped the boat into forward gear and with a twist of the wheel, Shady Lady started moving ahead. I felt exhilarated. This must be the start to a perfect two months of peace and quiet. I thought smugly.

2 - THE BURIAL

And How I Lost an Engine and found it Again

Shady Lady nosed out of the little Vigie harbour and eased into the main waterway, which ran at right angles to the dock. Once in the open water, Josh turned to starboard, keeping well clear of some nasty-looking rocks on the right that marked the end of the Vigie Airport runway. When I turned and looked over the stern, I could see the port of Castries, with all the customs sheds lined up in a neat row on the right-hand wharf. There was an old, rust-decorated freighter unloading, which looked as though it had seen better days. On the left was Pointe Seraphine, a large piece of waste ground that was to become the cruise liner berth. I turned back and looked straight ahead. There was an old gun emplacement on the left; on the right were some attractive houses on the hill towering above the water. These were mainly older properties and typical of the architecture of a past colonial age.

I put my right hand over my brow to shade the sun from my eyes.

"Looks rough," Liz frowned, as we approached the open sea.

"Yea, man, last couple a' days bin real bad out there," Josh yanked his thumb in the opposite direction, indicating the east side of the island.

26

The boat started to rock gently as it approached the harbour entrance. "This is the lee side though, so noo problem here," Josh grinned, but I could see he was starting to exert more pressure on the wheel, to keep the boat straight.

"We'll go a bit further out and raise sail," Josh was still grinning. Whether this was due to the sudden look of unease on Liz's face, or whether it was because once the grin was fixed, it stayed that way, I wasn't sure. Josh was gradually raising his voice the further the boat went out to sea in order that I could hear him above the wind and the noise of crashing waves. Suddenly, a white-faced Anne appeared from below looking rather alarmed and she scowled at me when she saw the roughness of the water.

Shady Lady started to pitch and roll. The O'Day didn't have a powerful engine, and the slow speed of the boat without its sails hoisted made it wallow in the water.

Anne's pallor started to acquire a tinge of green. The book she'd been reading fell from her fingers into a puddle of water in the cockpit and she sat down heavily trying to avert her eyes from the disturbed water, a difficult job for a bad sailor when aboard a small boat at sea.

I was suddenly aware that Josh was shouting at me.

"OK, man, I'll helm while you pull dem sails," Josh waited for my reaction, but I froze. I knew what a sail was of course, but because I'd never sailed a sail boat before I hadn't a clue about how to pull 'dem' up.

Josh looked at me, puzzled. He shouted again.

"Let's get de main up first. I'll give some slack on the boom," Josh turned the boat 180 degrees into the wind and started loosening a line. The boom is the beam on which the main sail sits when not in use; it started to swing wildly from side to side. I stumbled up in semi panic on top of the main cabin, and I saw the boom hurtling towards me. I ducked as it narrowly missed the top of my head. Josh took up some more slack on the line to steady it.

I stood unsteadily on the heaving deck and looked up rather foolishly at the mast.

"Er, which piece of rope do I grab?" I shouted.

"Use the winch handle man," Josh's voice now had a note of urgency.

"Okay," I answered diving for a handle that was in a holster fastened to the mast. The problem was that I wasn't at all sure what to do with it when I got it.

At that moment, probably because Josh was concentrating more on me than the boat's position, a large wave hit Shady Lady amidships. I became angry and frustrated, I tried to swear as the sea water swamped over me, but the blasphemous words were stifled with large amounts of it. I fell heavily on the now slippery wet deck just managing to grab the side rail and stop myself from pitching over the side.

"Owoooo" I yelled, as my shin cracked on a stanchion. The pain was unbearable, holding on to the side rail and nursing my bruised leg, I was sure that I'd broken something, but I somehow managed to cling onto both. This rather tended to negate my usefulness as an active crew member. The sails were still not hoisted. As I sat on the deck immobile from apparent injuries, Anne, who had just heaved the contents of her stomach over the side, gallantly sprinted up. She managed to prevent the winch handle that I'd dropped from disappearing into the sea. Liz, concerned for me as I was now in a foetal position on the deck with waves crashing over me, sprang to my assistance, but was dragged back by the rear of her T-shirt, by Josh.

Josh handed the wheel to Liz. "Jus' point 'er towards Castries," he said. "I'll give 'em 'an 'and," he wrenched the winch handle from Anne, and within seconds the main was tight at the top of the mast. Putting the handle in the holster, he jumped back into the cockpit and turned the wheel away from the wind. Immediately, like a racehorse let out of its stable, the boat heeled over and started moving forward.

Meanwhile after prolonged inspection of yet another damaged part of my anatomy, this time my big toe that had somehow encountered a protuberance on the deck, I decided that I'd no broken bones after all, just a much-damaged ego.

"Okay, man?" asked Josh.

"I think so," I answered, gingerly feeling my shin with one hand and toe with another.

"Let's get the jib up, then."

I groaned inwardly, while Josh explained in some detail what I should do. This time I took no chances. I crawled on all fours towards the bow, which was still taking in water, and opened the front sail locker hatch pulling the sail out of its bag and onto the deck.

I'd a sudden vision of a nice hotel room, dry and inviting as I grimly held on to the sail bag to prevent my hasty departure over the side. The more I pulled, the more there seemed to be of it. When I'd at last got most of it on deck, it started to fall into the water. Panicking, I tried to fasten the top of the sail to the fore-stay, but my leg was throbbing, and my fingers were so wet and cold that I couldn't get a grip on the small shackle. At last, I managed it pulling the part of the sail that was trailing in the sea back into the boat. When completed, I half limped, and half crawled back to the main mast and getting the winch handle from where Josh had stowed it. I steadied myself and manoeuvred around to the opposite side of the main, to where the winch was. Then, as Josh had instructed, I got hold of the correct line and wound it around the winch.

I now felt a surge of accomplishment, as I inserted the winch handle and started to wind, I could feel my face getting redder with every second of exertion. The line was solid; it didn't move one inch. It took me half a minute of frustration to realise that I'd wound it the wrong way.

"Oh, shit" I shouted, undoing it, and almost falling as another wave hit the boat. I'd just wound it round correctly when a further welter of water came over the side. I coughed and spluttered with exhaustion trying to get my breath back. Through a haze, I saw Liz back at the wheel, and Josh was by my side. He took the line.

"Here, tail for me man." I didn't understand him, but I took the end of the line and as it was winched, I took up the slack. Josh hoisted the jib in seconds, took the line from me and tied it off at the mast. In the meantime, I'd stumbled back into the cockpit, mollified by the look of sympathy received from Liz. This immediately counteracted by a look of contempt from Anne. Josh returned to the cockpit and took the wheel from Liz. The little yacht was now biting through the water like some highly tuned thoroughbred. Josh turned to me.

"You should really put up your jib when you're headed to

wind, same as the main, but it's only a light boat, so you can get away with puttin' it up reaching," he then looked at me quizzically. "You've not done much sailing recently, man?"

"Er not for a while," I said guardedly.

"He's never sailed anything but a motor boat before," said Anne. "Don't let him bullshit you,"

I cringed and glowered at her.

Anne shrugged and tossed her head in the air.

Josh nodded. "I guessed as much," he said grinning at my embarrassment. "We need to speak to the boss when we get back."

My heart sank.

The rest of the trip was uneventful; we sailed down the island for about twenty minutes, and then turned and headed back. Coming into Castries harbour we switched on the engine, the sails dropped, and Shady Lady was back in its berth within two hours of leaving it.

"Well, this is where I get off," said Liz firmly until she noticed the pathetic look on my face and relented. "Well, I'm not going anywhere, until I'm happy you can drive the bloody thing without going over the side."

I nodded, and looked at Josh pleadingly, as the latter finished tying the boat up on the quay. He started to climb onto the deck and inclined his head towards Fisher's office.

"'Tink we better see the boss."

Fisher heard the story in silence.

"Well, there's no question of you sailing out of the island now," he looked thoughtful.

I must have looked crestfallen.

Josh noticed and came to my rescue.

"It's noo big 'ting, Fishy. 'E jus' needs a bit of practice, dat's all," he flashed a grin at me. "Look," he went on, "I need to get down to Pittam's place in Soufriere by Friday. It's now Wednesday. I'll sail down with James, we'll stop off in Marigot Bay tonight, then Soufriere by Thursday, it'll jus' mean I'm a day early," Fisher nodded.

"Then, if 'e," Josh inclined his head in my direction, "can 'andle 'er by den, I'll get off an' let 'em go."

Fisher looked at me, "how's that sound to you?"

"That sounds fine," I answered gratefully. "I'm just a little rusty," I added, stretching the truth to its limits. "I'll be perfectly all right."

Fisher half smiled, but tactfully said nothing.

It was about 2 p.m. in the heat of the afternoon, when we finally got away. Josh, his ebony skin glistening, pulled the dinghy line close into the boat, to prevent it fouling the propeller.

"Right man, you take the wheel, and we'll reverse out."

I started the engine and waited for Josh to go to the bow to collect the lines. Liz was below, just finishing washing up the lunch dishes, and Anne was laying full length on top of the deck. There was no one on the quay, because it was lunch time, and I saw Josh looking round for someone to let off the bow lines.

"Anne," I shouted harshly, still smarting from her recent reproach. "There'll be plenty of time for sun-bathing. Make yourself useful and let the lines off on the quay."

Anne had frequent bouts of inertia, and the mood almost certainly worsened if she was unhappy about something, like the request to get up from sunbathing. She grumbled as she sat up and tried to fasten the straps of her swimsuit. She was still fumbling with them when she stood up and ambled slowly towards the bow. She stepped barefooted, grumpily, on to the hot stone of the quay. She let off the first line that was at an angle of 45 degrees to the bow and threw it on deck. She then started to move grudgingly towards the other line.

In the meantime, I'd put the boat engine into reverse, but realised too late that Anne wouldn't reach the second line before it became too taut to undo. I moved the gear lever to forward to ease the pressure on the line but because the lever was stiff, I pushed it too hard and then realised with mounting horror that Shady Lady was going forward too fast. In desperation I pulled the lever hard into reverse again, at precisely the moment when Anne was about to step onto the bow with the last line. There was a scream and a splash, and she disappeared between the quay and the boat. Josh, who had seen the accident unfold, ran back towards me shouting, "NEUTRAL MAN, GO INTO NEUTRAL."

There was a sudden crump as the engine stalled. For a minute, I thought that Anne had somehow gone under the boat and felt sick in my stomach but was quickly reassured by blasphemous yells coming from an area in front of Shady Lady, confirming that it was not the propeller that had damaged the beautiful body.

"Oh, man," said Josh sorrowfully.

I'd completely forgotten that the rear anchor was still out. Shady Lady had reversed into the anchor line, fouling the propeller. Now the freed bow of the boat was swinging round slamming with a crash of splintered wood into the galleon moored opposite. As the O'Day was made of fibreglass, I knew the damage wasn't to Shady Lady. I feared this was going to prove expensive. Within seconds of all this happening the dock seemed to come alive, there were people everywhere, some laughing and pointing, others scowling. There were also two worried looking people on the galleon, hastily putting down plastic fenders.

Eventually, by throwing a line back onto the quay, Josh pulled Shady Lady back into the berth manually. The damage caused to the galleon, a quarter of a million-pound vessel was used as a day pleasure boat, was fortunately slight, which was just as well as it was the boat that featured in the film Roots and was something of an historic artefact. I shuddered at the cost of it being out of commission for even one day.

The line around Shady Lady's propeller was rather more difficult to deal with however, and a diver had to come and unwind it. Josh seemed to take some pleasure in telling me that quite often when that happened, the propeller shaft, wrenched out of its bed, was often bent beyond repair.

"Yea, man, it's a very costly job to put right," He looked worried, but not half as worried as I felt as I could see our precious deposit money vanishing into the cost of a new drive shaft.

It transpired that I was lucky. The line hadn't caused any damage to the shaft and, apart from damaging my ego, my pocket to pay the diver and the whole scenario causing me considerable embarrassment, Shady Lady was able to sail out of Vigie under engine power just before five in the evening. Anne was still extremely unhappy, because the dirty oily water of the marina had left her smelling like an old oil barge.

She'd also lost the top of her swimsuit which gave the

locals much merriment when she extracted herself from the water, her hands not quite large enough to cover all the necessary parts. Liz eventually went to her rescue by throwing her a towel to wrap around herself. She got her revenge that night by staying in the only shower on board for almost half an hour thus using up all the boat's water.

The sail between Castries and Marigot Bay normally took about thirty minutes, but Shady Lady took about one hour to reach this small piece of paradise. Sailing from Castries harbour, I turned Shady Lady south and sailed past the La Toc Hotel on the port side nestled in the next bay. This was the hotel where Liz and I'd stayed on our previous trip to the Island. Shortly after that, we passed Cul-de-sac Bay where the Hess oil storage depot is. This is a lighter terminal for large oil tankers heading for the USA. The smell of oil pervaded this area drowning out the scent of nature, and we were glad to get past it. After leaving the oil depot to port Josh told me to start heading inland, but it wasn't until the boat was very close to shore that I realised we were aiming for a small and partly hidden inlet.

As we were approaching the entrance to Marigot, I recalled reading that large French ships were pursuing smaller British galleons during the Napoleonic wars, they are a small section of the British fleet. The story went that the British turned into Marigot Bay and dressed their masts with palm fronds. The French sailed straight past, apparently failing to see them. The suspicion was (no doubt put about by the British) that the French didn't particularly want to face their enemy, far preferring to get back home to their girlfriends, mistresses and the decent food in Martinique, the large French island to the north. Of course, as a total non-event, they reported it as another British victory.

Sailing into the narrow entrance of Marigot Bay, we saw that there was a little restaurant called Doolittle's on the left-hand side where Josh said they filmed Doctor Doolittle. Immediately after, there was an attractive sand spit with palm trees, that almost divided the enclosed bay in two. Beyond the spit was a small anchorage, just large enough for about ten or so boats. The hotel that served the southern shore was called Hurricane Hole, aptly named, as Marigot is

33

one of the best hurricane refuges anywhere in the Caribbean. At the entrance to the bay, the hills on each side rose steeply with lush vegetation. On the right, there were various types of small houses and bungalows, and on the left were wooden holiday chalets. Before them, in the inner bay, was a swampy area, with more palm trees at the edge of the anchorage and then another hill covered with green vegetation. At Josh's suggestion, I anchored well away from any other boat. After a light supper and because we were exhausted due to our unfamiliar exertions, we agreed that bed was the only remedy. Anne had made the excuse that as there was no water on the boat after she'd used it all in the shower, she had to drink white rum instead. After what she considered to be her trials and tribulations of the day, the unaccustomed heat, and her unexpected immersion in the marina, she soon became unconscious by the potency of the alcohol even before the food was on the table, much to Liz's annoyance.

After we'd carried the slumbering Anne down below, Liz and I fell onto our berths in our cabin and were sound asleep by 8:30 p.m. Josh slept on top of the main cabin, in the open. Fortunately for him, it didn't rain.

I awoke with a start. It was pitch black, but something had disturbed me because I was suddenly wide awake. The air filled with a high-pitched buzzing sound that I recognised at once. I felt my right thigh start to itch, then my arm, then an itch on my cheek.

"Jesus, we're being eaten alive," I yelled.

Liz was now wide awake, and she turned on the cabin light. There was blood on the sheet, and I knew that it was the remains of at least one overweight, overfed mosquito, and it was my blood.

"God, look at 'em," I exclaimed. "There must be a dozen flying around," I lashed out uselessly with a frontal Kamikaze attack, but there were others approaching from behind.

"This is no good," said Liz, getting out of the berth. "I think there were some mosquito coils in the provision pack."

She disappeared out of the cabin stumbling towards the galley. Within seconds, I'd grabbed an aerosol of foul-smelling fly spray and doused the aft cabin with so much of it that we'd to sit outside on the deck for ten minutes, where at least the slight breeze gave us some respite. After that, we lit the mosquito coils and placed them strategically in the cabin. Liz and I eventually got back to bed, but both of us continued to scratch at every conceivable part of our bodies, until total exhaustion finally enveloped us, and we fell asleep again.

Our normal waking up time was about 7:30 a.m. but subsequently we frequently found that when we were on board a boat, we woke up with the dawn. Even considering the midnight battle with mosquitoes, I was wide awake by 6 a.m. as was Liz. By 6:30, the boat was a bustling hive of energy, even Anne was up, but she was much the worse for wear. The mosquitoes had clearly given Liz and me up as a bad job and concentrated their efforts on Anne, even though Liz had put mosquito coils in her cabin too. She spent the next two days scratching her body all over like an orang-utan and my comment to her of the comparison didn't go down particularly well.

By 7:30, the smell of cooking bacon emerged from the galley and being civilised people, we laid the table in the open cockpit ready for an early morning feast. Josh climbed down from his sleeping quarters on the cabin roof and joined us. Everyone had just sat down to tuck in to the food when there was the roar of a powerful outboard engine. I was vaguely aware of an inflatable speeding towards Shady Lady from the dock, and I noticed Josh quickly picking up his plate of food and his coffee cup, but I wasn't nearly as quick. The inflatable veered away when it was within yards of Shady Lady and as I was about to take my first bite of toast, the boat heeled over to such an extent that it seemed momentarily to tip on its side. Plates shot to the cockpit floor, along with the newly cooked breakfast, and Anne screamed when hot coffee spilled on her freshly sunburned thigh. Liz was drinking her coffee at the time, but my cup landed upside down on my lap and its spilled contents created some days of extreme discomfort and celibacy.

Anne was the first to realise that the wake of the speeding inflatable had caused the problem and the ruined breakfast, I stored her shouted abuse into memory for a future discussion with that august lady, the headmistress of her supposedly high-class public school. The grinning driver of the inflatable turned and gave Anne a cheery wave before he disappeared round the end of the entrance to the bay.

"Oh, man," groaned Josh, "that's Peterkin," he nodded his head in the direction of the wake, which was all that was left of the speeding boat. "He's a stupid man, I tell you. One of these days he's gonna catch it, no mistake."

Liz didn't have the energy to cook another breakfast, so after I'd cautiously changed my shorts, we all climbed into the dinghy that, thanks to Peterkin was half full of water, and we slowly puttered towards the Hurricane Hole dock while baling the little boat out with two old bleach bottles with their tops cut off.

The dinghy that came with Shady Lady was marked Shady Lady 2. It was made of heavy fibreglass material, and had a bench in the middle, running from side to side. It had a raised bow area that could also serve as a seat, and two small, raised areas aft, one on each side. On the centre of the stern was a block of wood where one fastened the removable outboard. The dinghy was steered by an extension from the outboard itself, a device like a small tiller. Because this type of dinghy is heavy, we towed it behind the yacht, rather than hauling it on board. To avoid the outboard becoming water logged, we removed it before sailing and stowed it on a similar block of wood fastened to the aft rail on Shady Lady. They were robust little boats, but quite unstable and to make matters worse, its engine was so low powered that it gave the dinghy at full revs a speed equivalent to that of a slow walker.

After breakfasting on dry land, we called into the hotel shop for some anti-bite and anti-burn cream, the former that a frantic Anne promptly emptied over her well-bitten and now rather unattractive, lumpy body. Liz, who enjoyed walking, said she'd like to stretch her legs ashore, so it was after 10 am when we joined Josh back on the yacht. Liz, Anne, and I spent the rest of the morning learning how to reef a sail, finding out the location of the emergency tiller, and how to fix it on in the event of a wheel failure. *It was just as well to have this knowledge because Murphy's Law would ensure Liz and I'd suffer two such failures in the future while under sail, although not in that boat.* We filled the two water tanks again, and Josh reminded us how not to fill the diesel tank with water or vice versa. The latter was a useful trick to learn because an engine doesn't like water and we were rather averse to drinking diesel.

There was a story that Josh recounted of some poor man who had filled his water tanks with diesel and suffered abuse from his unhappy girlfriend after she'd inadvertently showered with the oily substance.

I spent some time with Josh, learning the rudiments of the main engine itself. The health of the latter was important, as the engine also acted as a generator and consequently it had to run for about an hour a day to ensure the boat had electricity. We kept all Butane gas cylinders used for cooking aft in a locker, one cylinder in use, one kept as a spare. Because of the danger of fire on board, we switched the gas off before sailing.

The four of us had a quick lunch, and by early afternoon, we were under way with engine power until Shady Lady was well free of Marigot Bay when we raised the sails. Josh reckoned it would take about two hours to reach Soufriere, which was the last St. Lucian town before heading south to St. Vincent and the Grenadines that we planned to be our first major stop. The trip in the lee of the island between Marigot Bay and Soufriere passed some of the most picturesque land anywhere in the Caribbean. We sailed almost within reach of beautiful sandy beaches, completely deserted, with palm trees growing on the sea line, and little fishing villages with pretty names like Anse La Raye and Caneries, where there were attractive small, coloured houses and traditional Caribbean fishing boats hauled up on the shore. Everywhere was green vegetation, with splashes of colour where one or another tropical plant had haphazardly put its roots into the ground. The whole scene was set against a back-cloth of Piton Floye rising to 1,850 feet in the north and Mount Beaujolais, reaching to 1,158 feet in the middle of the island. Because the centre of St. Lucia is mountainous, there's little or no wind when sailing close into shore on the lee side, this provided us with a perfectly stable and safe environment to continue learning the rudiments of sailing. No one pointed out to me however, the difference between tying a reef on a main sail in the calm and doing the same in a 40-knot wind. The latter is akin to changing a wheel on a motor car in normal conditions, and then doing so without a car jack.

Just before reaching Soufriere, we saw the resort of Anse Chastenet on our left. This is a little bay with the hotel chalets dotted around the hillside reminiscent of pictures on Chinese Willow Pattern pottery. The flora partly hid some of the buildings behind rushes of reds, yellows, orange and the ever present green.

"I don't think you ever realise just how many shades of green there can be until you visit the Caribbean," said Liz dreamily, as she watched the landscape drift by.

Just past the bay, Josh asked me to swing Shady Lady out to sea, to avoid Caille Point Shoal, some rocks just under the water line, a favourite spot for pleasure divers. Once we were safely past these, we turned to port and in to Soufriere Bay.

Soufriere, although the second largest town in St. Lucia is quite small and most of it is visible from the sea, it nestles comfortably in a flat spot at the bottom of the hills. The little coloured houses had started to dot the hilly landscape after the local builders ran out of level ground. We thought it the most picturesque and prettiest countryside we'd seen so far. The Catholic Church was, as always in the smaller Caribbean towns, the largest building there. As the yacht sailed in towards the town, the Pitons overshadowed us on the right. They rise straight from the sea, like two giant spears, one to over to 2,400 feet, the other to over 2,600 feet. They're at their most awe-inspiring when viewed from sea level, not so much because of the height, more because of the steepness of their slopes.

Josh and I pulled down the sails, and Shady Lady glided gently into the sheltered anchorage near to the Humming Bird restaurant, which is just off the beach on the north side of the bay. I dropped the anchor about 20 feet from the shore. Josh informed me that the water was quite deep around the Soufriere Bay area and because the land quickly drops away from the beach line, the holding isn't good. He advised me to put a rear anchor (called a kedge anchor) out as well, just in case. This was quite good experience for us as he'd warned us there were several anchorages in the Caribbean where it's advisable to put out two anchors, and he showed us the technique for accomplishing this simple task. After dropping the bow anchor, he let out all the anchor line, while I reversed the yacht, under his direction. When Shady Lady was as far back as the bow anchor line would allow, he called to me to drop the kedge anchor over the stern of the yacht. Despite this being smaller than the bow anchor, I needed Anne's help to lift it over the stern rail. It hit the water with a loud splash. When the rear anchor had time to drop to the bottom, Josh pulled on the bow anchor line while I let out the slack on the stern line. Shady Lady pulled forward until the line on both bow and stern was approximately equidistant, and then both secured. When he'd finished, he moved back into the cockpit, his throat waiting for the customary beer that I noticed followed any sort of exertion. He explained that with two anchors out, Shady Lady was less likely to find herself drifting out to sea or far worse, landing on a reef in the middle of the night.

"Yea, man, landin' on a reef can definitely have an adverse effect on your sense of well-being," he grinned. "In fact, it's been known to ruin a good holiday, or even a marriage."

On the sail down the island, Anne had kept referring to the various lines as ropes. Josh explained that nothing on a yacht is a rope.

"Yer see," he explained, "if yer in a storm, an' yer tell a crew member to pick up a rope they won't know which rope to go fer, which could be a problem. 'Cause of this, each rope has a different name, depending on what its used fer."

Josh pointed at the mast. "The lines that pull up the sails are halyards, and on Shady Lady you've a main halyard an' a jib halyard," Josh traced his finger along the boom, the mast-like projection that ran at right-angles to the mast that had a nasty habit of moving rapidly from side to side at head height, if not properly tied.

"These lines are sheets, there's the main sheet an' the two jib sheets. Then there's the line on the dinghy; that's a painter; and an anchor line is a rode."

Anne looked at Josh sullenly.

"They're all ropes to me," she said sulkily. Josh shrugged his shoulders, parted his lips in a grin, and downed the remaining beer in the bottle.

When I rowed Josh ashore in the dinghy, he suggested that we should try eating at the Humming Bird restaurant that night because good eating places further south were rather limited.

"Tell Joyce that Josh sent you," he said, giving me a brown-eyed wink as he jumped off the dinghy and on to the black volcanic sand. "That'll get you good service."

"Should I book a table," I shouted to the receding brown back as Josh walked swiftly up the beach.

He turned and shouted back, "Naw, s'not necessary, jus' call her on the radio, channel 16, 'bout 'n hour before you go," as an afterthought, Josh added, "we haven't done radio, do that tomorrow. See you, man." He gave a cheery wave and disappeared among the little coloured houses that came down to the beach edge.

It was about 3 p.m. and conscious that we were on this trip to find peace and quiet, if not inspiration, for my future book, I'd just finished mapping out the story-line synopsis, when the radio crackled down below.

"Shady Lady, Shady Lady, Shady Lady, this is Grampian."

No one on board reacted. Anne sat up from her sun-bathing on the deck. I noticed that she was looking even pinker and candy-coloured than before.

"Daddy isn't that a call for us?" she shouted.

I listened.

"Shady Lady, Shady Lady, Shady Lady. This is Grampian."

I put my papers on the cockpit seat, slid rapidly down the galley steps, and grabbed the microphone when I reached the bottom.

"This is Shady Lady, go ahead Grampian." The radio was set on channel 16, which was the emergency channel that boats and ships listen in to. Once contact is made, a more suitable channel for conversation of a non-urgent type selected. At least, this was the international agreement.

According to Josh, many a long, trivial transmission was made on the emergency channel 16, much to the annoyance of other boat users who are prevented from communicating until such morons had finished their mundane chat.

The voice at the other end said "switch to 27," which I did.

"Are you there, old boy?" I recognised Pittam's voice at

the other end.

"Copy to that," I answered, using flying vernacular.

"I wondered if you and your good ladies would like to come and have dinner with me tonight," he didn't wait for an answer. "I'll send Josh down with the Jeep about seven. Is that, OK?"

Without asking Liz or Anne, I said it was, and that we'd love to go. I informed Liz, who grumbled slightly because she felt she'd have to dress up rather more than she'd have done for the nearby restaurant. Anne took the news with equanimity. Food was food, and she didn't much care where it came from as long as she didn't have to cook it. The Caribbean languor, already inherent in her make-up, was now becoming more prevalent.

I spent the next two hours on my book project but by 5 p.m. I decided enough was enough for one day.

Liz uncorked the bottle of dark rum and mixed up a rum punch from a recipe given to her by Josh, a concoction that we decided was best described as delicious. It consisted of two parts dark rum, four parts cold tea, one-part orange juice all finished off with a touch of cinnamon.

"Ummm" said Anne. She quaffed the first glass down as though it were lemonade, her previous misadventure with the local spirit already forgotten.

By 7 p.m., we were quite a happy crew, and it was almost seven thirty before we heard a yell from the shore, by which time Anne was in no fit state to go anywhere. The rum and sun had taken their course, and she uncharacteristically declined dinner, saying she was going straight to bed.

Liz and I managed with some difficulty to climb down into the dinghy. I hadn't thought to put the outboard engine on beforehand but not wishing to leave oars in the small boat when leaving it on the beach. I moved the little boat around to the stern of Shady Lady so that I could unscrew the outboard from its current position. The rum punches didn't make me or the dinghy any steadier, and I shouted to Liz.

"Here, you hold on to Shady Lady and I'll get the outboard down." Liz swivelled the bow of the dinghy round until it was broadside to the yacht. She held on at the bow of the dinghy while I held on at the dinghy's stern. Once this manoeuvre had taken place, the dinghy was stabilised, at least that's what I thought. Unfortunately, I had to let go to unscrew the fastening clamps of the outboard motor so that I could haul lift it down to the dinghy. I was successful in undoing the screws and I felt pleased with myself as I lifted the heavy motor from its resting place. At the precise moment of lifting, however, I no longer had contact with Shady Lady, and the stern of the dinghy started to swing away, moving with the current. I tottered, still with the heavy piece of equipment held at chest level.

"Liz," I yelled in panic, "for God's sake hold the dinghy," Liz seeing what was happening sprang to help me.

This would have been most commendable on dry land, had she not in the process, also let go of the bow of Shady Lady, she had forgotten that a small boat moves underneath one if one moves. The dinghy tilted to an untenable angle with both of us situated at roughly the same place at the same time. For a split second, I'd both hands holding the heavy outboard in front of me, while at the same time trying to balance against the tipping dinghy.

Gravity won, with an almighty splash. The outboard motor hit the water first, with me rapidly following it. For some reason I clung on to the engine, dimly thinking I'd be able to swim up with it and triumphantly hand it to a waiting Liz. My brain engaged when I was about fifteen feet down and I realised that next to a hunk of concrete, an outboard engine is a great way of getting to the sea bed in the fastest way possible. I wisely let saw the motor settle among some seaweed and coral, before I lunged back to the surface, where I arrived gasping for air and in time to see a worried Liz peering over the side of the dinghy. In our confident mood, we'd previously untied the painter from Shady Lady and, as a result, it was now rapidly drifting out to sea. I was still in the water holding on to the side, unable to get on board without tipping it over.

"Here," Liz yelled, and threw me the painter, "you'll have to tow us back." I grabbed at the line but missed it. In the attempt, I'd let go of the dinghy. Liz drew the line back, and being practical, she tied it around her waist, and dived in. Between us, we swam back to Shady Lady, with one dinghy in tow, feeling a little soberer and slightly foolish. Josh had been watching the antics with some mirth, and I shouted to him from the water that we'd be with him when we'd changed into some dry clothes.

"Noo problem man," he shouted back. He was showing his two rows of gleaming teeth as he sat on the beach in the moonlight and lit up a cigarette. It was with some considerable annoyance that I could see that he was still grinning from ear to ear.

It was at this moment when we came across our next hurdle. Unfortunately, I hadn't left the ladder down on the stern of Shady Lady, so we now had the problem of getting back on board without it.

"Oh shit," I yelled in frustration, then I swam around the yacht rather uselessly looking for a way to get on deck and realising that the only way to get up was via the anchor line.

The problem with climbing onto an anchor line, as I was to find out, was, as you apply weight to it, the line sags, and the boat is pulled either forwards or backwards depending upon which anchor line is grasped. After many disastrous attempts and much guffawing from Josh on the shore, a very unhappy Anne, who had been awakened from a deep slumber, eventually appeared, and let down the ladder.

Within ten minutes, Liz and I'd changed and showered for the second time that evening. Afterwards, we untied the oars from the deck and put them in the now engine-less dinghy and rowed ourselves towards the shore, Liz was unhappy as she hadn't had time to re-do her hair.

On the drive up to Pittam's house, I confessed to Josh that we'd lost the outboard overboard.

He sucked his teeth. "Oh man, that'll cost you plenty," he shook his head sorrowfully.

"I'll have to dive and get it in the morning" I said, hoping that Josh might volunteer. I braced myself as we hurtled towards a sharp corner without any sign of the being brakes applied.

"You done any divin'?" Josh looked at me with raised eyebrows, guessing what the answer would be.

I was just shaking my head when I saw a strange creature in the road.

"Look out," I yelled. It was too late. We hit the creature with an unpleasant thud, despite Josh swerving wildly.

"Jus' a Manico," Josh grinned. He turned the jeep into a driveway and screeched to a halt.

"What's a Manico?" asked Liz, puzzled.

Josh looked back to where Liz had jammed herself firmly between the front seat and the rear to compensate for the fact that there were no seat belts.

"A Manico looks like a cross between a pig an' a rat, some locals even eat it." Josh grimaced. "Manico's are scavengers, jus' like rats, an' they've a pouch too, jus' like a kangaroo." I screwed my face at the thought of eating such a thing.

We'd arrived at what looked like a reasonably large house with a front veranda. We got out of the car, both of us feeling slightly weak at the knees due to our recent exertions. As we walked up to Pittam's house, Liz was trying to envisage an animal that looked like the cross between a pig and a rat and concluded that Josh was probably having us on.

(*He wasn't as we were later to discover to our cost*).

Josh said he wasn't joining us for dinner, as he'd to go back to Castries. This announcement caused a sinking feeling in my stomach as he wouldn't be available to help with retrieving the outboard motor the next day.

He remarked as he was climbing back into the car that "when you've found the motor, you'll 'ave to strip it and clean it, otherwise it'll not work. Lot 'a work, man. Betja don't do that again," he laughed.

Obviously, he would not be going through the radio protocol either, but this wasn't a problem for me as it was quite like using a radio while flying. My concern was with the idea of diving some 20 feet to get the outboard motor and even more so, on how I was going to get it working again once I had pulled it up.

Putting these thoughts aside, I looked at the surroundings as we were walking up the veranda steps. The house was in a superb position. About 500 feet up from sea level, it overlooked the whole bay of Soufriere, including the town and the Pitons. The view, even at night was breath-taking. The interior was open plan, as are so many Caribbean houses, with a veranda stretching the whole length of the front and back of the house. There was a small lawn at the back, which disappeared at the edge of a cliff. When Liz and I walked in, Pittam got up from a comfy chair on the rear veranda to greet us. We noticed that he seemed a little worse for wear.

"Hello old boy, nice to see you both," he boomed, shooting a cursory glance at Liz. "What'll you have, a Rum punch?" He'd steered us towards two similar chairs to his own, and he sat down heavily.

"I think James has had enough rum for one day," growled Liz.

Pittam ignored Liz's comment and turned to her with raised eyebrows.

"Do you have any white wine?" asked Liz. "Of course, my dear, Charlotte," Pittam yelled at the top of his voice. A little old black lady of indeterminate years stumbled out of a room that I supposed correctly was the kitchen.

"Yassir," she smiled.

"Open a bottle of white wine for our friends, chop, chop," he ordered.

Liz apologised to Pittam for being late, but seeing my scowl, decided not to tell him that a part of his boat was on the sea floor.

I changed the subject quickly, I'd noticed that Pittam was dressed rather formally for a Caribbean evening, and I remarked on it.

"Ah, yes, it's unusual. Fact is I just got back five minutes before you arrived. I've been to the funeral of a dear friend." Liz and I were suitably sympathetic realising that had we been on time, there'd have been no Pittam to welcome us.

"Most strange funeral I've ever been to. I'll tell you about it over dinner."

I didn't particularly relish the thought of discussing someone's death over dinner and from the look on Liz's face, I could see that she didn't either. Mrs. Charlotte Crombie, for that was the name of the lady doing the cooking, came through with two glasses and a bottle of wine and placed them rather unsteadily on a small coffee table. She filled the glasses to the brim, and then attempted with an unsteady hand to pass a glass to Liz without spilling the pale golden liquid.

She was unsuccessful, "Oh so sorry, ma'am."

"It's all right Charlotte, white wine will do no harm and anyway, I've been wet already," said Liz as she used a tissue to dry off some of the liquid from her dress. I glowered a warning at Liz and grabbed hold of the glass intended for me before Mrs. Crombie could get to it, congratulating myself on my forethought, I took a drink.

I prided myself on being a bit of a wine connoisseur, and I found it difficult to prevent my face wrinkling at the atrocious taste of what was 'corked' wine. I'd never drunk pure acid before, of course, but I decided that Pittam's wine must rate close to falling under that category. It was disgusting.

"Good wine, eh," Pittam smacked his lips. "Bring it all in from Martinique old boy. I can bring in some for you on my next trip if you'd like?"

I gave Pittam a watery smile, allowing the obnoxious mixture to trickle down from my mouth rather more gradually now, to give the lining in my stomach a chance to assimilate it.

I saw Liz's eyes bulging after she took a drink, she looked at me with a pained expression. Fortunately, shortly after that, Mrs. Crombie announced that the food was ready, and we all got up and went to the table that had been set on another part of the balcony. When we sat down, Mrs Crombie served us with Callaloo soup, which I said afterwards, tasted like old smelly socks. In order not to offend, I sipped the thick green slime from my spoon slowly, as Pittam started with his story.

"Yes, well James. My friend, John Paul Baptiste, was a very tall man, about six foot six, which is unusual for an islander," he added. "This meant that they couldn't get him into a standard coffin you see," Pittam broke a piece of Mrs. Crombie's leathery bread and dunked it in his soup, splashing the same appalling liquid on his shirt.

"It had been suggested that they cut his legs off, but the doctor wouldn't do it for less than $100, and the local carpenter who was called, flatly refused to have anything to do with a dead body," Pittam, who ate faster than most, mopped up the remains of his soup with another large piece of bread.

"Problem is you must bury people here within twenty-four hours, otherwise. . ." Pittam grimaced and sniffed allowing time for us to imagine the rest. "Anyway, the carpenter agreed to extend a standard coffin, for $40, and the widow agreed. All he did was to remove twelve inches from one coffin, and add it to another, just taking out the end. He fastened them together with battens on the outside. It didn't look very pretty, but it did the job. That's when the problem emerged."

Much to my relief, Mrs. Crombie came in and took away the soup bowls before I'd finished and brought in the main course. I peered at the meat dish, and assumed it was lamb but because of its severely charred appearance, I couldn't be sure.

"As is the custom here," Pittam continued, "the coffin was placed in the aisle of the church, and the short service began," he started to put large dollops of cabbage on my plate. I held up my hand and Pittam transferred his attention to Liz, a vegetarian, who had the sense to remove her dish and was helping herself to a small portion of the other vegetables, stringy green beans, and overdone carrots.

"The service started okay," Pittam went on, "but the gravedigger usually digs the grave in the early morning before sun up, and no one had told him until the last moment about the extra length. At first, he refused to work in the heat of the day, but eventually and with much haggling he agreed to do so for an extra $10."

I received my slice of meat and began to cut it into mouth-sized portions. Pittam didn't bother with a knife he simply shovelled in a whole piece, which temporarily halted the story. I wasn't sure whether I had a blunt knife or tough meat but found great difficulty in cutting the piece I had. I tried more forcibly and was embarrassed to see the whole charred portion skid off my plate on to the floor. I was about to pick it up surreptitiously when a cat pounced on it.

I sighed with relief. Perhaps, I thought, I could furtively send the rest the same way, but the ginger feline had clearly come across the stuff before and after a quick sniff it walked off, head held high, leaving the offending piece of burned flesh where it fell.

I was conscious that Pittam was still telling the story.

"It was a very hot day today, the gravedigger clearly wasn't going to dig a fraction of an inch more than was necessary and therefore during the service, we were interrupted by this little wizened man in a dirty sweaty T-shirt, who kept running into the church and measuring the coffin with a rather battered 12-inch ruler. He'd been in at least half a dozen times before the service finished, and each time there was a wail of anguish from the distraught widow." Pittam shoved another piece of meat into his mouth.

Liz had finished her vegetables and quickly turned down the offer of more.

I politely chewed on the remainder of the meat and wondered how people got pleasure out of chewing tobacco, which I supposed could hardly have tasted worse.

"And so, what happened then?" I asked, extracting a piece of chewed gristle from my mouth, and placing it on the side of my plate.

Pittam leaned over to pour me some more wine.

My reactions were immediate, and I just managed to pull my glass away in time.

Pittam didn't appear to notice.

"John Paul was carried out and duly lowered into the hole that had been dug. By this time, there were about thirty people, including the Priest milling around the grave. Problem was," Pittam broke off while he poured a large amount of wine into the glass from which he'd been drinking rum punch. "The hole was still too small, and the coffin jammed, so that the top was level with the ground, but it wouldn't go any further, probably because the gravedigger hadn't considered the battens on the sides of the coffin," Pittam smiled as he remembered the scene.

"The gravedigger obviously concerned that he might be involved in more manual work, suddenly broke through the crowd of mourners, and launched himself at the coffin. He jumped up and down on the top to get it to move. Nothing happened but on the third jump there was a sort of hollow shout," Pittam looked at Liz and me, to ensure that we were following the story, and then laughed. "The voice, came straight from the coffin, asking who the bloody hell was

48

jumping on his roof, and ordered them to get off at once."
Pittam straightened up in his chair, as Mrs. Crombie removed
his clean plate. "Well, there was absolute silence for about ten
seconds, you could have heard the proverbial pin drop, and
then there was a screech from the widow, and she and
everyone else, but me and the Priest, fled. They just
disappeared into the bushes."

"Would you like some pudding Ma'am," Mrs. Crombie
was talking to Liz.

"Oh, no thank you, I've had quite enough," said Liz,
truthfully. "Just some coffee would be fine," I hastily nodded
in assent.

"To cut a long story short," Pittam scraped his chair back,
"poor old John Paul had obviously had a tad too much to
drink and had become comatose, and this had been
misdiagnosed by the local doctor. The Priest and I got him
out, and he was extremely peeved to find that he was about to
be buried. Anyway, we got him home and he was fine, calling
for his supper. His wife wasn't too pleased, however, as she'd
already moved the boyfriend in, and he'd to exit via the back
window just as we took John Paul in through the front door."

Pittam guffawed, "welcome to the Caribbean."

Later in the evening, Pittam drove us back down to the
beach in an old Austin 10 of a type not seen on British roads
for at least twenty years. Somehow, it suited him

When we disembarked from the ancient vehicle on the
road next to the beach, Liz thanked Pittam for his hospitality.
"Think nothing of it, old girl, and you can now tell all your
friends that you've eaten the finest delicacy in the islands."

Liz and I looked surprised, even astonished.

"Hah. Hah," said Pittam, as though he were a magician
drawing a rabbit out of a hat. "A Manico, we had Manico for
dinner. Bet you thought it was lamb, eh?" I was quite unable
to answer, and suddenly felt decidedly nauseous. Liz grinned
all the way back to Shady Lady.

THE 'BURIAL' OF JOHN PAUL BAPTISTE...

3 - THE SAIL

And How We Nearly Didn't Make It

The next morning Liz told Anne Pittam's story, and she was understandably sceptical. "He was having you on," she laughed.

I wondered but was prepared to accept that it was true. I also wondered whether the meat really Manico had been, but when I remembered Josh's sudden change of plan, I understood that he'd known exactly what we were in for and had wisely left us to our fate.

I was quick to learn that retrieving anything from 20 feet down is troublesome enough without diving gear, but retrieving the heavy outboard engine proved to be extremely difficult. The human body is surprisingly buoyant. To dive from the sea surface down to the sea bed, twenty feet below, and stay there long enough to put a line around the motor proved to be beyond my diving capabilities, which I admitted weren't good to start with. Anne maliciously suggested that I tie some heavy fishing leads that we'd found on the boat to my ankles. I discarded the idea when Liz asked me to write my will before doing so. After several attempts to dive down from the surface, I thought I might solve the problem by diving off the stern of Shady Lady.

The extra height gave more power to the dive, but each time I reached the outboard, I couldn't get enough purchase on it to attach a line around it.

"Why don't you lasso it, daddy?" suggested Anne facetiously. She was thoroughly enjoying my discomfort.

"Actually, that's not such a bad idea," Liz said. Anne

looked pained.

Liz took some line, made a large loop with a slip knot, and handed it to me. After the third dive, I managed to get the loop over part of the engine. Now exhausted with my efforts, I climbed back on board, and we heaved at the other end of the line. To my delight, the outboard appeared above the water, but just as we were pulling it out of the sea, the knot slipped with a disconcerting SPLASH. "Oh no," I shouted at Liz for not tying a proper knot. "I wasn't a boy scout," she shot back, "and if you're so good at bloody knots," she growled, "do it yourself. I'm going to make some coffee," she turned and went below.

Chastened I got the end of the line and made a slip knot that would slip on the line but not become untied. After several more tries, I managed to dive down and attach the loop again, this time around the propeller. After I'd done that, and although by now completely exhausted, I hauled the offending machinery on board. Later in the day, when I'd partially recovered from my exertions, I set about stripping it and cleaning it as well as I could with the limited tools available. Despite my efforts, the outboard never did work again and we'd to row everywhere we went with the dinghy.

My attempt to recover and restore the engine took the rest of the morning and part of the afternoon, so we decided to head south for Bequia on the following day, which was a Saturday.

I reckoned it was some 10 to 12 hours sailing. The trip entailed crossing the St. Vincent Channel and depending upon visibility, I reckoned that we'd be out of sight of land for at least an hour of that time.

That evening, after supper at the Humming Bird, where the food was as delicious as Pittam's meal had been inedible, we planned our trip, spreading the charts out on the galley table and carefully taking bearings. I explained that St. Vincent was the next Island south in the Windward chain, and approximately the same size as St. Lucia, about 38 miles long north to south but rather more mountainous. I knew from the tourist guides that the northern end of the island had an active volcano that last erupted in 1979. Calculating that the distance between Soufriere and the northern end of

St. Vincent was about 28 miles, and the island of Bequia lay a further 6 miles south of St. Vincent, our total sailing distance was to be 72 miles. This would be the longest sail we'd ever attempted, but I was keen to sail straight to Bequia, because there were virtually no recommended stop-off points on the lee side of St. Vincent. The one that had been popular was Cumberland Bay, now notorious for the murder of a European skipper. So, we all agreed against stopping there. Wallilabou, the only other place frequented by yachts, was at that time the haunt of thieves. Josh had told us that the holding there was so bad, that yachtsmen had to rely on a local helper to tie a bow line to a palm tree. If the gratuity weren't good enough the line would be untied at some ungodly hour of the morning, with rather unpleasant results. In any case, I decided stopping at Wallilabou would mean us putting out a kedge anchor again and after the day's exertions, I much preferred to take the safer and less stressful option and sail the extra two hours or so necessary to get us to Bequia.

Liz and I had heard a lot about Bequia.

Fisher had enthused about it being a sailor's paradise. A small island shaped rather like a horseshoe, with the inside of the U to the lee of the wind, making it one of the largest natural harbours in the Windward Islands. Historically, the indigenous people are reputed to be a mix of North American whalers, Scottish farmers, French freebooters, and Negro slaves, and although administered by the island of St. Vincent, they're fiercely independent. It was one of the few inhabited islands not to have any airstrip, so the only way to reach it was by boat. (*No longer, unfortunately*).

To try and reach Bequia before sundown, I determined that we should set off at first light, which is about 5:30 a.m. almost all year round in the Caribbean.

Liz, not wishing to go below while in the channel, wisely prepared sandwiches from the only ingredient available, which was peanut butter. We later discovered that peanut butter sandwiches were excellent for inter-island trips, when the seas can run quite high at times, for they seemed to settle the stomach. Liz reckoned she could stay below just long enough to make coffee without throwing up, but I put some fruit juice in the cockpit, just in case. We all got to bed early, and because there was a pleasant breeze in Soufriere, we didn't experience the problem with mosquitoes we had in Marigot.

Shady Lady was a hive of activity by 5 a.m. next morning, but it was just after six before we got away. Picking up the kedge anchor proved to be more difficult than I'd thought, as it was well and truly wedged. In the end, we used the jib winch to release it.

While Anne steered a course across the bay, heading south, we secured the kedge anchor on board, then Liz paid out the dinghy painter until the little boat was following like a faithful dog about three yards behind. The breeze was quite light in the lee, so I'd no difficulty in pulling up the mainsail without turning from our course, leaving first Petit Piton and then Gross Piton, to port. The mountains are most impressive from the sea and there's a very small, pretty bay between the two huge monoliths, which was deserted. (*It now houses the expensive resort of Jallousie*).

I took over the wheel and Anne went back to her usual horizontal position on the deck. I noticed that she was now wearing a T-shirt. Shady Lady sailed on a bearing of about 185 degrees, and as we left the Pitons behind us, the wind began to freshen. I handed the wheel to Liz, and I went forward and pulled up the jib. Almost immediately, we started to catch the wind and with some minor adjustments to the main sail, we could feel Shady Lady surging forward. I felt a sense of accomplishment as I ceremoniously turned off the engine. There's nothing quite like the peace that envelops a yacht when moving under sail I thought, as we started to enjoy the scenery sliding silently behind us. After an hour, Shady Lady encountered some heavier seas, but the day was sunny and the most the waves managed to do was remove Anne from the forward deck.

There was some considerable excitement on board when a school of dolphins joined the yacht, playing around the moving boat for half an hour or more much to the delight of Anne who watched them from the bow.

At about 11 a.m. St. Vincent appeared in the distance, and I felt a surge of pride that I'd passed my first major test in sea navigation. Liz produced coffee and sandwiches at about twelve, and as the sun was now extremely hot, we all wisely put-on long-sleeved shirts and hats. Liz and I, like all newcomers to the Caribbean, had been warned to cover ourselves up while sailing, as the breeze masks the full effects of the sun, and the painful consequences wouldn't be fully felt until port is reached.

"What's that?" Liz pointed to a dark patch on the eastern horizon.

I looked in the direction she was pointing. "Just a dark cloud," I shrugged, but couldn't avoid feeling just a little uneasy.

St. Vincent was now quite large in our sight, but I kept a wary eye on the cloud, which was growing more rapidly in size than the island of St Vincent and starting to cover the entire sea area on the port side. I became more concerned as the phenomenon drew nearer; it looked like a huge water spout, certainly, there was no difference between the sea and the sky at the point of contact. I racked my brains for an answer. I'd read that there were no water spouts in the area but then the locals always said there were no sharks in the Caribbean. After waiting for the customary look of relief on the visitor's face at this welcome information they'd then add, 'ye see, they (*the sharks*) have all read the tourist brochures.'

Liz stood up in the cockpit, "I don't like the look of it, it really looks menacing," she said worriedly watching the now black cloud racing towards us.

Neither did I, surely it wasn't a hurricane I thought, but my heart was thumping. "It's just a rain cloud," I replied as much to bolster my own courage as Liz's and Anne's. My voice couldn't have carried much conviction.

"Shouldn't we be doing something?" asked Liz.

"Like turning around and heading back," added Anne.

"It's too late for that, in any case. . ." I was cut off in mid-sentence when WHOOOMPH, a blast of wind hit Shady Lady, and we heeled over so much so that the sea was now surging over. the starboard rail WHOOOMPH..., Whoomph..., WHOOOMPH, this time the wind was even stronger than before, and for the first time I was quite frightened. It took all my strength to hold the yacht on course, and as I looked up at the flapping mainsail, I worried that it would rip. Then it rained. It wasn't just rain, it was a deluge, with even more wind, and it became suddenly and surprisingly cold. Visibility was virtually zero, and I was grateful that we were out in the channel and clear of any known rocks.

I desperately reached over to let off some line on the boom, which I reckoned would take the strain off the main, but my fingers were now cold and wet. As I uncleated it, the wind pressure on the mainsail simply whisked the line through my hands. Foolishly, I tried to hold on and as a result, I suffered quite a bad friction burn on my hand. I yelped with the pain and let go seeing clearly that we were now in trouble. The seas had become alive, and it felt as though we were riding a bucking bronco. The boom swung dangerously from side to side, and I knew that if I couldn't secure it, it could snap at any moment. I recollected reading a sea book somewhere, Hornblower perhaps, that said when a bad storm blew up the galleon ran with the wind, in other words with the bow pointed away from the wind direction. In desperation, I turned the wheel. The pressure on the sails appeared to ease immediately, the sea stopped coming over the cockpit and came over the stern instead, but the boom was still swinging now even more wildly, and I knew we would have to get hold of the whipping line, which was now out of reach over the side. I passed the wheel to a reluctant Liz.

"Hold on to this course," I yelled.

Liz peered at the compass needle, which was gyrating all over the dial.

"What course?" she shouted.

I threw my arm out to indicate direction, but as I couldn't see anything to head for, I'd no idea whether the direction was correct or not. "Just keep the wind behind us," I yelled.

I turned and shouted to Anne, "Anne, help me get hold of the boom line," I pointed in the direction of the cavorting piece of line that was teasing us, one moment whipping in our faces and the next going out of reach.

Anne shouted something rude in reply, but went to assist anyway, neither of us helped by the instability of the yacht, the slippery surface on deck and the incessant downpour.

The line caught me and Anne several times in the face, but

we managed to get hold of it during a lull, and Anne immediately wrapped one end around a winch. This done, Liz drew in the boom until the main sail no longer flapped. It was then that I was conscious of the jib making a strange sound; it had ripped straight down the middle. Groaning inwardly, I knew that there was no way to reef the main to reduce the amount of sail presented to the wind. Lowering it and tying off a portion around the boom would normally be simple, but the wind was simply too strong to attempt it. I did the first sensible thing since the rain had hit us by turning on the engine, which enabled Liz to get some control of the direction of the boat. Realising that I had to get on deck to let down the tattered foresail, I half slid, and half crawled my way to the bow, being deluged with sea water every fifteen seconds or so as Shady Lady rolled in the rough sea. Eventually reaching the forestay, I turned and shouted at Anne, who was in the cockpit.

"Let off the jib lines," it was like pissing into the wind. Neither Anne nor Liz could hear me, they could only understand that I was getting more and more frustrated, as I hung grimly on to the bow and gesticulated to them. Liz, aware of my precarious position, lost her concentration and instead of steering the boat downwind, allowed the bow to come around. Immediately, the wind caught the now billowing main, and I felt my grip slipping.

"For Christ's sake, steer away from the wind," I shouted again gesticulating with my hand. Liz couldn't hear but understood the message and I saw Anne gamely crawling along the deck towards me. When she reached the bow, I told her that we needed the jib halyard released and told her where to find it on the mast.

Unfortunately, none of my children were able to distinguish their right from their left therefore, after Anne got back to the mast and had struggled to stand up-right she got hold of a halyard. I saw what she was doing but it was too late.

"The other side you idiot," I shouted and watched with dismay as the main dropped into the water.

There's a time in any crisis I thought, when one feels that, the odds of winning aren't commensurate with the effort put in and when it would be best to let fate take its course while you lie down and die. I groaned, with no pressure on the main, the boom started to swing wildly again, and I saw Liz duck as it swept inches from her head. Anne had the presence of mind to grab the boom line and haul it in. She then went back to the mast and let off the jib halyard. Nothing happened. I looked up at the two flapping bits of sail and realised that the top had wound itself around the forestay, and that I'd have to hoist myself up the mast to release it. I also realised that there was no way I could accomplish that in the present conditions and abandoned the idea. I pushed back my wet hair and headed unsteadily, on all fours, back to the cockpit. I pulled in the mainsail that was now dragging in the sea and just as Anne and I were bringing the last bit of sail into the cockpit, we were conscious of a sudden calm.

Almost like magic, the wind dropped, the rain stopped, and the seas were almost back to normal. Within a minute, the sun was shining as before and we all looked at the offending squall, for that's what it had been, fast disappearing like some huge express train, towards the mainland of St. Vincent. We looked at the eastern horizon, it was clear, and Liz sighed with relief. Now was the time for taking stock. I looked at Shady Lady from the cockpit and imagined that this was what a shady lady might have looked like after a night out. At that moment, Liz raced for the side and brought up her peanut butter sandwiches, probably due to delayed reaction rather than the rough sea. After pulling in the main, we hauled it back up, but this time with one reef, kept in for the rest of the trip. I secured the flapping jib sail, at least the part I could reach, and changed course back towards St. Vincent, now completely blotted out by the squall we'd just experienced.

The whole episode had lasted only about twenty minutes but realising just how dangerous a position we had been in we resolved to go over the lessons we'd learned once we reached Bequia so not be caught again.

Shady Lady reached the northern end of St. Vincent at about 2.30 p.m. and once in the lee of the island, there was no wind, so we folded the main and kept the engine running to try and make up for lost time. Josh had told me how to use the Boson's chair to get up the mast, but I never thought I'd have to use it. In the event, it was easier than I'd thought and although Liz had visions of me crashing to the deck from the top of the mast, as had I when I got up there and looked down, I managed to unwind and release the twisted and torn jib while we were still under way.

While stowing the offending sail, I noticed that there was another, smaller fore sail in the sail locker, and I decided to hoist that once Shady Lady caught the wind again off the south end of St Vincent.

The scenery on St. Vincent is stupendous when viewed from the sea and we all enjoyed the relaxing atmosphere, as the yacht chugged gently south. The island is much more mountainous than St. Lucia, the volcano at the north end rising to over 4,000 feet. It's also a much more primitive and rugged terrain, covered in a tangle of dense rain forest. The colours were predominantly green except where huge lava trails lead from the volcano down to the sea.

There's a funny story about the volcano told in Chris Doyle's 'Sailors Guide to the Windwards'. I had read it somewhere and the words came to mind now. It goes like this: *'I'd a friend who was anchored under the Volcano in April 1979 he'd an amateur geologist on board. Together they scaled the volcano and peered into the depths. The geologist declared it was safely dormant. That night, which happened to be both Friday the 13 and Good Friday there was a rumbling from the very bowels of the earth, and it erupted with a massive cloud that landed dust hundreds of miles away.*

'It created a fog so thick they couldn't see the bow of the boat they were on and had to sail completely blind, steering by compass to get away from the volcanic dust.'

It was about 3.30 p.m., and I was just dozing off when Anne, whose turn it was to be at the wheel, yelled, "Daddy, daddy, There's a submarine straight ahead of us."

I snapped out of my doze.

"Don't be stupid," I snapped.

I suddenly thought 'ROCKS'. The charts had shown a jumble of rocks, called appropriately Bottle and Glass, extending from the coast line of St. Vincent for about quarter of a mile about half way down the island. I jumped up, catching my head on the boom as I did so, and peered ahead through slightly blurred eyes. I thought Anne had perhaps steered too far inland and that we were about to visit St. Vincent in a way that had not been planned. A quick look made me realise that she'd correctly kept the boat about a mile offshore and I knew from looking at the charts the night before that there were no rocks on the course, we were taking.

"Look over there," Anne was pointing straight ahead, panic in her voice.

Sure enough, there was a huge black bulge protruding from the water only about 200 metres ahead. It was moving slowly and certainly looked like a submarine. I searched for the tell-tale conning tower, as I grabbed the wheel from a mesmerised Anne and swung the boat sharply to starboard. The suspected submarine must have heard us, because it suddenly developed a huge fin–like tail and immediately disappeared beneath the waves. I half expected it to surface with Shady Lady on top of it and steeled myself for the impact. Liz, who had been asleep, joined Anne and me on deck, and then we realised that we'd seen our first whale, probably dozing in the sunshine.

"That was too bloody close for comfort," I said.

We realised that until we'd seen one at close quarters none of us had been aware of just how large these mammals are, but we were fortunate in getting so close to one, although none of us felt so at the time.

I turned Shady Lady back on course, and we remained alert from then on, but our new-found friend didn't reappear. A school of dolphins escorted us for about five minutes at the southern end of St. Vincent, but other than that, the rest of the trip towards Bequia was uneventful. I started to worry though, as it was clear we weren't going to make the island before nightfall. The lower Caribbean authorities in those days were not renowned for marking out where the reefs were and certainly, any buoy or marker that was there would not be lit. I knew from the charts that there were two hazards in Bequia, one was a shoal to port, to avoid when passing the end of the horseshoe, before entering Admiralty Bay proper, appropriately called Devil's Table, the other was in the middle of the anchorage, between the town of Port Elizabeth and the

Princess Margaret Beach, which is on the south side of the inner horseshoe. I also knew that in the moonlight, we'd be able to give the first shoal a wide berth, but I wondered about the second.

As it happened, I needn't have worried. As Shady Lady manoeuvred gingerly around the headland, two young boys in a small rowing boat met us. Rodney and Wilbur descended like African vultures who knew their prey was at its most vulnerable. Staunch boat boys, despite their young age, they quickly sensed that we weren't seasoned sailors, perhaps the torn jib lying on the fore deck gave them a clue. After hitching a tow, Wilbur came on board and pointed to some lights ahead.

"You go there," he pointed.

We anchored safely in no time. After promising to let our two new friends show us around Bequia on Monday morning. I gave the boys EC$2.00 and they rowed away happily into the night.

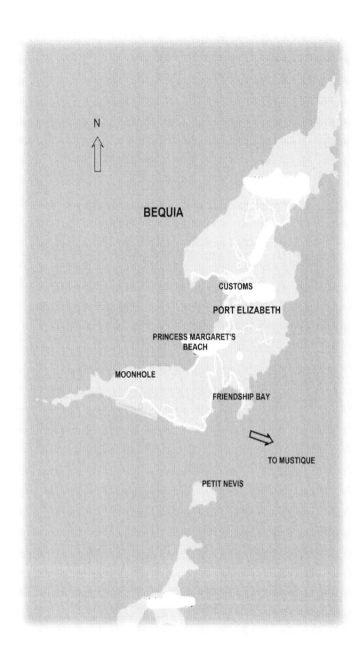

4 - THE CALM BEFORE THE STORM

And How Liz and I Lost a daughter

Although Admiralty Bay is in the lee of Bequia and because the island is small, about 8 miles long by 2 miles at its widest part, the wind whistles down through the hills behind the town.

At times, the force of the wind is such that I wondered if the anchor would hold the boat. Consequently, I was up several times during the night to ensure Shady Lady wasn't dragging. Alone on deck my mind returned to the previous days and the dangers of sailing without proper experience. I then began to think about setting up some sort of time plan for my book, but the empty starlit night swallowed that idea up in a deep but short sleep.

One of my many appearances on deck awakened Anne, and she asked me rather crossly, what I was doing stamping around the deck in the early hours of the morning.

"I thought it was dragging," I said tiredly.

"Dragging?"

I took a deep breath and explained.

"Dragging is when your anchor has dropped on the sea bed but, for whatever reason hasn't dug in to the ground under the sea," I continued patiently, "this can be because there's an old bicycle that someone threw overboard or due to a coral

63

bed that disintegrates when a heavy object drops on it.

"The result," I continued, "is that your pride and joy will quickly move backwards until something stops it, like rocks or, if you're lucky another boat. The only remedy is to re-set the anchor, often in another area. It's just what you need after a hard day's sail, a heavy dinner and enough rum punch to guarantee that you invariably drop it in the wrong place again, again and again," I scowled at the taut anchor rode.

"Why didn't you check it, like we used to in the motor boat?" asked Anne reasonably.

"You mean, reverse backwards once the anchor has been dropped?"

"Yes,"

"Because I didn't," I confessed angrily. I'd forgotten the procedures we used to adopt when we owned our own boat, unhappy too, that it had to be Anne who reminded me.

Anne shrugged her shoulders, "Seems to me to be the obvious thing to have. . ."

She saw my fists clenching and decided that it would be better to leave the goading for another day. Hastily she went below.

The next morning was cool and sunny with a steady pleasant breeze, which is the second reason why Bequia is so popular. The first reason is that they reputedly grow the best 'grass', more commonly known as ganja, in the Caribbean.

All the shops closed on Sunday, as it was a holiday, so we enjoyed a full day doing nothing. On Monday, the good weather continued, and Wilbur and Rodney rowed up to Shady Lady while everyone was having breakfast and offered to fetch ice, water, food, and with a sly glance at Anne, 'grass.'

I settled for the boys rowing us all into the town of Port Elizabeth so we could look around. Anne noticed that they'd a dinghy very similar to that of Shady Lady, and it reminded me of one of Commander Fisher's last warnings.

"Oh, and lock your dinghy to your boat at night, dear boy. You'd be surprised at how many goes missing." I'd nodded sagely, and deliberately refrained from asking the price of replacing one. I also realised that I'd forgotten to lock the dinghy the night before and resolved to make sure that didn't happen again.

Shady Lady was anchored well out in the bay, no doubt Rodney and Wilbur had assessed our sailing competence, or rather the lack of it at an early stage and decided we should drop anchor before becoming tangled up with the sixty or so other boats that had anchored in the area. This meant that rowing into Port Elizabeth was no easy task, particularly as there were five people in the dinghy and a twenty-five-knot head-wind. I was pleased that Rodney was doing the rowing. Wilbur explained that he, Wilbur, was the captain, and Rodney the first mate. Quite how Wilbur got away with this most unfair demarcation, I never found out, but he was clearly the boss, even though he was only thirteen years of age and Rodney fifteen. During the row in, the wind came in fierce warm gusts, and it amused us to see a man in a dinghy coming towards us. His only motive power was a large black umbrella, which he held in front of his craft.

During the time it took to reach the shore, I had time to take stock of our surroundings. To the left and astern of the small dinghy, the land rose from the area of Devil's Table like an accusing finger pointing due west. The ground swept up to a ridge that spanned the full length of that side of the bay, only to disappear into another larger hill in front of us. On the shore line, the first sign of habitation was one or two little houses with corrugated iron roofs and then a small dock built on stilts before the town proper started. The town of Port Elizabeth spread out to the left and the houses on the hillside were interspersed with deep green foliage, as though someone had said, 'I would like a house here,' and simply built it. There seemed to be no order, no planning, no concern for what others may think, just practical little dwellings, most of them with superb views. The whole small town looked wonderful, and I couldn't help feeling that it would do no harm for some of the supposedly skilled planning authorities in the western world to look at Bequia and understand that everything doesn't have to be organised or even be in a straight line to be functional.

We arrived at the Frangipani Hotel boat dock and stepped ashore where small and not so small boys accosted us.

"Look after yer boat man," the leading one said.

A string of invective flowed from Wilbur's lips.

Because we'd got out first, while Wilbur held the boat, the other local boys hadn't noticed him. The throng glowered and passed on to another boat just drawing in.

"Rodney'll look after de boat," Wilbur broke off to chastise another youth who had the temerity to approach within a yard.

"An' we go to town." Wilbur threw his hand out expansively and pointed towards the two dozen or so shacks that comprised the shopping area of Port Elizabeth.

The Frangipani Hotel stands on the bay-shore and whilst there was no beach there, the gardens were indeed full of blossoming pink and cream frangipani. In the front of the small hotel was a patio where one could sit in the shade and have cool drinks. A sandy path led from the hotel and along the shore. It went past a small boutique and then became a tarmac road. The whole of Port Elizabeth is basically one street running parallel with the shore and apart from some market stalls, two small supermarkets (*a small corner shop in England would be larger than these*), a branch of the ubiquitous Barclays Bank and a book shop, said to be one of the best in the Caribbean, that was it.

It took us precisely ten minutes to establish where everything was and then we all trundled into the customs where we had to register our arrival, having crossed into a new country. The formalities were slow and ponderous, but thirty minutes later, we emerged some $130 the poorer, having paid entry fees and cruising fees for the Grenadines.

I'd no intention of rowing the quarter mile each day to where Shady Lady was moored, and in any case, as Anne had used up all the water, we had to move in order fill up. I managed to do so without Wilbur's help, and it peeved him no end that I'd done so. After replenishing Shady Lady's water tanks at the small marina for some exorbitant amount of dollars, we anchored the yacht much closer to shore. As water was so costly, Liz suggested to Anne that she attempt to restrict her shower time somewhat. This didn't meet with Anne's approval however, nor did it make the slightest difference to the time she appropriated the shower for, much to Liz's annoyance.

We spent the next five days in Bequia, and I made good

progress with the outline of my book and wrote a couple of chapters. Computers were in their infancy, so I was writing everything in longhand. I'd reached the first sex scene but was finding great difficulty in putting my thoughts on to paper, I discussed the passage with Liz and asked her advice.

She read what I'd written and grimaced.

"I should leave sex out of it if I were you, you're no good at it." My jaw dropped in a pained expression.

Anne's head swivelled round, in anticipation of further revelations.

Liz smiled, "at writing about it, silly."

"But I must have sex in it, for it to be commercially acceptable," I argued.

"Why? I read lots of books without sex and I enjoy them," Liz answered.

"I don't," said Anne, who had been listening intently, "Of course you've got to have sex, daddy. If you can't have it, the next best thing is to read about it," she said ruefully.

Liz glowered at her.

In the end, I managed to convey the love of a couple without unnecessary detailed descriptions.

We had now been in the Caribbean for 12 days, and so we decided to take the next step in our journey south. About three hours sail from Bequia, almost due south east, is the island of Mustique, which means Mosquito in French. Liz thought it would be a good idea to stop off there for at least a day, before going down to the Grenadines proper. After lunch, everyone felt lethargic. The stay in Bequia had been uneventful and we'd been lulled into a feeling of peaceful euphoria, a state that was about to be rudely shattered. We all turned in early. Although the next day's sail wasn't a long one, I was beginning to realise that the earlier one does things on a boat, the more time there is to cope with disasters.

I woke up to a large bang on the side of Shady Lady. In a container made of fibreglass, which was what Shady Lady effectively was, any sound however slight reverberates and amplifies. This had sounded as though something large and heavy had hit the boat hard. I went into a cold sweat. My immediate thought was that the anchor had come free, and we were on the rocks.

Unfortunately, I still hadn't learned that one shouldn't move too quickly on a boat, particularly just after wakening. When we had gone to bed, the hatch to our cabin roof had been open. I naturally expected that it still was. In my haste to stick my head through to discover the cause of the bang, I found out that it was closed.

"Ooooww," I shouted, as my head made contacted with the Plexiglas and I was catapulted straight back towards the berth. "F***, F***, F***," I hissed, as I nursed the already painful and tender parts of my body still not recovered from previous ill use.

Liz was now fully awake.

"Do you mind NOT using four letter words," Liz's Methodist upbringing came to the fore.

"Why the hell did you close the hatch?"

"Because it started to rain, anyway what on earth are you doing? It's after midnight," Liz was looking at her luminous clock by the side of the berth.

"Didn't you hear the bang?" I asked.

She hadn't.

I heard someone moving on the deck above us and I immediately thought of the murdered skipper in Cumberland Bay. Only the previous day, we'd also heard a similar story of an unfortunate Canadian knifed and killed while asleep in his yacht over in Friendship Bay. Friendship being on the south end of Bequia. I swallowed hard, and gently opened the hatch. It was Anne. She was already up and apparently having an urgent conversation with someone.

I hastily put on some shorts, and carefully negotiated the cabin entrance, climbed onto the aft deck, and quickly established what had happened. A French boat had come in late and anchored too near to Shady Lady. As their vessel was made of concrete and therefore much heavier than Shady Lady, it didn't swing in the wind as quickly. which is why it had made contact. It was an immediate relief to me to find that the anchor hadn't moved but it became clear that Anne was having a very acrimonious exchange with someone on the offending boat.

"Degagez, degagez," (Push Off).

The small man on the French yacht was gesticulating

wildly.

"And you, fuck off, you little creep, we were here first," shouted Anne. "I wonder where she learned that language," I muttered to Liz, who had just joined me on deck.

The Frenchman let off a string of verbal abuse in return.

"He'd look rather like a stick insect if he didn't have that mop of dark hair," whispered Liz

Anne was in her element. While she didn't comprehend the content of the Frenchman's speech, the way he delivered it was crystal clear. She snarled something that questioned the Frenchman's lineage and put a fender down between the two boats. The Frenchman became even more agitated. Liz noticed that three small children and a youngish woman, whom she assumed was the mother and an older woman, who appeared to be Grandma, arrived on the deck of the other boat. Their yacht started to close with Shady Lady again, and the Frenchman became quite hysterical, jumping up and down on the deck, shaking his fist. Another stream of French came across, and my confrontational ire was now up. I went and stood by Anne to give verbal support. By this time, the young woman and Grandma had joined in, the young woman gesticulating wildly. The noise was such that various disturbed yachtsmen were switching on cabin lights around the area. Liz came up behind me.

"For God's sake, let's move," said Liz. "It doesn't matter who's right and who's wrong, the whole bay will be awake if this goes on," I was about to give an answer, when Anne turned around to Liz momentarily suspending the exchange of good plain English invective.

"Not bloody likely," she growled. "Do you know what he just called me?" Before she'd a chance to tell Liz, the Frenchman made a big mistake. He had picked a long boat hook up off his deck and was prodding it into the side of Shady Lady. His idea was to push the boats further apart, but at the expense of Shady Lady's free board. We heard a scrape on the side of the yacht and Anne moved with unfamiliar speed. She grabbed the end of the hook and pulled. Unfortunately, the Frenchman was caught completely off balance and he didn't let go. He was standing between a gap on the surrounding wire structure that most boats have allowing people to climb into a dinghy, and he had been bending forward slightly. For a split second, he teetered on the brink, with a comical expression on his face and then he went overboard with a loud splash. The young woman, who had seen what was going to happen, tried to catch him, and only just managed to stop falling in too. Anne dropped the boat hook just as the Frenchman was surfacing, and there was a howl, as it caught him squarely on the top of his head. Anne's honour was satisfied and as there appeared to be no more abuse to exchange, she left what she clearly thought was the 'mopping up' to those less skilled in the art of international diplomacy.

She returned to her cabin, grumbling, and growling as she went, missing seeing the Frenchman's toupee floating to the surface like a black wounded jelly fish. I assumed that the combined effect of immersion in the water and the boat hook falling on his head unstuck the ghastly apparition.

I watched long enough to ensure that the man could swim, and then turned my attention to the main problem, which was that unless one of the boats moved the banging would continue unabated throughout the remainder of the night. The crew on the French boat were now much more concerned with retrieving their man overboard than they were with Shady Lady, so it was unlikely that a solution would come from the French boat.

"Well, I'm not going to move," I said to Liz.

Liz pursed her lips.

"James, there can only be one winner in a contest between fibreglass and concrete and that's not going to be us,"

"Anne put fenders out," I remarked ignoring Liz's plea, "so they should take up any further impact,"   but I knew that fenders wouldn't be enough.

I stroked my chin thoughtfully, "I know," I said.

"Let's bring the dinghy in from the stern and tie it to the side. If Frenchie boy," I inclined my head in the direction of the French boat, which due to a wind change, was now several yards away and whose crew were just about to haul in a dripping, and very bald Frenchman, "makes contact again, he'll scratch his free-board on the row-locks."

"Great idea," agreed Liz. "You're a genius."

"I know," I said. We made our way aft and I looked for the dinghy painter. 'Liz, where's the dinghy?" Liz looked over the stern. There was nothing. I quickly walked around Shady Lady. There was no dinghy in sight.

I frowned, "Have you moved it?"

"Of course, I haven't moved it," growled Liz.

"Are you sure," and without waiting for an answer, "has Anne?"

"No, Anne hasn't touched it either," answered Liz.

"Did you tie it on properly?" asked Liz.

I thought back to the early evening. I knew I'd tied it securely, but I also knew that I hadn't locked it to Shady Lady with the steel painter provided for that purpose.

"Yes, of course, I tied it on properly," I answered irritably.

"Surely, they haven't pinched it," Liz peered into the gloom at the French boat.

"Well, if they have, they're in real trouble," I answered grimly.

"Not if they sail off before morning," answered Liz, almost to herself.

I thought about what she had said.

"I'm going in," I said.

"What?" Liz looked startled.

"I'm going to swim around the bastard's boat, to see if it's on the other side. If it's there, I'll bring it back."

Liz became alarmed. "Don't be silly. You couldn't reach their deck from the water, and if they had it, they'd certainly have it tied to the deck."

I noticed that the entire crew of the French boat seemed to have gone down below and, one by one, the cabin lights started to go out.

"I'll take a carving knife with me. I've a good mind to cut his bloody anchor rode too," I said in frustration.

Liz was even more alarmed.

"Don't be a fool that could be dangerous, and besides, his anchor is attached to a chain, I heard it clatter down when they anchored," Liz said finally.

I realised she was right, but I also had to be sure that they didn't have the dinghy. I fetched the carving knife from the

71

galley and silently slid down the aft ladder into the water. It was surprisingly warm. Carefully inserting the long knife into my mouth and making sure the sharp end pointed away from me, I swam towards the bow of the French boat, with the knife clamped firmly between my teeth

I felt a bit foolish when I reached the other side and found only one dinghy in evidence, which was not ours. I decided it would be quicker to swim right around the boat to get back to Shady Lady and it was while I was doing a silent doggy paddle, about ten yards from the starboard side of the concrete hull, that I heard a yelp from the French yacht. The little man, who was still completely bald, had obviously been calming himself down with a cigarette on the side away from Shady Lady, and had spotted me swimming in the water. Within seconds the whole family was on deck again and pointing towards me. The young woman was saying something earnestly to the man. I caught the words "Allons, allons," and I saw her making stabbing signs.

It was then I realised that I must have looked rather threatening swimming around their boat, pirate fashion with a large knife between my teeth and plainly visible in the moonlight. I hurriedly changed to a crawl and gave the French yacht a very wide berth indeed, as I swam back to Shady Lady. Because of the detour, it took me some minutes. I climbed the aft ladder, removing the knife as I did so, and Liz helped me on board.

"Well, you must have done something." she said in admiration, "because they're moving." I looked across at the French boat and heard the throb of the engine. I saw the young woman engage their electric windlass, which pulled up the anchor chain, and the vessel was under way. The Frenchman turned his boat in front of Shady Lady and passed about twenty feet away, headed in the direction of the sea.

As he drew level, he put his finger to his head and shouted something quite impolite. Anne once more emerged from the depths of the cabin, looking extremely pugnacious. The Frenchman was concentrating so much on me, that he hadn't seen a large wooden hulled yacht that had swung around in the wind, clearly silhouetted by the lights on the shore, and was now completely blocking his path. I instinctively shouted a warning.

"Look out, you idiot," I pointed ahead of the Frenchman's yacht.

Plainly taking this as provocation, the little man left his wheel unattended and rushed to the side of his boat nearest to Shady Lady, where he performed a little jig, with his thumbs in his ears and tongue out.

"The man is bonkers," Liz had been watching.

The young woman, who had been stowing away the anchor walked back towards the wheel. She suddenly realised why I'd shouted and turned around to look towards the bow. She turned back and yelled in desperation. "Andre, attention, attention," The Frenchman looked but he was far too late.

There was a sharp sound of splintering wood, and then a TWANG, as the Frenchman's fore-stay snapped under the impact, he'd ploughed into the bow of the wooden boat, removed the bowsprit in the action and become tangled up with their anchor chain.

He clasped his bald head in his hands in disbelief.

"Mon Dieu," he cried plaintively, as two rather rough and belligerent looking Swedish sailors appeared on the deck of the wooden boat.

Liz tugged at my arm.

"Time, we went to bed, I think," Anne had already gone down below again in disgust, and I felt that she was probably a little disappointed now that the battle was plainly at an end. Liz and I took one last look at the French boat; its mast was now leaning at an angle of forty-five degrees with the Swedes advancing ominously towards the instigator of the damage. I smiled, Liz smiled, and then we howled with laughter. It took us some time to get to sleep, as one or the other of us kept having a fit of giggles. We'd both forgotten the missing dinghy.

I was somewhat chagrined to wake up at first light by a pounding on the hull.

Liz looked worried.

"It's the bloody Frenchman," I said as I swung aggressively out of bed, pulled on my still wet shorts and with gritted teeth, charged out of the cabin. I stopped short. In front of me was a fierce looking bearded local, who was hanging on to the side of Shady Lady.

"This yer dinghy man," he nodded his head in the direction of a small fibreglass boat, which was tied to his own inflatable. I looked and my heart jumped.

It had Shady Lady 2 painted on the side.

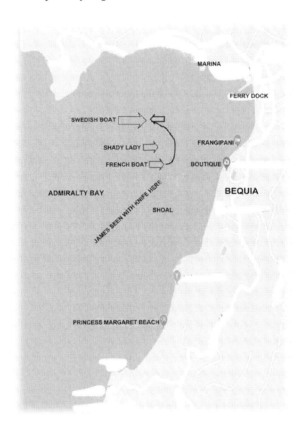

"Yes," I answered, looking puzzled, "where did you find it?"

"Way out man, Way out," the black man pointed airily in the region of western horizon. "You must've tied 'im bad," he explained.

I knew that I hadn't, and that it was quite definitely secure when I left it, but I didn't feel that I'd achieve anything by arguing.

"Well, thank you very much," I said, trying to smile. It

soon became obvious that the black man wasn't about to part company without an exchange of cash, so I offered him a wet $10 dollar note from my pocket.

The man shook his head contemptuously.

"Noo man, I lost a whole day fishin' to get this boat for ye."

"How much," I asked grimly,

"$200," he growled. Eventually, the amount fell to $50, because I was able to convince him that we'd no more cash on board. He reluctantly parted with the dinghy after accepting the money with bad grace and sped off towards the shore.

I was glad to get the dinghy back at almost any price as without one we would have had to swim everywhere, and I shuddered at the thought of the cost of replacing the damn thing. When Wilbur and Rodney turned up to say good-bye, I told them what had happened.

"You shouldn't have given 'im anything," said Wilbur

"He does it all th' time, steals dinghies, then takes it back and demands $20 for findin' it," added Rodney.

I didn't wish to lose face by letting them know that I'd parted with $50, "why doesn't someone report him to the police?" I asked.

Wilbur shrugged.

"They prob'ly take a cut," he answered cynically. "In any case, the guy is a witness for the police in a murder, so they say they wanna keep 'im sweet."

"So, until he testifies," said Liz, who had been listening from the cockpit, "the police won't act against him?"

"Yea, another lesson learned in the rich tapestry of life," answered Anne, who had been listening in and grinning.

We sailed Shady Lady at about 10 a.m. The Swedes were working on the bow of their boat, and they gave a cheery wave. I suspected that they'd turned their disaster into a cash windfall.

I had established that there were two ways to reach Mustique from Bequia. One route would take us around the north end of the island, along the channel between St. Vincent and Bequia itself, the southern route was between some small uninhabited islands just south of Bequia. The small island nearest to Bequia on the south side is Petit Nevis, where an average of one whale a year ends its life.

We had been warned that the smell on the little patch of land was usually putrid from the remains of the last unhappy creature, which was no doubt another reason for the island being uninhabited. For those interested in the environment, Bequia is the only country in the world approved by Greenpeace for killing whales. This presumably is because they still use the old methods of hand-harpooning from an open boat and the whale probably has a better chance of damaging the thrower than the reverse.

The distance from Port Elizabeth to the far western end of Bequia is about two miles or so 'down-wind' and because Shady Lady had only one undamaged jib that was too small for anything but the fiercest wind, we had to use the engine as well. I'd given the larger torn jib to a sail-maker in Bequia, who, after berating Fisher's company for supplying the yacht with rotten sails, promised he'd have it repaired and ready before Shady Lady left to sail south. Unsurprisingly, he hadn't completed the task in time, so I resolved to collect the sail on our way back up to St. Lucia in about two weeks' time.

Anne picked up Shady Lady's anchor and we sailed out of Admiralty Bay, heading due west. I looked back to where the little coloured houses of Port Elizabeth spilled over into the next bay, called Princess Margaret's Beach, separated only by an underwater reef of coral. The beach is a beautiful strip of yellow sand that merges with the warm Caribbean water sloping gradually away under the sea, making it ideal for family swimming. Just after the beach, the land becomes rougher and twists into a second finger, again heading for the western horizon, parallel with the land opposite. This land on the south side stretches for almost two miles before reaching the end, which culminates in two areas of broken rocks with the sea swirling in between them.

As Shady Lady neared the end of the southern point of the horseshoe, Liz was the first to notice some very strange houses built into the hillside on the port side. All are a concrete grey colour, with holes instead of glass windows and in some cases, the houses were built into the rock. Anne remarked that they looked like something Fred and Wilma of the Flintstones might live in. I heard later that an American architect called Tom Johnson, believed that dwellings should fit into the landscape. He didn't believe in the use of glass, which inhibited a free flow of air. The place was appropriately called Moon Hole. To me, the buildings were a not very attractive, but Anne argued that they were a sight worth seeing, if only for their strangeness.

"I've just read a story about one of those houses," Anne announced smugly. "I'll share it with you if you like."

Liz urged her to continue.

"Well, there is one house that was partly built inside a cavernous piece of rock jutting out from the mainland. If you go close enough, you can see straight through the house because it's empty, and this is the funny bit, the owner left after part of the top of the cave fell on to his bed, fortunately just after he'd got up. They reckon that the only toilet in the house, was carved directly out of the cave's floor, allowing the unmentionables to drop straight down into the sea. I wonder if they posted notices up advising tourists not to fish in that area when the owner was in residence."

We sailed our way around the southern end of the horseshoe and tacked east towards Petit Nevis, so that we could anchor there and have lunch. However, Liz suggested that we abandon that idea when we met the smell of dead whale meat some 100 yards off shore. Instead, we headed straight through the northern channel between Bequia and Petit Nevis towards Mustique, which was now in full in view, but because of the danger of hitting the Montezuma Shoal on a direct route, we took a northern tack to arrive at our destination in one piece. After about ninety minutes sailing, we turned due south, to approach Mustique from the north.

Anne excitedly pointed out the wreck of a huge passenger liner that had foundered on the rocks at the northern end of the island. Because the area was very rocky, we couldn't get too close, but Liz wondered what on earth a liner captain was doing sailing in an area of clear shallow water.

Like most stories in the Caribbean, the truth turned out to be rather blurred, but not to be outdone by Anne, I told Liz what I'd read. "The official story was that the cruise liner Antilles belonged to the French government. It had a relief captain on board who liked to give his passengers a close view of the shore. He certainly succeeded, by running the ship onto the rocks. After the grounding, dirty bilge oil was allegedly thrown onto the main drive shaft causing a fire, which was then blamed for the disaster. There was one couple on board who had won a free holiday for being the happiest married couple in France. The story doesn't indicate what happened to their marriage afterwards, but because the French government had no insurance for the vessel, none of the passengers received a penny in compensation. It may be that the real story will never reveal what happened, as the French captain, and all the crew arrived back in France before even all the passengers had been taken off the stricken vessel, and there the story ended. Of course, there were plenty of rumours about the incident and they continue to this day. The silver cutlery, crockery, glass, and every other conceivable movable item now resides in many homes around Bequia and the Grenadines. It's even alleged that the entire staircase, which was a feature on the ship, now adorns a house in St. Vincent. How it got there, no one can say. Eventually the wreck became the property of Colin Tennant, the then Chairman of the Mustique Company," I bowed low at the end of my story. "Thanks, daddy," said Anne, suppressing a yawn.

We soon reached the northern end of Mustique and just before anchoring, we sailed past Colin Tennant's Indian temple, which is in the garden of his home on the north-west side of the island. Shortly afterwards, Liz dropped the anchor in Britannia Bay where sits the well-known Basil's Bar restaurant, which is built partly on stilts and jutting out into the bay. There are two hazards in Mustique. One is that the sea developed a most uncomfortable roll, partly alleviated by putting out two anchors and the other hazard came from large birds. They must have seen Hitchcock's film of the same name.

They were an absolute menace and unsuspecting holiday sailors made the problem worse by feeding the brutes. Boats always left Mustique adorned with bird dirt, inside and outside the boat.

To describe Mustique as a Caribbean island is a misnomer. It is simply Beverley Hills in the Caribbean. The only indigenous people living on the island were those who worked for the Mustique Company, the remainder were wealthy Europeans, Canadians, North and South Americans, who built expensive properties for their leisure use. Princess Margaret, Lord Lichfield, David Bowie, Raquel Welch, and Mick Jagger were just some of the house owners.

This time it was Liz, who enjoyed reading about the titled and the rich and was able to give information about the island. "Would you like to have a house here mummy," Anne asked, giving me a sideways glance. "Not really," said Liz loyally. "It seems to me to be a rather artificial life."

Later during our life in the Caribbean, we made friends with a man called John Golds who had been the chairman of the Mustique company, and who was asked to solve a problem created by a Prince of the realm. The Royal concerned and a 'model' called Koo Stark booked on a British Airways flight from London to Barbados, the nearest International airport to Mustique. Mrs. Stark, Koo Stark's mother, and Koo Stark's secretary a Miss Grey accompanied the party. The names under which the Prince and Koo Stark booked was Mr. and Mrs. Cambridge. The press was tipped off about the flight. (The chief suspect was Miss Grey). The hullabaloo it caused at the time is well known. Shortly after they all arrived at Princess Margaret's house in Mustique, John received the urgent communication at his house in Saint Lucia from Buckingham Palace. Its essence was, 'for God's sake get them out of there...' As the world press converged on the small island, John knew he had to act quickly. The first thing he did was to send his forty-four-foot yacht with his Captain, Leopold to take the Prince off the island for a sail.

This accomplished, he then organised a dawn flight from the little airport in Mustique to fly Koo Stark and her entourage to Hewannora airport in St Lucia. From there they would be flown to the USA and thence to Canada. John lived at the Northern end of St Lucia, while the international airport is in the south, so he set off early in the morning to reach the airport before the Starks and secretary arrived.

Before leaving, he had telephoned the head of St Lucia's Police force and asked him to waive immigration and customs for the incoming flight from Mustique. He told him that he could not explain why at that stage, just that he had some 'special' VIP's who would be transferred to the Eastern Airlines USA flight. The chief of police, no doubt guessing who Mark's visitors were, agreed to his request, and told him he would phone down to the airport and make the necessary arrangements.

Mark arrived about ten minutes before the Mustique Airways flight was due and was concerned to find that no call had been received from the police headquarters. It later transpired that, the chief of police had not been able to contact the airport, because of downed phone lines. In desperation, John got hold of the head of immigration at Hewannora and told him that even though he did not have a call from the Commissioner of Police would he please accept Mark's word for the agreement he had struck that morning with the Commissioner. John knew that if the party was seen to enter the country, or if an immigration officer realised the potential 'pension' he could earn from tipping off the international press, then the plan would be blown. Fortunately, the head of immigration knew Mark, and he acceded to the request, even arranging for a private office to be made available, so that his visitors would be kept from public view. John just had time to collect the tickets from the Eastern desk before they arrived. Meeting them in the office allocated to him, he found Koo Stark to be very sweet, and indeed, he was quite smitten with her (Mark was over sixty years of age and a committed bachelor).

The mother was also pleasant, but the secretary was not such a happy person.

The Eastern flight came in and soon the passengers were ready to board.

Everyone else was boarded first, and as John said his good-byes, Koo asked him if he could do her a favour. John agreed and asked what he could do. She said that the press had taken some photographs of them on Mustique, which were to be published the next day. Would John mind obtaining copies and send them to her. John said he would not mind at all, and if she would give him her address, he would ensure she received them as soon as possible. She scribbled something on a piece of paper, which John stuffed in the top pocket of his jacket, and then as the flight attendant was getting jittery because of the time, they left to board the aircraft.

Mark breathed a huge sigh of relief and started to find his way out of the airport back to his car. Someone who knew him stopped him, and as he was chatting, he heard the engines of the Eastern airliner start its taxi run to take off. John excused himself and headed for the external door of the airport when suddenly there was an urgent announcement for a Mr. John Golds to report to the Eastern Airline desk. John retraced his steps and was hurriedly taken into the privacy of the airline office. The manager told him that the pilot had just radioed in that cabin crew had three people on board who were insisting on being upgraded to first class, and if they could not be, they wanted to disembark. The tickets arranged by the palace had been for economy class only. The pilot said correctly that neither he nor his staff had authority to upgrade the people, and as they were causing so much trouble, he was taxiing back to the apron. John knew that if the party were offloaded, the story would almost certainly break, as some of the people on the plane must by now know who the three passengers were.

"Is there room in first class?" he asked.

He was told there was.

"Will you accept my cheque for the difference?" Eastern affirmed that they would, and John paid for the upgrades out of his own pocket. He was to tell me later, that one of the sweetest noises he had heard for a long time was the sound of the Eastern Airliner taking off.

On his return trip to the north end of the island, he was somewhat pleased, when listening to the British Overseas Service, to hear that his ruse had worked. The programme apparently had a direct line with their correspondent on Mustique, and the narrative, in a low voice was saying, "I am just near Princess Margaret's house now, and everything is quiet, the curtains tightly drawn, the occupants still in bed. The rumour is that the Prince and his party will try to move out sometime today...." Of course, at the time of this transmission, John knew the 'birds' had already flown.

81

The next day when he got the newspapers, he remembered Koo Stark's request, so he cut the relevant pictures out and put them in an envelope. He then dug into his top pocket for the address. He read for the first time:

MISS KOO STARK,
C/O,
BUCKINGHAM PALACE,
LONDON.

The last piece of this story came some three months later when John received a cheque from the palace reimbursing him for the upgrading.

We all had a good evening at Basil's Bar, but because of the uncomfortable anchorage we resolved to sail to Tobago Cays the next morning, when we would reach the Grenadines proper.

We passed some small uninhabited islands sailing south from Mustique. The first is called Petite Mustique, then Cavan Island and finally Petite Canouan before reaching the main island of Canouan on the port side.

There is an interesting story about Petite Canouan, which caught my attention having worked in Ghana in West Africa as a young man. During the days of the slave traders, most of the Africans were transported from an area called the Gold Coast of which Ghana is the main country. Located in that area is a tribe called the Ashanti who were similar in many ways to the Zulu in that they were aggressively militaristic. It was this tribe that worked with the European slave traders to catch people from the other less aggressive tribes who then sold them into slavery. Subsequently they became involved in a civil war, and many Ashanti's from the losing side were also sold into slavery. It came about that many slaves revolted once in situ, and the British realised that the trouble was usually caused when there were Ashanti's in the area. It was decided therefore, that all the Ashanti's from the various islands be rounded up and placed on Balliceaux. (In 2019, this island is for sale for £3 million). It was realised however, that the island was far too small to contain them, so the question was asked, 'where do we have the strongest military contingent able to deal with troublemakers?' The answer was Jamaica, and so they were all moved onto that island. It is suggested that the Jamaican is the most aggressive of all the peoples in the Caribbean Islands and arguably the most intelligent. My apologies to Jamaicans reading this book and to the other islanders too. But that's the story.

Tobago Cays was the piece de resistance of the Grenadines. About three hours sail south of Mustique it's a collection of four small, uninhabited islands surrounded on the eastern side by a huge coral reef. This is where the Caribbean meets the Atlantic. The sail is an easy one, passing the small rock islands noted above and then the larger island of Canouan on the port side. The latter is an island almost as big as Bequia, yet sparsely inhabited. The next island south is Mayreau, where Salt Whistle Bay, a tiny inlet at the north end, large enough only for half a dozen boats is to be found. One could spend many happy days swimming in Salt Whistle Bay, which affords an ideal anchorage.

Salt Whistle does have one danger however and that's the number of Manchineel Trees (Hippomane Mancinella) that grow there. It's a pretty tree, with yellow-green apples and it's normally quite safe to take shade under it but if you take cover during a rain storm, you're likely to get nasty blisters from the acid that runs off the tree. Liz and I had heard about these trees from a young couple we'd met in Bequia.

They thought it would be romantic to 'sleep' under one and they covered the ground with the leaves to make a bed on which to lie. The next morning, they were red and very swollen in some very embarrassing places.

From there onwards is an area of dangerous reefs and shoals that lead in to Tobago Cays, about two to three miles east of Salt Whistle. This area is dangerous with all the reefs and great care if needed sailing in the area. Josh told us that a boat going aground on a coral reef doesn't often come off again in one piece.

I'd studied the local charts and to ensure maximum room for manoeuvring we'd dropped sails shortly after passing Salt Whistle Bay to starboard and used engine-power to proceed to the first small island in the Cays, Petit Rameau. If one were looking down from the air, you'd see three islands side by side running north to south, with a further island close by to the east. Sailing between the islands of Petit Rameau and Petit Bateau, Shady Lady negotiated the very narrow channel, and I noticed the easternmost island, Baradal ahead. When we were clear of Petit Bateau to starboard, I turned Shady Lady heading south, to leave Baradal Island on the port side and Petit Bateau to starboard. We passed a second channel on our starboard side, between Petit Bateau Island and the fourth island called Jamesby, which was now clearly visible some 100 yards or so ahead.

The two navigable parts of the channels running east to west between the three islands are less than fifteen metres wide and the gap between the two northern islands and Baradal Island isn't more than thirty metres, which gives an indication of how tricky it is to enter the Tobago Cays area. The coral reef surrounding the Cays is like a huge U encompassing the islands on the eastern shores and it is teeming with all types of tropical fish, underwater coral, and flora. From studying the charts, I knew where to anchor and as Jamesby Island came abreast of Shady Lady, we turned east towards the coral reef, always watching the depth gauge very carefully. Once it registered six feet, Anne dropped anchor.

A note on the chart told us that the holding was excellent there, and the wind speed is rarely less than 25 knots.

We found it exhilarating yet peaceful. The exotic sea bottom simply asked for visitors to go snorkelling. That evening, when we rowed the dinghy around to the channel, we had originally gingerly steered through, we came across some fishermen who tended to camp on Petit Rameau in the season. Liz bought fresh, live lobster from them and these were cooked while we waited.

The next three days, Monday to Wednesday, we spent on the Cays, but Liz insisted that we must find some civilisation if we were to eat anything other than lobster, so it was with sad hearts that we left for Union Island early on the Thursday morning.

The channel between Petit Bateau and Jamesby Island is dangerous and I wanted to leave in the early morning so that, with the sun behind Shady Lady, I could see the reefs clearly. This we did and when we came into deep water, the sails were hoisted and a course for Union Island set, it being about eight miles away to the south-west.

Union has so many dangerous reefs that it's relatively well marked. Passing a beautiful little island called Palm on the port side.

We turned into Union, negotiated the numerous hazards, and moored at the dock to pick up water and diesel. Leaving Anne to supervise the filling up, Liz and I walked up to the only hotel on the island, which boasted a small supermarket.

Union is a small island with a strong French influence.

The hotel was French owned and most of the Grenadine day trips started from there. Immediately behind the hotel was the most extraordinary aeroplane runway I had ever seen.

Arriving flights are all short-landing aircraft and they virtually dived down the side of a hill and levelled out, to land. They then brake hard to stop the plane and passengers disappearing into the sea at the end of the runway. If one takes a walk to the runway end as I did, there, lying in the water,

were old aircraft engines, the sad remains of those that failed to make it.

Liz was intent on replenishing our dwindling food stocks, so we went into the small supermarket and over to the large open freezer in the corner. It was empty. An indolent young shop assistant was painting her nails behind the counter.

"Have you no frozen food?"

"Yea, we 'ave cold food," the girl didn't look up from her nails.

"Well, where is it?" Liz asked patiently.

"In store," answered the girl, still talking to her nails.

"Well, do you think you could get me some frozen peas?" Liz was now becoming a little edgy.

"Can't," answered the girl, at last putting down the nail varnish and crossing her arms.

Liz looked at the girl incredulously. "Why not?" she adopted the tone of voice one uses to try and establish communication with a petulant child.

"'Cause it's in th' store."

"Well, could you kindly get it out *of the bloody store*?" The last four words spoken by Liz out of the girls hearing.

"No, I ain't goin' in there," the girl pursed her lips. "Noo ways,"

Liz was becoming exasperated.

"WHY NOT?"

"They got a cadaver in there."

"A what?"

"A cadaver,"

"You mean a dead body?" I intervened.

"Yea, man, an' I ain't goin' in there till the cadaver's gone, noo sir."

It was no good, she wouldn't let me or Liz into the cold store either, and she was certainly not going in herself until they removed the body. Further questioning elicited the fact that the authorities would take the corpse to St. Vincent by plane later in the day. Apparently, a tourist had died of a heart attack while sampling the delights of West Indian hospitality, although it was never divulged what kind of hospitality, he was sampling.

To guarantee reasonable freshness for the body's trip home, the local police had insisted they use the freezer to keep the body fresh. We had to do without frozen food until our arrival in Grenada.

After filling up with water and diesel and paying an even more exorbitant charge than at Bequia, we sailed Shady Lady across to Palm Island and anchored there for lunch. Here the beach is arguably the best in the Caribbean, with pink coral in the sand. The hotel takes up most of this small island, although there were one or two private houses on it.

There was an amusing story about the owners of the island, the husband lived in the small hotel and the wife lived in her own house. The ideal paradise had not worked as well as expected. The son and his wife lived in the hotel as well but didn't speak to the father who prevented them leaving the island. However, once a year on the son's birthday, it was common news that his wife gave him 'a blow job' as a present, whether the rest of the year he was forced to be celibate is not known. One night they crept out of their room and escaped from the father along with their young child. Sailing to Miami to start a new life.

We felt that the anchorage at Palm was too exposed for an overnight stay and so at about 3 p.m. we reluctantly got back on-board Shady Lady and sailed for Petit Saint Vincent (PSV), an even smaller island, about four miles south of Palm, which is completely occupied by a luxurious hotel. With dangerous reefs in this area, I dropped the sails early, motoring carefully through the Pinese and Mopian reefs and into the anchorage near the hotel entrance.

PSV hotel was famous for its unique method of room service. All the hotel rooms were in individual chalets and if one wanted room service, you pulled up a flag on the flag-staffs provided near the chalet's front door. Service came in a small electric car. Double hammocks were slung at intervals along the beautiful white beach, and many visitors spent a romantic evening in them.

I pondered the technique of lovemaking in a hammock, and whether it may result in me capsizing and my partner falling heavily on top. I imagined that being battered and winded wouldn't be at all conducive to the desired result. Would it, or would it not work, in my rather neglected novel. I hoped for an opportunity to investigate before committing it to paper.

Liz however put a stop to that idea.

PSV is the last island in the St. Vincent administration. From then on south, all the islands were under the administration of Grenada then ruled by a rather offensive communist regime.

Petite Martinique is the first island of the Grenada chain and nestles in the same bay as PSV, but to the south. There's an impassable reef joining the two islands to the east, which is why the anchorage at PSV is so sheltered. Liz and I were acquiring considerable geographical knowledge, as well as deepening sun tans, while Anne concentrated solely on the sun tan.

I couldn't help wondering how they originally organised the allocation of these islands to their various administrations. I imagined civil servants sitting in London, and saying one for you, one for me. . .

I also knew a little of the recent history of these romantic places and understood that Petite Martinicans had no truck with their communist rulers. When the government on the mainland, some thirty miles south, decided to curb the frequent smuggling that went on between Petite Martinique and the islands of St. Vincent, they sent a customs official to set up a post on the island. He arrived by the only ferry and was standing next to the captain in the wheel house while the vessel manoeuvred to the dock. He remarked that he was happy to see a cheerful welcoming committee on the jetty. The captain grunted. As the craft reached its berth, the customs man noticed a coffin standing on a table just near to where the ferry would tie up.

"Who's died?" queried the customs official.

"Noo one man," the captain avoided his eyes as he made last minute manoeuvres to bring his ship alongside.

The customs man frowned, "Well, why the coffin, then?" he asked, with some unease now.

"It's for you man, if you set foot on the Island," explained the captain in all seriousness.

The customs man promptly and wisely locked himself in his cabin and refused to come out again until he was sure the boat had docked back in St George's, in Grenada. The smuggling continued unabated. I wondered how I could work this into my plot since it seemed worth a second airing, but it didn't quite fit in with the City of London.

To the west, across from Petite Martinique is the island of Carriacou. To the south of that, the furthest southerly destination in the Windward Islands and our destination south was Grenada.

We anchored in PSV for two days and then sailed the next day, Sunday, we sailed for Grenada. We had now been sailing for just over two eventful weeks.

Just after leaving Tyrell Bay, which is on the south-west of Carriacou, Grenada was plainly visible in the distance although still six hours away, after two hours we passed a group of high-profile rocks north of Grenada, of which the most notorious is Kick 'em Jenny. The stories of rough seas and strong easterly currents around this point were legendary. When Shady Lady sailed past, the sea couldn't have been calmer.

We sailed to Carriacou, where we booked in at the police and immigration post in Tyrell Bay. We only stayed there one night and on the island.

I decided not to sail to St George's, which is the capital of Grenada and like many of the islands, it is situated on the south western side. Josh had said that even winches had gone missing from boats berthed there, never mind dinghies. He had recommended a lovely little inlet just around the corner from the capital, on the southern end of the island called Prickly Bay. It was the only other place that one could anchor as the rest of the coast was restricted by order of the communist government.

Prickly Bay afforded a delightful anchorage. The landscape is a tapestry of attractive flora, with the usual green backdrop forming a contrast with the brilliant splashes of colour. I negotiated the unmarked reef in the middle of the bay and anchored about one hundred yards from the rather broken-down dock. There were only a few boats around, so we had the bay almost to ourselves. After spending two days recuperating in Prickly Bay, Liz decided that as the next day, Thursday, was to be the last full day on the island we should all travel to St George's by taxi.

I am interested in all things historical, so I was keen to have seen the old British Fort George on the hill overlooking the town, but when I enquired, I was told in hushed tones that political prisoners were kept there and not wishing to become one of them, I wisely gave the place a wide berth.

Grenada is similar in size to St. Lucia, but arguably prettier. The people were very pleasant, but the area we could travel was so restricted, that Anne said it was pointless staying longer.

We decided to sail back to Union, to spend the night there because we couldn't 'book' in to PSV, there being no customs post on that island. From Union, we planned to take a leisurely trip back to St. Lucia via Tobago Cays and Bequia.

The best laid plans, however, obey only Murphy's Law. I remembered Robert Burns' poem:

'Th Gang aft agley,
an' lea'e us nought but grief an' pain,
for promis'd joy!
e best laid schemes o' Mice an' Men,'

On Thursday morning, the day planned for the trip, the weather was foul. A tropical depression hit the area and it poured with rain incessantly for two days. I was all for sailing, but Liz and Anne objected so strongly that we decided not to venture out until the weather had improved. It didn't do so until the Saturday. That morning dawned bright and sunny, the wind had freshened somewhat, and it was therefore agreed by us all that the long sail north could be attempted.

The seas on the southern end of Grenada after leaving Prickly Bay were rough but as we turned north into the lee of Grenada, the wind dropped and although the sky was overcast, it was quite pleasant. I was mildly surprised that we could sail up the lee of the island without engine power and this should have warned us of what was to come.

When Shady Lady cleared the northern end of Grenada, the sea was even rougher than it was on the southern end and the wind speed increased to thirty-five knots. I'd taken the

91

precaution of putting a double reef in the main and as the second jib was quite small, we weren't over-sailed. Nevertheless, the boat kicked and bucked and generally it was most unpleasant. Apart from anything else, it was cold and frequent large waves came over the side soaking us. The wind veered more to the north, and we weren't making good headway, so we turned on the engine to give some support. We were two miles south of Kick 'em Jenny when Anne went below to get herself a sweater; Liz and I were already wearing foul weather gear under our life jackets.

There was a sudden shout and Anne appeared at the top of the galley steps looking alarmed.

"The boat's full of water. Quick, look daddy," she went back down below. I handed the wheel over to Liz and peered down into the main cabin area where Anne was ankle-deep in water that was swishing dangerously from side to side as the boat heeled over in the high seas. I knew we'd taken on some water, as waves had been breaking over the cockpit area, but I wasn't aware that any had got down below. Shady Lady had an automatic bilge pump that should have activated once the water got to a certain level and any surplus water pumped out.

To check why it was not working, Anne and I lifted the section of cabin floor above the pump. The boat was gyrating wildly, the fibreglass floor was extremely slippery and neither of us was feeling too great, it's one thing being up on deck in a rough sea, quite another to be below. It was clear that the electric pump had failed, probably because of faulty maintenance. I cursed Marine Charters under my breath. I could only think that Shady Lady had sprung a leak.

I realised that the dinghy wouldn't last five minutes in the present seas, even if we had an outboard engine that worked.

"Get the bilge handle from the cupboard over there," I pointed at Anne and then to a cupboard behind her.

She opened it, and immediately pots and pans flew all over the cabin. Liz, hearing the sound, left the wheel and rushed to the entrance of the main cabin. I saw her worried face looking down on us. At that moment, a large wave hit Shady Lady, throwing Anne and me across the cabin floor. I quickly gathered myself together and looked up; Liz's face had disappeared from the doorway.

"Oh, no," I shouted, my heart pumping as I scrambled up the galley steps. Had the boat hit anything, I wondered. My mind went back over the last few days, but I recalled nothing of relevance, nevertheless, we had occasionally seen empty oil drums floating on the surface and realised that to hit one in a small boat could cause substantial damage.

One thing was certain; if we couldn't get the water out faster than it was coming in, our destiny was straight to the bottom of the Caribbean.

The wheel was spinning wildly, with no one around.

I looked over the side of the boat nothing, not a sign.

Having a 'man' overboard is a very serious matter, particularly so in a rough sea. I knew just how quickly a human being can disappear. I was aware that Liz was a strong swimmer, so I felt that she would be able to stay afloat. The main problem would be finding her. I remembered being told that in a 'man' overboard situation, one should throw everything over board that will float, to mark the spot. After that, the vessel could turn around, and the crew still on board would be reasonably sure of getting back to the same area where the person went over. I grabbed one of the cockpit cushions and a split second before throwing it overboard, I felt someone by my side.

"Are you, all right?" It was Liz. I swore at her furiously.

"I'm sorry," she said, "I just had to go . . ."

We got control of the boat again, and as we regained our heading, I noticed grimly that we were now roughly abeam of Kick 'em Jenny. I learned later that Kick 'em Jennie is a huge underground volcano similar in many ways to Yellowstone Park in the USA. If it ever blew, the Caribbean Islands would disappear.

I made sure that Liz had the wheel and that she'd inform me the next time she felt an urge and I went back down below.

Anne had already connected the bilge pump handle to the manual pump, and was pumping steadily, but the water had increased in volume. I noticed that she'd been sick, which didn't improve the reactions from my own stomach, so I decided to concentrate on the problem in hand and that was to find the leak and patch it. To this end, I started taking up all the floor boards but there was no sign of a leak; I was getting desperate.

Another large wave hit Shady Lady, and I was thrown on my back, the water in the cabin swept over me and I swallowed what felt like half a gallon.

As I recovered my balance, I suddenly realized that the water wasn't salty. I dipped my finger into the liquid swishing around on the cabin floor. It was fresh water. Eventually I found the culprit; a very rusty connection on the port side fresh water tank had simply corroded and the water had flowed out. I told the white-faced Anne that she wouldn't have to pump out the Caribbean Sea after all, only the contents of the burst tank. I grabbed a toolbox and made some hasty repairs to try and stem the flow, which reduced it to a mere trickle. Leaving Anne still gamely pumping away at the manual bilge pump, I went on deck to see how Liz was faring, she wasn't happy.

"I think we're going backwards," she pointed to Kick 'em Jenny. "Fifteen minutes ago, we were abreast of the rocks," she said, "but now they're definitely on our right front."

"Starboard bow" I corrected her in the middle of another breaking wave.

Liz scowled.

She was right, I decided, we certainly had appeared to lose ground, and that with an engine going too.

Then I realised what was happening.

"We're sailing too close to the wind," I explained, as though I'd been sailing all my life. Indeed, I felt as though I had. "The sea swell is almost head on, we'll have to tack," I grimaced as the new heading would add about two hours to our intended trip and make it certain that we arrived in Union after dark, not a pleasant prospect, considering the lack of navigational aids on the southern end, in the dark.

"But that'll mean we won't get to Union until after its dark," Liz had been thinking along the same lines.

I nodded.

"We'll never get in to the harbour; there are far too many reefs. Let's turn back," said Liz.

I considered her suggestion for a minute, but I persuaded myself that the sea had eased since bearing away from our more direct heading and it was obvious that we were now making better headway. I didn't particularly relish a similar trip the next day, so I thought carefully about how we might sail into Union harbour after nightfall. All the charts I'd studied indicated that if the yacht lined up with a certain flag pole and with the corner of a red-roofed house further up the hill in Union, it would ensure a reef-free channel. The problem was that these landmarks wouldn't be visible at night even if there was a moon, and they would probably not show up through the overcast sky. I turned to Liz.

"Let me dig out the chart again and I'll see what may be possible,"

I went below, where Anne was still pumping.

"Do you think you could take over?" Anne said, reasonably. "I really would like to get some air. Without waiting for my reply, she scrambled up into the cockpit and I took over the manual bilge pump with my free hand and managed to get the chart out despite the lumpiness of the sea. Pumping with one hand and spreading the chart out with the other, got it thoroughly wet in the process and I wondered why charts were not on waterproof material. I subsequently found out they were, but because of the extra expense, our charter company hadn't considered it. It took a further half an hour to pump out all the water and from then on, we spent about ten minutes every hour at the pump to keep the cabin dry. When I'd finished peering at the chart, I folded the soggy piece of paper and went up to the cockpit.

Anne had disappeared.

"She's lying down in the aft cabin," Liz inclined her head.

"I hope she's not sick in there too," I growled.

I received a nasty look from Liz.

I explained that I thought we could get within a mile of Union, without any problem.

"What I suggest is that we go in under slow engine, with me and a flashlight at the bow."

Liz looked doubtful. "That might be fine in a calm sea, but on a day like today. Are you sure about this?" She asked.

"Well, can you think of a better idea?" I said irritably. "In any case once we're near Union, the sea will be much calmer," I claimed, not sure of my facts.

"We could use Channel 16 to call for someone who knows the area and ask them for the best route in to the mooring," answered Liz practically.

I had to admit that it seemed a sensible idea. Of course, in Europe there are Coast Guards listening out for people in trouble, not so in the Caribbean. If you were in trouble, then you had to sort it out for yourself.

"That's not such a bad idea - for a woman," I answered patronisingly.

Liz stuck out her tongue.

It took over thirty minutes to get an answer on channel 16. Had we been sinking; we'd have been under the waves by the time someone answered.

Eventually the radio crackled. "Blue here, mate" I thought the voice on the radio was American at first, but then realised it was Australian. Then, for a fleeting second, I thought a freak radio wave had connected me with someone 'down under'. We changed to a different channel, and I quickly learned that 'Blue' ran a day-charter motor yacht out of Union and knew the area well.

"Okay, mate," he said, "this is what you do," he then told me that the lights from the hotel were distinguishable at night in that they were red. "To keep the bugs from getting' interested" he explained. "If you line up the furthest red light on the eastern side with the house on the hill, you can't go wrong."

"But how will I find the house on the hill?" I enquired.

"It's the only house there and it's always lit. The French guy who owns it has a phobia about thieves, so he leaves his outside lights on all night." I was relieved and thanked him. Blue said that if we got into trouble, to call him again and that he would leave his radio on 'watch,' which was comforting.

Anne thought she heard someone calling Shady Lady later that evening, but when I got to the radio, I couldn't raise anyone.

Shady Lady approached the entrance to Union Harbour at 10:30 p.m. after sailing for over twelve and a half hours.

We were all wet, hungry, and totally exhausted.

Reefs protect almost all the way around the natural

harbour at Union. Although I fully expected to hear the bottom of the boat ripped out from under us as we sailed through the narrow channel of the perimeter, we arrived inside safely. There were many boats already anchored and I decided to anchor in a spot some way from the rest. The wind was veering quite sharply, and I didn't want another occurrence of the French experience we had in Bequia. We dropped the anchor with some relief but by the time, we had done that we were all too tired to eat. Liz went down to the galley to make some strong coffee and we sat huddled in the cockpit, sipping the hot mixture.

"We're moving," said Anne, suddenly. She was becoming the deliverer of bad news.

"Just with the wind," I answered hopefully.

"No, daddy, we were roughly next to that boat over there." She pointed to a wooden-hulled, broad-beamed yacht that had been about 100 yards away from us on our port beam. It was now quite definitely well in front of Shady Lady.

I realised that the anchor was dragging and unless we did something about it, Shady Lady would end up on the reef behind us. With a heavy heart, I turned the engine on as Anne and Liz pulled in the anchor line and then the anchor, I moved Shady Lady forward. Anne dropped the anchor in another spot close to where we'd been, but it became clear that we were still not holding. The procedure was repeated a third time still no good.

"Let out more line," I shouted, becoming irritable. "The less the angle of line to the sea bed, the better the chance of the anchor catching," Liz, who was on the bow with Anne, helped her to do so.

Still, it didn't hold.

"Jesus," I exclaimed, gritting my teeth in frustration.

"Let's try again, in another spot," shouted Anne from the bow.

We did and still the anchor dragged. Six more times we tried, but to no avail. Putting a heavy anchor down isn't so much a problem, but Shady Lady had no electric windlass, that useful electric winch found on more advanced yachts that pulls up the anchor.

Therefore, each time, the heavy piece of iron pulled up by

Anne had to be done manually. Adding this exertion to the twelve difficult hours we'd all just spent at sea wasn't conducive to good tempers and some very colourful language drifted across the bay between Anne, Liz, and me. I then told Liz to take the wheel and I went up to the bow.

We tried again. It was no good. It simply wouldn't hold. Anne suggested that we sail to PSV.

"Not likely," shouted Liz. "I'd rather we sailed around inside the harbour all night than repeat that experience," she was referring to our entrance into Union. It was then we were conscious of a small dinghy approaching.

Its engine cut as it came alongside. There were two men on board. One stood up.

"Hi mate I'm Blue."

We made the necessary introductions.

"We bin watching you since you came in," he grinned.

"You won't catch here," he swung his head in the direction of our anchor, "its coral underneath mate, that's why there are no other boats anchored in this area.

It was on the tip of my tongue to say, "why the devil didn't you let me know about an hour ago, when we first came in?" but discretion won the day, and I just nodded. Of course, I should have guessed, when there are a lot of boats anchored in a bay and one spots a nice empty space, there's usually a very good reason why it's empty.

Blue and his friend came on board, and I willingly let them take over.

Within five minutes, Shady Lady was anchored among the other boats. I was past caring whether we bumped against another craft in the night, and I was sure any noise, however great, wouldn't wake us.

It was now well past midnight and Liz had made another pot of coffee for our new friends. I sipped mine gratefully, knowing that I'd soon be in bed. I realised in a half doze that Blue was talking.

"Yea, mate, we tried to call you a way back, but got no reply." I remembered that Anne had said someone was calling the boat, and I explained that I hadn't been able to get back to him.

"Ah! You probably got behind the headland," nodded Blue. "VHF is line of sight, so you'd have bin cut off from us for a while. Thing is, we were worried about you guys, because there was a power cut on the island. It's not unusual," he added with a grim smile.

I answered in surprise. "But we came in on the lights as you suggested," I must have looked puzzled.

Blue shook his head.

"Naw couldn't have done. The hotel lights were okay, 'cause they've their own generator, but Francis's house definitely blacked out." I frowned and looked around the harbour.

There was only one yacht with mast lights lit and I realised that it was that light I'd mistaken for the house light. Because they were closer, it seemed to me from a mile away that they were up on the hill. I went quite cold. If the yacht in question hadn't been in exactly the right place, at the right time, Shady Lady would almost certainly have been on a reef with no bottom to the boat. I gulped silently and wisely decided to say nothing.

CARRIACOU

CARRIACOU TO GRENADA
APPROX 4 MILES

N

THIS IS WHERE
SHADY LADY
SAILED BACKWARDS

KICK EM JENNY

3 KNOT CURRENT

RONDE ISLAND

2.5 KNOT CURRENT

THIS IS WHERE
SHADY LADY
TOOK ON WATER

GRENADA

"A power cut?"

The next morning brought a calm and sunny day and for the first time on a boat, we all slept past 9 a.m. After I'd repaired the water tank leak with some borrowed silicone, we took on water at the dock and were ready to sail up to Bequia.

Anne had been over to see Blue and came back highly excited.

"I've been offered a job as a hostess," she exclaimed cheerfully.

Neither Liz or I were happy at the prospect, and it must

have shown on our faces.

"Now listen," said Anne, with a determined look on her face, "I've had quite enough of sailing with you two," she looked at directly at me. "I'd like to live past thirty and frankly, I need to do my own thing anyway." I had rarely got on with my elder daughter and there's no doubt that by having Anne on board and in such proximity, created a certain amount of strain. On the other hand, I knew that our relationship was sometimes a love/hate affair and felt guilty that Anne found it necessary to leave. Suddenly, I had a lump in my throat.

After Liz and I had discussed it and thought about it, we realised that there was some sense in what Anne was doing.

In any case, she was old enough to make her own decisions, and there was little that we could do if her mind was made up, "when do you intend to start?" I asked.

"In three weeks', time, when we sail back down in the Sunshine yacht, you can drop me off," said Anne, quietly triumphant.

I was much happier with this as it would give Anne time to rethink her new life, and with that thought, the matter was closed for the time being.

5 - THE YACHT SEIZERS

And How I Avoided a Fight

We decided against going back to Tobago Cays on this trip as we were now running short of time. We determined to head straight back to Bequia, where we arrived without incident just before 5 p.m. on the Sunday evening.

This is by far the best time of the day to arrive at any anchorage, partly because one could see what one was doing at that hour and partly because one had time to wash off the salty water, relax with a rum punch and hope to see a green flash.

We'd been told about the green flash and thought it was probably a myth or, more likely a result of too much rum punch but we were about to experience the phenomenon for the first time. As the sun sets in west, providing there's no cloud on the horizon, the watcher sees a distinct bright green sun during the last second as it disappears. Greatly excited by this experience, we rowed ashore in the evening and had dinner at Mac's Pizzeria, run by a Canadian girl called Judy, from a small wooden shack near the waterfront. It was probably the best pizza we'd eaten anywhere in the world, before or since. We decided to stay in Bequia until our return

103

to St Lucia, which Liz suggested, should be the following Thursday, one day before the boat was due to be returned to Marine Yacht Charters.

On Monday morning, I collected the sail from the sailmaker, who had done an excellent job of repair and Liz completed her shopping. After a lime squash at the Frangipani hotel, we got back on board at around 11 am.

I was determined to finish writing my novel before we left Bequia, so that I could get it typed while in St. Lucia. The manuscript had fallen on the cabin floor while we were sailing up from Grenada, and while sorting through the pages and putting them in some sort of order, I heard someone hailing us from the stern.

Out of the corner of my eye, I noticed a large motor cruiser moving towards Shady Lady, but it was a beam of us before I realised what was happening. Fortunately, I'd put fenders in place, ready for the odd boat boy who stopped by, selling everything from fruit to carvings and black coral, but Liz jumped up and put out another one when she realised the motor launch was coming alongside. A man of about thirty-five hailed us, "James Dalby?"

I was puzzled as to how this stranger knew my name. "Yes," I answered with raised eyebrows.

"Do you mind if we come aboard?" The man's tone was polite.

I noticed that apart from the man who had hailed us and the driver of the boat, the other person on board was an attractive young woman. The hailer and the girl wore smart suits as though they'd come straight off an international aircraft, which would have been impossible for Bequia as there was no airport. They looked odd, dressing up on the island equalled shorts and T-shirts. I nodded and went to help the girl on board.

The West Indian driver of the motorboat fastened lines to Shady Lady but stayed on his own vessel.

Anne had lifted her head from her normal position on deck, found it was nothing to concern her and turned over to toast yet another part of her anatomy.

"What can we do for you?" I asked

The man smiled. "My name is Ruben Heinzweiller, and

this is my friend Dinga." A strange name I thought to myself, more like a dog. I guessed from the man's accent that he was either German or Dutch, but Dinga appeared to be English. They sat down at Liz's invitation, and she went below to make coffee.

After some pleasantries about weather and what a beautiful place Bequia was, Ruben got down to business.

"We've come to seize the yacht," he explained, "what, this one?" I asked incredulously. "Ja," Ruben nodded his head vigorously. "Well, not just this one, but all the O'Day's run by Herr Pittam-Bagshaw."

He pointed to a similar boat anchored a few hundred yards away.

I asked him on whose authority he was acting.

The woman chipped in.

"Mr. Heinzweiller is representing the owners," she explained.

"I was given the impression that Pittam owned the boats," I said in surprise.

Ruben shook his head. "No, he's the owner of one only, the rest have been in the care of his charter company."

I frowned.

Liz appeared with the coffee, which gave me some time to think. "Do you have any documentation to support your claim?" I asked.

Ruben took a fat briefcase Dinga was carrying and opening it extracting a bunch of documents in a file and passed them over to me. I saw that they were all signed affidavits from owners authorising Mr. Ruben Heinzweiller to take charge of the yachts. There was more information including detailed allegations of money received and not passed to the owners, lack of agreed maintenance of the boats and various other complaints. Certainly, I couldn't disagree with the lack of maintenance. These were all set out in legal jargon. I handed them back.

"I sympathise with your owners," I said, "but as far as we're concerned, we chartered this boat from Marine Yacht Charters and our agreement is with them. As I see it," I went on, "that is the company to whom we'll have to return the boat. You must appreciate that we don't pick up our

105

replacement boat until next Friday. If we moved off this one, we'd have the expense of a hotel, including flights back to St Lucia."

Herr Heinzweiller scowled.

"I'm authorised by the owners to pay for your air fare back to St. Lucia," he smiled thinly.

"And what about the intervening time?" I asked.

"And what about our deposit?" chipped in Liz.

Herr Heinzweiller seemed surprised. "Deposit, what deposit?"

I told him that Fisher held £400 of our money as a deposit, which was returnable after the charter.

At that moment Anne, who had appeared oblivious to the discussion, leaned up on one elbow, from the deck in front of the cockpit.

"But you only get that back if you haven't smashed something-like the outboard motor," she added gleefully.

The looks that Liz and I shot in Anne's direction abruptly ended her interest. She lay back on the deck and closed her eyes.

Fortunately, Herr Heinzweiller had been in earnest discussion with Dinga, in what I now recognised was German, and hadn't heard what Anne said.

Herr Heinzweiller turned from his conversation with Dinga.

"I am afraid that's not our business," he answered rather sourly, the smile gone.

"Well, it is ours," I said, and stood up, indicating an end to the discussion.

"You can't have this boat until the end of the charter," I added.

Liz could see that Heinzweiller was sizing me up.

"I'll get a court order," he threatened.

I smiled, "you must do what you must do, but I frankly doubt whether any judge will give you possession of this boat, which we've a legal right to until 15 December. If you can find a judge this side of Christmas, good luck to you," I continued, "who takes the yacht after that, isn't our concern, providing we get our deposit back," I stared at him, sure of my ground.

"I'll fetch the police," Heinzweiller stated.

I scowled and was starting to consider tipping the little man over the side.

Anne, who had obviously been listening to every word, rolled over from her static position, "why don't you throw the bugger overboard daddy?"

Dinga quickly interrupted in German, recognising that an acrimonious situation was developing that may not be in their interest.

She obviously knew that the Bequia police wouldn't get involved with what was clearly a civil matter and it was apparent that she was trying to persuade Heinzweiller to take a different tack.

Heinzweiller nodded, and the smile was back, albeit a little fixed.

"Okay, okay," he sighed and waved his hand for me to sit back down. "I'd be grateful if you'd do one thing for me?"

"Which is?" I asked, suspiciously.

"Just let me know the day you are sailing to St. Lucia and when you reach the southern end, radio me on channel 44 to let me know the exact time and place of your arrival there."

"And in the meantime," suggested Dinga, "we'll get permission from the owners to pay the deposit back to you."

I knew that we'd nothing to lose by doing so and as I was worried that our deposit might now be at risk anyway due to the outboard motor, I nodded and agreed. We were all smiles again and after finishing their coffee, they climbed back on board the motor cruiser.

Liz pointed out that they were headed towards the other O'Day anchored in the bay.

"I wonder what that was all about," I mused, "but the affidavits were damning. However," I added, "let's try not to get caught in the cross fire."

Half an hour later, I noticed the couple from the other O'Day boarding the motor cruiser, with all their baggage.

The woman, who was being helped on board by Dinga, looked quite pleased with herself, "I know how she feels Liz murmured," as she watched.

Liz suggested that we ask Marine if we could hand over the yacht in Rodney Bay rather than return it to Vigie Marina. Suggesting that we get agreement from John Peachcombe for us to moor next to the yacht we were taking over. "This will make it much easier to transfer all our luggage and whatever provisions we still have on Shady Lady," Liz was always practical.

After the yacht seizers had gone, Liz and I walked up to the hill above Port Elizabeth and down to Friendship Bay on the other side of the island. It was a long haul, and very hot, but the view from the top of the hill was worth it. Anne, who we invited to join us, indicated that we were out of our minds to go walking on a hot day, and declined the offer.

We arrived back in time for lunch and that afternoon made plans for the following week.

Our young children, Robert, and Jessica were flying out on the following Monday and Liz felt that it would be nice to have everything ready so that the whole family could sail straight off back down to Bequia, where we planned to spend Christmas Day. We were due back in St Lucia by 15th, but we decided to return one day early, so it wouldn't be such a rush.

I had one more chapter of my book to complete and as this was the one that was to include the 'twist in the tale,' I felt it important that I gave it some time. To this end, I worked hard on the story during the rest of the day and was satisfied that the result provided the reader with the surprise I'd hoped to achieve.

I felt I'd done quite well, as I'd originally estimated that it would take two months to write a full novel, whereas now I could get the longhand manuscript typed in St Lucia and use the typewritten version for revision purposes, thus getting it away to a publisher well within the original time frame I'd set myself.

That evening before we sailed, I telephoned Fisher from the Frangipani Hotel. Fisher was out, so I spoke to his wife, being careful not to mention Heinzweiller. I asked her if it would be okay to change venues. She told me she was sure it would be all right, but if there were any problems, Fishy would contact Shady Lady on the radio.

We left Bequia the next day at 5 a.m. just before sunrise and arrived in Rodney Bay, the northernmost bay in St. Lucia on the leeward side, just after six in the evening. I tried several times to radio Heinzweiller on channel 44 but received no answer and I subsequently discovered that Shady Lady's radio didn't have a crystal for channel 44, so Heinzweiller wouldn't have heard the transmission anyway.

Sunshine Charters left a berth open for Shady Lady on the dock and we slid in next to Mary Anne, a Peterson 44, which was to be our home for the next four weeks. When we looked around the 'new' yacht, we realised just how light the O'Day was and immediately appreciated the solid stockiness of the Peterson, which we reckoned could ride the higher seas with much greater comfort.

We had already found that sleeping in a boat on a dock isn't a pleasant experience. It was hot and noisy, with the wind whipping the halyards against the masts of other boats nearby and Sunshine dock was no better than Vigie, except we didn't have to cope with aeroplanes landing and taking off.

Friday brought another sunny day and we waited on Shady Lady for someone to turn up, but when neither Heinzweiller nor Fisher had arrived to take over the yacht by 11 a.m., Liz and I decided to go to Castries for provisions before the supermarkets closed at 12 noon. We left Anne on board, contentedly reading a book. It was soon after we had left, that Pittam and Josh arrived.

Anne climbed off the yacht and greeted them cordially, but Pittam brushed rudely past her, climbed on the yacht, and demanded the keys, saying to her that her we had broken the contract.

Pittam wasn't to know it, but he couldn't have chosen a worse person to bully.

"I think you should wait for mummy and daddy to get back," said Anne, politely. "They won't be long." "I've no intention of waiting," snapped Pittam, "give me the keys."

"Oh, and what about our luggage on board?" asked Anne.

"Your mother and father can collect that from Vigie Marina, where they should have delivered the yacht," he snarled and advanced towards her threateningly.

Anne stood her ground. "If you so much as touch me, I'll scream that you're molesting me," she looked around to ensure that there were enough people on the dock to react.

Pittam was caught off guard and as he hesitated, Anne quickly avoided him, which wasn't too difficult and ran towards the office at the end of the dock, where John Peachcombe the manager of Sunshine Charters was working. She told him what had happened and gave the keys to him. John promised that he'd hang onto them until we returned.

Anne went back down to Shady Lady and told Pittam what she'd done and although he was most unhappy, there was little he could do, but he ordered Anne to leave the boat. She flatly refused, dropping her previous polite manner and the three of them sat around in the cockpit in silence for well over an hour.

Liz and I arrived back at Sunshine Charters well laden with groceries and as we were carrying them down the dock, John Peachcombe, who had seen us arrive, caught up with us before I reached Shady Lady. He told us what had transpired, and added, "Pittam isn't liked here, so if you've any problems, just let me know and we'll give you a hand." I thanked John and walked on down to the boat.

"Thank goodness you're back," said Anne, with obvious relief. She started to tell us what had happened, but I cut her short.

"Yes, I know, I've just seen John. Well done," I added, as I climbed over the side to greet Pittam. I'd decided to start out by being friendly and acting as though nothing had happened. I smiled and held out my hand, Josh who was busying himself with the rigging, appeared rather embarrassed by the current confrontation. Pittam however refused my hand.

"I want the keys to this boat, and I want them now," he glowered fiercely. "I also want you all off this vessel," he added, glancing at Liz climbing on board. "You can collect your cases and personal effects from the office in Vigie and you've lost your deposit." Pittam threw his chest out and extended his hand for the keys. I sat down in the cockpit.

"No and no," I said firmly.

"What do you mean, no?" Pittam almost yelped.

"I mean what I say, I don't part with the key until I've received the deposit back." While I knew that I'd been at fault with the outboard motor, there were many other things on Shady Lady that had gone wrong that shouldn't have done, so I felt no compunction in demanding the return of the full deposit.

"In that case it'll be necessary for us to eject you physically from the boat," warned Pittam belligerently.

He called out for Josh, who came down from the deck, trying to look fierce, but I could see his heart wasn't in it.

I smiled.

"Look, Pittam, I know you've some problems with your boat owners, but that's not my affair. You must be aware that I telephoned Fisher and told his wife that we'd be berthing here," I threw open my arm for emphasis, and noticed Pittam took a step back giving me the impression that he was a bully type who wouldn't stand firm if confronted.

"Fisher's wife told me that if there was a problem, Fisher would call me on channel 16, which he didn't." I was watching Pittam closely for a reaction, and guessed that Fisher had passed on the message, otherwise how would he have known we were at Sunshine.

"Now," I continued, "Liz and I are going to move our effects from this boat to the Peterson," I pointed to the boat lying alongside. "And when we've done that and you've given us our deposit back, we'll give you the keys."

"I'll get another set of keys," shrugged Pittam.

"Yes, of course, you can do that, but we're not moving from here until we've finalised our arrangements," I stated firmly. Pittam looked even more menacing, and as he came closer, I could smell drink on him.

"You're not going to intimidate us Pittam, and you can use violence if you wish," I said. "but you'll have to physically throw us off and not only will we resist, but we shall certainly call for help." At that precise moment John Peachcombe, who had been walking down the dock, approached.

"Everything okay James?"

"So far, John, but we'll sure as hell yell if there's any rough stuff." John gave Pittam a dirty look and moved away, but he kept within earshot.

Pittam stood glaring at me and then he promptly sat down in the cockpit.

"All right, all right, I accept your story," he pulled out a cheque book.

I shook my head. "No, Pittam, I gave you cash, and I'll only

111

accept cash in return."

"I don't carry that sort of money around with me," Pittam snapped.

I stood up ready to go but sat down again.

"In that case we're all in for a long wait because we," I looked at Anne and Liz, "aren't going anywhere, until we've got our deposit in cash."

There was a pregnant silence.

Pittam stuffed his cheque book away and sheepishly reached into his back pocket, where he extracted exactly £400. I took it and counted it deliberately in front of him.

After that, it took us only a few minutes to move the luggage over to the Peterson and Josh kindly helped with the transfer.

"Don't 'tink too unkindly 'bout the old man, he's had lot's 'uv hassle recently." I nodded and thanked Josh for his help, after that I walked up to the Sunshine Charters office and retrieved the key, which I gave to Josh. I'd the certain feeling that we'd not heard the last of Pittam.

Later in the day, I took my finished manuscript and took it to a secretarial agency in Castries for it to be typed. There were over five hundred pages of tightly written longhand words, which Liz had edited so that a normally perceptive typist could decipher them. They told me that it would be ready in the New Year, and I gave them a deadline of 14th January because we'd booked to return to England on 16th of that month.

After taking over the Peterson, we sailed her down to Vieux Fort, the town nearest to Hewannora International Airport. I got a taxi and picked up the over-excited Jessica and Robert from there that same evening. The next day, we sailed straight to Bequia and were pleased to see how much more proficient we'd become, even though we were now sailing a much bigger yacht.

We all enjoyed our Christmas in Bequia and spent many happy hours snorkelling in Tobago Cays where we had sailed to after Christmas Day. It was, therefore with some sadness that we returned to Rodney Bay in time for us to catch our flight back home.

I was surprised to receive a letter on our arrival at

Sunshine Charters and was even more surprised to see it was from one of the major publishing agents in New York to whom I'd sent a description of my novel some five weeks before. Joan Hargreaves, the agent concerned was most enthusiastic, and asked me to send the manuscript as soon as possible, as she'd a publisher interested.

That evening I sat down with Liz, and we discussed the situation. "I feel that if there's real interest, as it appears there is in Joan's letter, we'd be better staying here rather than going back to the UK," I argued.

Liz agreed in principle, but ever practical she set out the problems of doing so:

"We've a car in the long-term car park in London airport, we've an empty house that needs to be kept warm in the winter, you've a job to go back to if you want to and finally, we don't have unlimited funds." . . . "And" she added, "you wanted to get away from stress, but the last few weeks have not all been completely free of it."

We both recognized however that the prospect of staying in West Indies was attractive particularly as the weather in the UK at that time was foul.

We discussed it some more and finally agreed that Liz would go back with the children and sell the car and do all the other things that needed to be cleared up before returning to the Caribbean by the end of January. In the meantime, I'd look for rented accommodation in Saint Lucia and we'd stay in the area for another six months until the end of June, Liz was also aware that having left Anne to take on her new job, she'd be closer to her in case things went wrong.

6 - BACK ON LAND

And how we met Laurie

I collected the finished typescript of my novel, read it through, made several revisions in pen and then had five copies made. I already had a further list of people I was going to send it to, including the literary agent in New York and one publisher and one literary agent in London. I kept the final copy plus the original for myself. We spent the 15th looking at rental properties and found a chalet in Marigot Bay that was perfect for our purposes, and we took a six-month lease at an exorbitant cost, it still being high season.

On the 16th we hired a car, and I took Liz and the children back to the airport in the south, I was sad to see them go, but we were quite excited with our future.

Liz returned at the end of the month, and we settled in to Caribbean living. The next few weeks went by quickly and I received word that the American literary agent had received the manuscript and that she was getting positive vibes from a publisher but was suggesting some changes to the book to make it more acceptable to the US market. When I started the major revision that the literary agent had suggested, I realised that it would be easier to carry out a total rewrite, so I set about it encouraged by the positive interest.

During this time, Liz and I took various short-term

charters to help a new charter company that had opened in Marigot, which provided some help towards our expenses.

While I was rewriting the book, I had a small table and chair on the front veranda of the house where we were living. The property was about half way up the side of a hill and afforded us an almost panoramic view of the whole of the Marigot Bay inlet. I'd noticed that once a week a very large sailing ship moored below almost directly in front of us, the tall masts reaching almost as high as our rented house. It was always a hive of activity when it visited the bay and Liz guessed correctly that it was probably some sort of sailing ship for tourists. It was during the third week after our arrival at Marigot that we met the skipper of the vessel. I was having a cool drink at Doolittle's, when two men entered the bar area. I knew they were from the ship as I'd seen them leave it in a large tender; one of the two that the ship carried with it when sailing. The younger man sported a neat black beard, was quite stocky in build and had an intelligent face. The second man was older, but somehow, I guessed that he was the junior of the two. His large blond moustache was wet with sweat, as was the rest of him. He appeared troubled.

As often happens in bars in West Indies, the two newcomers and I soon got into conversation.

Liz, who'd been cooking in the house, joined us after about fifteen minutes.

"By the way, my name is Mark," said the younger man holding out his hand "and" he jerked his thumb towards the second man, "this is Laurie."

I introduced myself and Liz. "Are you on holiday from the large schooner?" I asked. "Hell, no," said Laurie. "Mark here is the skipper an' I'm the first mate." His accent was harsher than Mark's, although both were obviously North American.

"So where do you sail from and to?" asked an interested Liz. Mark replied "the ship is named the Atlantic Clipper and we set off weekly from St. Maarten, now we go down as far as Mustique," he went on. "The ship is owned by an American company that offers weekly sailing trips for the adventurous at reasonable prices."

Laurie screwed his face up as though in pain as Mark put over roughly word for word what was in their company

115

brochure.

"The ship was originally laid down in Bremen, Germany and designed as a clipper for the Atlantic trade running out of Boston," Mark said. "It was decommissioned when trade deteriorated and eventually it was bought as scrap by a German industrialist in the early 1900's and he spent a million dollars on converting it into a private yacht."

"Then what happened?" asked Liz.

Mark grimaced. "It became a war prize after 1945 and the American navy used it for training. Later, they auctioned her off with a load of other surplus US navy stores. My boss, who runs several of these types of ships world-wide, bought it and converted it to what it is today." He turned and looked at the newly painted vessel. "It's 200 feet long and has sixty cabins . . ."

Laurie interrupted. "Bloody tin coffins packed with cockroaches if you ask me," he said sourly.

Mark smiled. "Well, I guess you couldn't call 'em luxury cabins, but it's sold as an adventure holiday."

"Jesus," snorted Laurie grimacing, "some fuckin' adventure."

"What sort of people . . ." I didn't finish my sentence.

"Oh, we get all sorts," answered Mark, ignoring his first mate's cynicism, "mainly the younger set because comfort isn't the highest priority."

Laurie snorted again but more loudly.

Mark continued, "we often get older people on board, too. It's a great holiday for the price. We pick up in St. Maarten, and during the week we stop off at Antigua, Martinique, St Lucia, Bequia, Mustique and sometimes get as far down as Union and Palm island."

We got to like both men, although they were very different types and we chatted on until nightfall, when Liz invited them both back for supper. They were most appreciative of her cooking and a firm friendship formed. The next day we received an invitation to board the Atlantic Clipper for lunch and we had a thoroughly pleasant day. Each week after that, we'd meet up with Mark and sometimes Laurie as well.

About five weeks later, I was surprised one morning to see Laurie climbing the steps to the veranda of the Marigot house. He looked totally exhausted and even more depressed than when we'd first met him. I knew it wasn't the normal day for the Atlantic Clipper to visit Marigot, but I smiled and ushered Laurie into a seat.

Since the initial meeting, Liz and I'd learned quite a lot about Laurie. Mark had told us that he was an ex-Vietnam veteran and he'd clearly had a bad time over there to the extent that it had somewhat screwed up his personality. Everything he did appeared to end up disastrously, but he was a wonderful storyteller and could keep us all in fits of laughter for hours at a time.

"The really funny thing is," Liz said, "that Laurie never shows any amusement when telling his tales of woe, which tends to make them all the funnier because he tells them with a completely straight face."

Laurie was about my age, but after three divorces, he'd given up on any long-term relationship. His girlfriend's rarely lasted longer than a cruise and according to Mark, one left the ship after only a day's sail. "He's the only man I know," said Mark with a grin, "who has anti sex appeal." Laurie's physical characteristics played a part in the stories he told and doubtless had some effect on his lack of attraction to women. He had a long Wyatt Earp type blond moustache, which appeared to be straight at times when he was relaxing, but often it would droop either side of his mouth when he was stressed, which was most of the time. His physique was small, slightly built, bordering on skinny and he had a pigeon chest. He walked with a pronounced stoop as though the world really was on his shoulders.

On this day, he walked on to the veranda, barely acknowledging my smile, and headed straight for an armchair, conveniently situated near the drink's fridge. He slumped down and sighed dejectedly. Hearing Laurie's footsteps Liz came out onto the veranda. She offered him his favourite beer and sat down beside him. Liz and I sensed that we were in for a good story.

Laurie tipped his head back and slurped his beer down in huge gulps. It was only after the second can that his thirst appeared slaked enough for him to begin his tale.

"Well, you'll remember when you came on board for lunch

the other week. I told you that I'd been fired from my last job as a skipper on a charter yacht owned by a pig rich Yank, jus' because I threw his fuckin' complaining wife overboard." We both smiled and remembered.

Laurie took another swig of beer from the can. "Well, I never told you how I joined the present outfit, did I?" We both shook our heads.

"Well, I thought I'd had enough of chartering, so I looked around for somethin' more meaningful. While I wuz lookin, I met a friend of mine who worked as the first mate on the Atlantic Clipper. He told me that he'd met an heiress who'd booked a trip on the ship and he wuz goin' back to the States to get married and become a multi-millionaire," Laurie grinned and squeezed the beer from his long moustache. "Jesus, that sounded great to me, an' I asked him if he'd put in a good word fer me to take over his job. Much to my surprise, they were desperate to get someone quickly, so they employed me almost straight away.

"The first skipper then was a young guy called Bernard, but as he wuz busy shagging all the girls that came on board he didn't have much time to run the ship, as his second in command, that was basically left to me.

"Yer see the idea of a sailing holiday on the Atlantic Clipper, according to the fuckin' brochure, is to experience the excitement of sailing on a large ship in the Caribbean and to explore various tropical islands.

"But the real idea is to attract guys with money to take a trip on the ship, knowing that an ample supply of girls wuz provided, this wuz done by the company's policy of offering special low-priced deals to airlines, for air hostesses and any other industries that have lots of females. It's a sort of single's bar with sails an' beds down below."

"Sounds reasonable to me," I said, my smile being quickly wiped away when I noticed Liz frowning at me, followed by a kick under the table between us.

"Yea, problem was the broads usually ignored the spotty white-faced male creatures that had paid, an' concentrated on the crew. I found it real difficult to do my job properly. To try an' organise things a bit better, an' to ensure the crew didn't fall out over all the 'available' on board, I set up a system of entitlements."

"Entitlement?" I queried.

"Yea, it worked well for a while. As soon as people came on board, they had to give us their passports.

"Once we had 'em all, we sorted the males from the females. Then the skipper would take first choice, me second, and so on."

"You mean you targeted specific females?" Liz sounded alarmed.

"Yea, well, I thought it was better than individual crew members being targeted by half a dozen of the sex-crazed women, particularly as the ones that targeted me were fat, spotty ones. The idea was that once you struck up a relationship the rest'd leave you alone."

"But what happened in the case of females coming on board with their own friends?" I raised my eyebrows.

Laurie laughed, swigged down the rest of his beer, and grabbed for another, which Liz was just pulling out of the fridge.

"It didn't seem to make any difference, I guess. I did slip up badly once though." His face crumpled at the thought.

"Oh?" I raised my eyebrows.

"Yea, well I wuz busy one day at the start of a trip that usually lasts for a week. I quickly picked my future bed mate from the pile of passports. Trouble was I hadn't bothered to look at the date of birth. Fuckin' bitch hadn't had her picture changed for ten years and had put on about two hundred pounds in the meantime, Jesus that was a tough fuckin' week that wuz." Liz got up to get drinks for herself and me, giving me a sidelong glance.

"It seems to me that with everything else going on you didn't have too much time to do much sailing," Liz said.

"Yea, that's right. Bloody Bernard spent most of the day in his bloody cabin while I did all the work. We'd a specific itinerary laid down, an' I had to sail to about six islands in week, re–provision at Philipsburg each Saturday, an' then take off on the merry go round again. I wouldn't have minded if I'd met a rich bloody heiress who wanted to lavish the sort of life style on me that I deserve, but the ones I had were all piss poor, an' in two cases they borrowed money from me to

119

get 'em home."

"What a shame," smiled Liz, not particularly sympathetic.

"Yea, that's what I thought. I spent my day making sure the local crew didn't fuck all the females."

"Jesus, the blacker they were, the more the females went fer 'em, it wuz like carrying the proverbial bucket of cold water when you've got a fuckin' bitch on heat. One day, I found the chief engineer in his cabin with three of 'em, how can you run a ship like that?"

"So, your passport method didn't work too well?" Liz asked.

"It did to start with, but there were just too many of 'em and too few of us, I guess.

"Consider what happened last week."

I cast my mind back to their previous visit. Mark and Laurie had enjoyed a drink on the veranda of our house and afterwards had gone off to meet the guests who had gone ashore to the Hurricane Hole jump up across the bay.

"What happened?" Liz asked.

"Well, by the time we got over there, the party wuz in full swing. There was one guy there with a wife about half his age, an' he was drinking himself into the floor. She wuz damned attractive too, sort of Marilyn Monroe type, big, you know?" Laurie stole a sly glance at Liz with his hands moving up to his chest, palms cupped upwards. "Well, they wuz big, she'd on a very tight dress too, an' she seemed to be a bit lonely, so I asked her if she wanted to dance. When we got on the floor, she came real close an' I thought that I'd scored with a good looker fer once. I'd one dance with her and it wuz starting to make me feel all hot an' sweaty. I guess I started to get a little horny. Well jus' as I was feelin' good, she whispered in my ear that she fancied the captain an' asked if I would I introduce her. Jesus, what a let-down, I consoled myself with the thought that nothing could happen, with her husband nosing around."

"Did you introduce her to Mark?" I asked.

"Yeah, and he took her over an' had one dance with her, but when she came over all amorous, Mark told her to go back to her husband, he wasn't like the previous shit, Bernard."

"And did she?" Liz asked with interest.

"I didn't see what she did. I wuz being propositioned by one of the spotty brigades an' I'd my hands full in trying to extricate myself.

"Next mornin', Mark told me what had happened," I raised my eyebrows.

"Mark saw the broad goin' back to the table where her husband was. Next time he looked; the guy was still drinkin' with some other guests an' the girl wuz nowhere around.

"Mark told me he'd had enough, so he went on back to the ship, had a quick drink at the bar on board and went down to his cabin. When he opened the door, he sensed someone wuz inside, so he switched on the light, expecting some guy to attack him. What he saw was the Marilyn Monroe type lying naked on top of his berth, all ready and waitin' fer you know what."

"What did Mark do, throw her out?" Liz asked.

I thought Laurie was about to have an apoplectic fit. Finally, he got control of himself, "throw her out." He looked at Liz in amazement, "Oh, yeah, sure. Pigs' can fuckin' fly, I wouldn't have minded, but the bastard came to breakfast the next mornin' with a fuckin' grin all over his face as wide as. . ." For once, he was lost for words.

"But surely, there must have been good times for you too," said Liz, this time a little more sympathetically.

"Oh, yea I got the real intellectual types, who would come up on the bridge and ask me to tell 'em how many times a wave breaks on the beach. Jesus, can you believe it?"

"What was your answer?" I asked, grinning.

"432.6 times per ten minutes. The fuckin' idiots used to nod knowingly and say gee that's real 'inneresting'. As though I'd know how many times, a wave broke. The other question we used to get when we anchored off some beach somewhere was, 'can I swim to the beach?'

"I'd say I dunno can you swim to the beach? I used to get my own back, though. When they hit the water, I'd shout, look out for the killer sharks, this is their breedin' ground. The look on their faces, when they tried to get back on board, made the job worth-while.

"Getting back on board wuz difficult, the deck is about fifteen feet from the sea as you know," Laurie looked me to confirm. "After one of the guys had a heart attack, tryin' to claw his way up the freeboard, Mark, who'd taken over by then, insisted we throw down rope ladders. It spoiled the fun a bit though." Another beer consumed; another can open.

I could tell Laurie was warming to the story now.

"One guy who I'd told about the killer sharks came straight back on board an' asked me if I'd any shark repellent.

"I told him I would get him some for $20. That night I sprayed a tin of shaving cream with some ship's paint, to cover up what it was, an' the next day, I gave it to him and told him he mustn't tell anyone that I'd got it specially fer him, as it was normally reserved fer the crew only. I told him that he should spray it in the water every thirty seconds when swimming, I watched the stupid fucker swim towards the shore, followed by little heaps of white stuff.

After that I made a tidy sum on the side as the word got around that I could supply shark repellent and I'd to buy a couple of cases a week from the supermarket in Philipsburg."

I glanced at Liz as she turned her eyes towards the sky. Laurie continued unaware of Liz's impatience.

"Jesus, some of the things that happened, you just wouldn't believe. Jus' recently, we took a party ashore at Palm Island in the Grenadines and one macho male trod on a sea urchin. The spines shoot into the foot and can be quite painful.

"The guy was crying like a baby because one of the crew had told him that it was fatal to tread on one. I told him that he'd bin' given a bunch of crap, and providin' he took quick action, he'd live."

Liz laughed. "What was the quick action?"

Laurie looked mildly uncomfortable. "I told him to piss on his foot." (*Correct advice: the acid in the urine relieves the symptoms*). "Well, you'd never believe it, but the guy was so scared that right on the beach, surrounded by loads of guys an' women, he jacked his thing out and performed. Seeing this guy standing on one leg and pissing on his foot, which he held as close as possible to the source of the stream, was . . . well, it made my day. I told him he'd to do it every fifteen minutes for the next hour if he wanted to stay alive."

We both laughed. Although such a story seemed highly

unlikely to the uninitiated, we had seen enough of tourists in the Caribbean to believe the tale completely. Some were very gullible.

Laurie drank another beer. "Then there wuz the guy who came up to me when we were doin' a night sail, which we used to do one night a week, he looked up at the sky and asked me the names of the stars. As there are about a billion of the fuckers, I told him that they were all named by groupings. I pointed to the west to the constellation called Pluto. I pointed east but he interrupted me. 'Good God he said, I didn't know they were all named after Disney characters.'

"I asked him if he ever went to school. Then I said, anyone knows that in the east, over there's Goofy, an' we're headed straight for Mickey Mouse in the south."

"Jeez, I wish I were so knowledgeable,' he said.

"So, what brings you here today?" Liz was starting to tire of the stories and looking at her watch.

Laurie looked mildly uncomfortable. "The bastards have sacked me."

"Why," I asked, with feigned surprise.

"That's another story, all on its own."

I thought it would be," murmured Liz, under her breath.

Laurie shifted his body to a more comfortable position, took another gulp of beer and a fistful of the salted nuts that Liz had put on the table. "Twice a year, the company encouraged a queer's trip."

"Do you mean gay people?" Liz interjected.

"Yea, you know homos, they come in their droves."

"Did you still do the passports?" Liz asked seemingly innocently. I grinned.

"Jesus no, I used to keep well away from the buggers, although, in fairness, most of 'em came with their own companions."

Liz got up and excused herself, she'd got certain things to do she said, and I suspected she didn't wish to hear any more of Laurie's story.

"So?" I asked when she'd gone.

"Well, I wuz at the wheel on another night sail, when someone came up behind me and put their hands over my eyes.

"It wasn't that I objected to, it was the hard feeling that I felt at the back of my trousers. I tore the hands off and turned around to see this pot–bellied guy with a hard on, telling me he fancied me. I was fuckin' beside myself and I grabbed a broom and went to hit the bugger, when he saw that I wasn't exactly fallin' in love with him, he turned to flee, but tripped. I only meant to scare the fucker I didn't mean the end of the pole to go where it did.

"We had to put the guy off the ship the next day and when he got back to the States, he got a medical report and last week he issued a writ on the company. I wuz asked if it was true, an' I told 'em what had happened. I also told 'em that as he was fuckin' queer, I would've thought that he'd enjoyed it. Mark put in a good word fer me, but I was fired the next day, that was yesterday," Laurie concluded.

"It does seem a little unfair," I said sympathetically.

"Story of my life," Laurie said mournfully.

"So, what are you going to do now?" I offered him a fifth beer, as he finished the one, he was drinking.

"I guess I'll mosey back to the States and see if I can find me an heiress there. If not, I'll buy myself a dog an' settle down. Perhaps buy a skunk farm," he mused.

I was thinking how to help Laurie and I said, "why don't you approach Sunshine Yachts? I hear they're looking for crews." Something inside me told me I had just made a bad mistake, but it was too late.

Laurie brightened perceptibly. "Gee, that's a real good idea, I reckon I'll just do that."

Liz came back onto the veranda.

"Hey, what's fer dinner Liz?" After Laurie had cleaned us out of beer and food, he departed rather unsteadily into the night.

"Was that wise?" asked Liz.

"What?" I replied.

"Recommending Laurie go to Sunshine."

"Why not, he needs a job and they're looking for skippers?" I said.

"Yes, I know," said Liz, "but does Sunshine need a Laurie."

In the early spring, to our total astonishment, Pittam, approached us like long lost friends. He asked if we would be interested in leading flotillas down to the Grenadines. He explained that a flotilla consisted of all six O'Day's, each charter party having their own boat.

We assumed he'd overcome the problems with the owners.

The idea was that Liz, and I would teach the other crews the rudiments of sailing, make sure everyone had a good time and ensure that no one ended up on a reef while 'down island'.

When we returned from the third and last flotilla, Pittam informed us that he'd experienced more problems with the owners, and they were now definitely withdrawing their boats.

He couldn't therefore pay us for our work, but he hastily offered his own boat free for four weeks.

We accepted and sailed north, to Martinique, Iles des Saintes, Guadeloupe, Antigua, St. Kitts, Eustatius, Saba, St. Barts, St. Martin, St. Maarten, Montserrat, and Anguilla.

By the time, we returned, we were seriously over our budget, but there wasn't much of the Leeward chain of islands that we didn't know about.

On the return, there was another letter waiting for me and it was good news. The literary agent had written from New York to say that she was dealing with a company who used to publish the Ludlam books and the chairman's wife had taken a liking to my novel. The upshot of it was that she wanted me to go to New York and meet the lady concerned. We were both delighted and on the

strength of the agent's letter, we invested in a return ticket to New York and left, booking into the Waldorf Astoria.

The literary agent telephoned me at the hotel the next day and arranged to pick us up for lunch. We were both excited at the prospect of me becoming a famous novelist.

Joan Hargreaves was a tall willowy woman of about forty, with a quiet American east coast accent and very smart clothes. She drove Liz and me in her new Cadillac to an expensive restaurant in the centre of the city. It was only then that we learned of a problem. Joan explained that she'd arranged for us to meet Monica Puesett for lunch. When she telephoned her office the day before, just to tie up final arrangements, the Chairman's secretary told her that Ms Puesett no longer worked for the publishing Company.

Knowing that she was the Chairman's wife, Joan pressed for more information and was confidentially told that the Chairman and his wife had had an enormous row and Monica had walked out of both job and home. No one knew where she was.

"Well folks," Joan said with a sigh, "you can guess my embarrassment. It was too late to get hold of you guys, and here we are, sort of at a loss."

Liz and I were dumbfounded and extremely annoyed.

Joan saw the expression on my face and tried to be conciliatory. "Look," she said, "I'm sure I'll be able to get hold of Monica within a few days. Can you guys stay over?" I looked across the table at Liz.

"I'm afraid that we've to be back in a couple of days," I said truthfully, "as we've an appointment we need to keep," Liz nodded in agreement, and it was left at that.

Two days later Joan rang to say she still had no contact with Monica but was sure it would be okay in the end.

"She was really excited about your novel," she insisted.

We returned to St. Lucia in an extremely dejected frame of min

INSTANT MEDICATION...

7 - THE FREEBIES

And How I Had My First Encounter

We got back to the little rented house in Marigot and prepared for a meeting requested by John Peachcombe of Sunshine Yacht Charters, from whom we'd chartered a yacht over the previous Christmas holiday.

In the morning, we hired a taxi to take us to the marina where Sunshine was located.

John Peachcombe welcomed us warmly with two cups of hot coffee and brought up the fact that he knew we had been working for Pittam. We laughed, "Yes, it rather came out of the blue," Liz said, "but in the end he couldn't pay us for the work we did for him."

I shrugged, "but he gave us the free use of his boat for a month, which allowed us to explore all the islands in the Leeward chain, so we didn't do too badly."

"And we received some very good tips from the trainee crews, from the flotillas we ran for him," Liz added. John Peachcombe nodded, "It doesn't surprise me that you weren't paid I'm afraid, but that's the reason I wanted to talk to you."

"Oh," we both said in unison.

"I've a problem," John explained. "We're taking on extra yachts and it's going to be extremely busy at the start of the new season, I simply can't find the right type of crews to run them and certainly there are very few, if any, who know all the areas we sail as well as you two do."

Liz laughed, "it sounds as though you're offering us a job John?"

John looked serious. "Yes, I certainly am, how about it?"

"Would we get paid," I asked.

"Yes of course you would. I'd start you off on a Gulf Star, which is a 50-foot sloop that would be no problem for you, and then once a Nautilus 60 becomes available, I'd move you onto that. Your pay would be $1,000 a month, you'd always live on the boat, so you could dispense with your costly rented home in Marigot, and you'd survive on the generous food allowance we give for charters. On top of that, you'd almost certainly receive generous tips from satisfied clients."

"What sort of tax would we have to pay?" I asked.

"Nil, nothing," answered John, "as you wouldn't formally be attached to any particular tax area, so what you earn, is what you keep."

Liz had a few questions about provisioning, the type of charters we were likely to get, and John answered them all to her satisfaction.

"Can we think about it?" I asked.

"Of course, but I do need someone very quickly for a charter this weekend, so I'd be grateful if you could both let me know by tomorrow."

We left John's office deep in thought, and as we were passing one of the Gulf Stars, Liz took the opportunity to buttonhole one of the girl cooks to discuss what was involved. I went on to take a close look at an empty Gulf Star further down the dock.

When I emerged, Liz was waiting for me, she smiled. "I've

had a long chat with one of the girl cooks and it all seems straight forward. It means that if there are no charters, we've the yacht to sail in, and although there's no provisioning if you don't have a charter, it appears that the allowance is quite generous, and one can live perfectly well for at least a couple of weeks free. I also enquired what the average tips were, and it seems to be between 10 and 15 percent."

I remembered that crewed yachts cost the guests around $3,000 a week, which would bring in an extra income of $300 to $450 a week.

"I'll work out the finances when we get back to Marigot," I told Liz, "and then we can make a decision."

"Oh, by the way," said Liz, "I've just been told that Laurie, did get a job with Sunshine."

"I'm surprised," I answered, "as he didn't have anyone to do his cooking."

"Well, I think he found someone, but how long that'll last is anyone guess," said Liz, as she got into the taxi to take us back to Marigot.

Liz and I discussed the offer and we realised that the money we earned would easily pay for our children's expensive school fees in the UK and that we would have plenty over. It didn't take long to make the decision. The next morning, we rang John Peachcombe and told him we'd accept the job for at least the new season, and he asked us to go over and see him that morning.

I hadn't really noticed the day before but John's office at Sunshine was chaotic. I noticed journals, yachting magazines and old brochures piled high on his desk. The floor area around him packed with old and new parts including boat engines, water pumps, rigging, winches and even a boat's lavatory seat with a cracked basin sat in a corner. Liz reckoned afterwards that the office hadn't seen a duster for many years.

John was behind his desk as we walked in. After greeting

us, he took us into the main office and introduced us to Ellie who looked after the charter bookings. He then left to meet someone who had arrived on the dock.

"Let me see now," Ellie turned her swivel chair to face the charter schedule, which consisted of coloured bits of paper spread across the wall in front of her. "I've a large charter booked for this weekend comprising of three boats. It's quite important for us, as these are all travel agents from the USA, so they're freebies, no tips I'm afraid," she turned to us smiling. "I know John particularly wants you two on this charter, so you'd better get your things over here ASAP and get settled in. When you return tomorrow, I'll introduce you to Laura, she's our accountant who deals with the cash and wages as well as all the paperwork."

We thanked her, shook hands warmly and left.

That night I gave notice to the owners of the rented property in Marigot Bay, and we moved on to Silver Fern the next day taking her out for a short sail, just to get used to the vessel.

The day after Liz and I had moved onto the boat, we went ashore to pick up some cleaning items from the store and afterwards went back to see Laura. She was a nice looking, pale-skinned St. Lucian girl of about thirty, who wore her hair straightened and tied behind in a sort of ponytail. She wore a mocha–coloured dress, which was the colour of the Sunshine uniform.

After offering Liz a seat, the only other one in the office besides hers, she pulled out a brochure, which I'd already seen. She didn't give it to us.

She provided a wealth of information about the company, explained how it operated and gave the low down on some of the people involved, without betraying her private opinion of her employer.

"Of course," she smiled, "I was forgetting that you'd

131

chartered from us, so you'll have seen this," she held up the brochure. Laura had a mild Caribbean accent and I guessed correctly that she had spent some time in England.

"We'll start at the top," she said efficiently. "Willum Gothenburg owns the company and lives in Annapolis, on the east coast of the United States." She got up, walked across to a wall map, and pointed to a red coloured pin. "The USA operation does all the marketing and books all the charters."

"Does he own all these yachts?" asked Liz, looking out of the window at the twenty or so yachts tied up on the three separate docks.

"No, all the charter yachts are owned by individuals.

"They buy them because USA law in some states such as Delaware allows substantial capital tax breaks to the owners," she explained. "Willum's US operation really makes its money from selling the yachts in the first place, but we're necessary 'cause it's important that the owners' expense of keeping the yacht are covered. We do that by chartering them out. Most owners have never even seen the boat they've bought, and John says he prefers it that way. Owners who like sailing are a bloody nuisance, he says," she grinned.

"Are they all crewed?" I asked.

"No, only about ten of them, we've over sixty yachts altogether, although some are up in St. Maarten, that's on the Dutch side." I remembered that St. Maarten, one of the principal northern islands is divided into two parts, the northern end being French and the southern part Dutch. My mind began to wander when Laura started to talk about washing facilities and what sort of food the crews served.

I'd read that the French and the Dutch couldn't agree on a border between the two states, so a representative from each delegation was appointed to agree on a method of demarcation. They decided upon a unique method of settlement. Early one morning, a Dutchman and a Frenchman met on a beach at the westernmost part of the island, and one walked north, the other south. When they met again on the perimeter, a line between the second meeting place and the first indicated the border between the two countries. Unfortunately for the Dutch, the Frenchman was either the fitter man, or more likely, keen to get back to his mistress in Marigot Bay (a different Marigot to the one in St Lucia) located on the French side of the island. Whatever the case, by the time they met up later in the day, the Frenchman had covered more than 60% of the coast, which is why they have the larger section. However, because the Dutchman walked to the east, the Dutch got the main port, which is Philipsburg. Since writing this, I understand there is some doubt that this happened.

I was conscious of Laura talking again.

"Most crews are youngsters, usually in their early twenties. They stay for a season, and leave," she walked over to the window and pointed to the shining water. "The Peterson 44 is usually chartered as a bareboat, that's the one you chartered recently. The Gulf Stars are all fifty footers and about eight are crewed. We've twelve of those down here, although most are out on charter now. Then we've two Nautilus 60's, They're the Rolls Royce's of the fleet, very luxurious, they even have a king-sized bed in the aft state cabin." she giggled, "and," she added, "a trash compactor and all mod cons," she adopted a look of mock sorrow.

"'Fraid you've got to be with Sunshine for years to get one of them though."

We walked back to her desk, and she sat down.

"Has John told you what you'll be paid?" I nodded, "a $1,000 a month." "Well, it's split $600 a month for the skipper and $400 a month for the cook. Of course, you receive a provisioning allowance for each charter, and most crews earn more in tips than their basic wages and they generally do quite well on the provisioning, but it's important that the guests aren't sold short," Laura grimaced. "We'd one

South African crew who offered their charter guests scrambled egg and cheese on toast for dinner and restricted their booze. The guests justifiably complained, and the crew were sacked, so they didn't gain much as they obviously didn't receive a tip."

Laura was looking closely at me, "it's not bad when you think that your rent is paid, you've a free boat to live on and cruise on when you don't have a charter and you'll almost certainly receive gratuities. Your food and booze are usually covered by the allowance, so what other expenses do you have?" She shrugged her shoulders.

"*Bloody school fees,*" Liz said under her breath.

"How often do we get a charter," I asked.

"Almost back-to-back in the season," Laura answered, "and if your rating is good from client's comments, you'll be very busy most of the year.

"Of course, if you're lucky enough to get a Nautilus 60, the skipper gets a $1000 a month and the cook $500 and the tips are much bigger," She threw out her arms to emphasise the point. "And strangely the 60's usually has less people even though they're much larger. Oh, and one other thing, you can have your money paid direct into a US bank account, which we can open for you," I frowned, "what about the exchange?"

"Exchange," Laura looked puzzled, "yes from the EC dollar to the US$."

"Ah, yes, the current exchange rate is 2.68 EC$ to 1 US$, but all the figures I've been giving you are in US currency, and you'll be paid in US$."

We went through some accounting paperwork and then Laura showed us around. There were only three offices, hers, Ellie's, and John's with a small reception area in between where a young girl operated a small switchboard. There was also a shower, lavatory, and small kitchen area. Outside there were some buildings that housed a parts store, a sail loft, and a smaller building, out on its own, where they stored the butane gas. Finally, there were some more shower cubicles and lavatories specifically for guest use in a separate building. We were introduced to the dock master, whose name was George, and Nigel the parts' manager. As we walked down to the dock, I noticed a large diesel tank built on brick supports, and the usual sickly oil smell that emanated from it. The dock was split into three parts, two outer legs built straight out into the Rodney Bay Lagoon, and the boats were tied to both sides by the bow. The centre dock was wider and had a large 'T' at the end.

"The end of the 'T' is reserved for boats taking on charter guests," explained Laura, as we climbed into the dinghy.

Liz thanked Laura for her time and as she returned to the office, we rowed out to Silver Fern. Later in the day, we moved the rest of our personal effects onto the yacht and set about cleaning the inside ready for the charter in two days' time. John had asked us to keep the radio turned on during the day, as it was easier to contact us that way, rather than getting someone to row out to the boat.

It was later in the evening when we received a call and John asked if we'd both go across to the Marina, which was about a five-minute row from where we anchored. With some trepidation, we rowed across the lagoon, tied the dinghy to the dock and walked up to John's office. He looked up from his desk as we walked in. He looked grim.

"Hi guys, I'm really very sorry, but I'm going to have to move you from Silver Fern, there's been a change of plan,'' My heart sank, and Liz looked totally crestfallen as she'd virtually finished cleaning the interior of the Gulf Star.

"I suppose the Silver Fern crew have decided to stay," I said mournfully.

"No, it's not that, the crew of one of the Nautilus yachts has given notice and want to leave immediately. Normally we allocate these larger yachts to people with the longest service, but the owner is insistent that we find someone a little older and as you guys are the oldest, the job is yours if you want it. It's also important that you take over immediately because our boss, Willum D. Gothenburg has arranged a charter for this bunch of travel agents coming down for a freebie. Personally, I think these people are a waste of time, but what the boss says, we do.

"I have to tell you that these types of trips aren't popular with the crews," John added.

"Why not," Liz asked.

"Because Freebie's don't tip, so Joan and Michel, the present crew have decided to hoppit early."

"When?"

"We've suggested to Michel, that he and Joan move on to Silver Fern as their plane doesn't leave until next week and you and Liz get straight on to the 60. Silver Star is the yacht's name by the way. The travel agents arrive the day after tomorrow, so it'll give you a bit of time to familiarise yourself with the boat and get her provisioned. There'll be twelve of 'em all together."

John saw the look of horror on Liz's face and grinned. She had forgotten what Laura had told her.

"Don't worry Liz there'll be two Gulf Stars going on the same trip so that'll be three yachts all together. The trip is only going to be a short one, they're only staying one night on the boat, so it'll give you a gentle entry into yacht chartering proper, But the people on your yacht will be the most important ones."

"One night, are we just sailing locally, then?" Liz asked, realising that the Grenadines were out.

"The suggestion from Willum is that you take them up to Martinique and anchor off St. Anne as they want to check out Club Med at the same time."

I knew that St Anne was a pretty bay situated on the south eastern end of Martinique. Club Med was built on the point as one sailed into the bay proper. I remembered that we'd stayed two nights in the St. Anne Bay area when we had sailed north in the much smaller O'Day 35, and we were told that we couldn't go into Club Med, because they only accepted residents. I mentioned this to John.

"No, that's not correct. They've a special deal for yachtsmen and are always glad to see you, but you should enter the complex from the sea side, tell reception that you're on a yacht anchored in the bay and they'll sell you your beads."

"Beads?" I must have looked puzzled.

John smiled, "yes, you can't buy anything with money in Club Med you buy beads and use them as currency," John shrugged his shoulders. "But in this case, everything is arranged. You just report to the manager when you get there, and he'll issue you beads for the party. You won't have to pay anything. Oh, and one more thing, I'm putting Margo Feldman and her husband on your yacht. She's the leader of the party, so make sure you look after them, 'cause she's bound to report back to Willum."

The next day was very busy, as we swapped boats and provisioned for the coming charter. Because the guests were travel agents, the crews had an extra booze allowance, which was useful, as we were able to get off to a good start in building up a bar.

Liz wasn't happy with the cleanliness of Silver Star, and she spent her time scrubbing and polishing inside, while I made sure the exterior was in good shape and familiarised myself with the rig.

Silver Star was a ketch, with one main mast, an aft mast for the ketch sail and a foresail. The main difference from anything we'd sailed before was the roller furling on the main and jib. The jib was a delight because it meant an end to pulling the sail out from the sail locker each time we sailed. By just pulling in the roller sheet, the sail rolled magically around the forestay. To let it out, it was enough just to uncleat it and if there was any wind at all, the sail would open on its own. If not, a simple tug on one of the jib lines and hey presto, the jib was ready for sailing. It's more unusual to have a main furling and I came to understand why they were not popular. In theory, it should have made things easier, because instead of dropping the main, by simply letting go of the main sheet halyard, the sail disappeared into the mast pulled in by the main line. This meant no folding and should have made reefing much easier too. The problem was that it was the very devil to furl, particularly if it was wet and many a time it seized altogether, making it a major job to extract it. The ketch sail was much smaller and often left up even at anchor. The main bonus was that Silver Star had an electric windlass, which took most of the physical exertion out of pulling up the anchor. On the other hand, it was a great finger-breaker, if one was careless.

The inside of Silver Star was quite spacious. It had been built specifically for the yacht charter trade and the designer had packed in four cabins, a large one aft, that had a king-sized bed and even a bath in the head, there were two cabins forward, both with their own heads. The crew's cabin was behind the navigation area and had two berths, one on top of the other with a small head behind. The main cabin was quite large and very well equipped to seat at least eight people. The water tanks, which were under the seats, were not adequate for people who spent a long time in the shower, and we were to have problems keeping up with charterer's needs in this respect. Generally, the finish was good, and all the wood was light mahogany. I was pleased to find that the dinghy was a large inflatable with a powerful outboard, both of which could be winched aft when sailing. The very large engine was underneath the aft cabin and accessed from the crews' cabin. The large cockpit was aft of centre with strong canvas covers in case of inclement weather.

We managed a trial sail before the charter guests came on

board and felt reasonably confident about the four-hour sail to Martinique with our prospective passengers.

We met the crews from the other two yachts accompanying us, Geoff and Budgie were English and married, and Gerald and Judith were South African and living together. All of them were much younger than we were, but considerably more experienced sailors. The South African couple had sailed from South Africa in their own small ketch and Geoff and Budgie had come over in a small wooden-hulled boat from Portsmouth, in England.

The travel agents arrived on the island the night before and stayed in one of the local hotels. They turned up on the dock with much fanfare at 11 am. I soon sorted out our party and it was quite clear who the leader was.

Margo Feldman was a large Jewish American woman in her late forties, with heavy make-up that looked as though it had been applied with a spatula. She and her husband Wayne were from New York. Wayne was a big man, with a big belly that his multi-coloured tourist shirt almost failed to cover. He was particularly sweaty and smelled of body odour. The other two, Madge and Robin, seemed a quiet and an unassuming pair and hardly spoke during the whole of the trip. Robin was tall and thin, with rimless glasses, and Madge was a little mouse of a woman who, it soon became obvious was clearly the boss. The other two who were supposed to be on our yacht had developed a bad tummy complaint and declined to sail. The rest of them were allocated to the other yachts.

Liz settled our four on board and offered them a Rum Punch, which was gratefully accepted by all save Madge, who only drank orange juice. Liz found that Wayne had an insatiable need for alcoholic liquid, and she quickly realised that the extra allowance might not even cover his needs alone.

It helped that they all knew each other, but it surprised me to learn that none of them had sailed before. We set off in

Silver Star just after midday on a glorious Saturday afternoon. Liz had prepared some peanut butter sandwiches, which were very successful although they apparently would have preferred jelly with them, Liz found them some black current jam and so they were happy with that.

Sunshine had their marina in Rodney Bay Lagoon, set inside the Bay, and connected to it by a narrow man-made channel. I sailed the yacht through that and into Rodney Bay proper, putting up the main sail as we did so. Passing Pigeon Island (*that had been an island but now joined by a man-made causeway*) on the northern side of the bay, we turned to starboard and within twenty minutes, had cleared the north end of St. Lucia. The sea was short and there was plenty of wind, so the boat made good time to St. Anne. The skippers had a race on the way across and to my surprise; we won, which pleased Margo immensely.

Sailing into the St. Anne area was straight forward, and the yachts anchored in front of the main Club Med building. Wayne was very keen for us to anchor Silver Star further north just around the point in what appeared to be a more sheltered spot. I acknowledged that the area was indeed more sheltered, but as there was a reef two feet below the surface in that area and the yachts drew six feet, I told Wayne that there was no way that we could move there.

The big man seemed most disappointed. After we'd anchored safely, I looked across the bay and saw the other yachts were just coming in; the women went below to shower and get ready for the evening. Liz was pleased that she didn't have to cook as Club Med had invited us all to dinner on the house with the traditional show afterwards. All the Sunshine Yachts anchored in plenty of water. Five minutes later, Geoff from Tiger Lilly came alongside Silver Star in his dinghy.

"All the guys want to go snorkelling," he said giving me a funny look.

I looked at my watch it was just after 4.30 p.m.

140

"Well okay," I said thoughtfully, "but the sun's a bit low for snorkelling, isn't it? Besides, I didn't realise that there was anything to see in this area."

Geoff laughed and stroked his wispy beard.

"Well, they want to snorkel over there," he pointed to the sheltered spot where Wayne had wanted me to anchor Silver Star.

"But there's no coral," I stopped because Geoff was shaking his head.

"No, but that's where the nude beach is."

"Nude beach?" I clearly didn't understand.

"Yes," grinned Geoff.

"You're joking?"

"Sadly, I'm not. You'll find that Yank men go bananas over nude women."

"But surely if they go to the nude beach, they'll have to strip off, too?" I was still wondering if Geoff was teasing me.

"Yea," said Geoff, "but they're not actually going on the beach they're going to swim around the area."

"In two feet of water, well, count me out," I said. "I'll go and arrange things across at Club Med while you show them the sights."

Geoff seemed keen to do so and agreed. He motored back to Tiger Lilly picked up his two male guests and returned for Wayne and Robin. Wayne was climbing down the Silver Star ladder rather unsteadily and Robin was hastily sorting out some snorkelling gear on board, which Sunshine had provided, when Madge came up from below.

"You aren't goin' nowhere," she snarled. "I know what those bastards are up to. I overheard Wayne talking to one of the other guys this morning," Robin put on a look of pained surprise.

The dinghy had reached the side of Silver Star and looking down over it I couldn't help but smile. Geoff, the skipper, was himself considerably overweight, but the three Americans in the boat were all larger, ensuring that the dinghy was sitting very low in the water. It was clear that if Robin got in, slight though he was, it could disappear beneath the waves. I looked around and noticed Robin taking off his flippers.

"You're not going?" I asked, in feigned surprise.

"Naw, I think I'll have a swim around the boat instead," he made a face at his wife's retreating form.

"I don 't think you'd have got in their dinghy anyway, if it's any consolation," I said, as I let go of the line of Geoff's dinghy. I shouted to Geoff to go ahead without Robin, and I could see that Geoff was greatly relieved.

The small boat delicately chugged on past the stern of Silver Star. I could see the men in the boat pulling on flippers and snorkel masks as they made their way around the point, water occasionally lapping over the side. I was curious about what they'd do, so I sat on the deck to watch. Liz came up on deck and I called her over to where I was sitting and whispered to her what they were doing.

"They've even taken binoculars and cameras with them."

"What snorkelling?" said Liz in amazement.

She hadn't understood the point I'd made to her. Geoff's dinghy reached the middle of the bay area, where the nude beach was in full view. The occupants slid over the side of the dinghy, almost turning it over as they jumped into the sea. The water where they were was very shallow and I could clearly see three large guys, complete with flippers, snorkels, masks, and snorkel tubes, standing in shallow water staring at the beach through their binoculars. I thought it funny, and I laughed loudly as Liz sat scowling. They'd been in position for about thirty seconds, when a lithe, fit looking young man, completely naked, sprang up from where he was lying on the beach and raced for the water heading in their general direction.

Caught completely off guard, panic ensued. Wayne in his haste dropped Geoff's binoculars in the sea and all of them swiftly turned around and pointed at the hills, which were in the opposite direction from the nude beach. The young man, who had obviously been taken as an aggressor, took no notice of the throng and swam off quite unconcerned.

I was still chuckling when Margo joined me on deck. She obviously knew what was going on and showed considerable contempt towards Wayne when he returned.

Nevertheless, the conversation over the whole of the evening to come, was predictable.

"Did ya see the tits on the one near the large palm?"

I was so amused at the spectacle in front of the nude beach that I hadn't been aware of a drama unfolding on the other side of the anchored Sunshine yachts.

Another charter yacht, a Morgan 47, owned by a different company, had come in to anchor about thirty feet the other side of Geoff's boat, which was the furthest Gulf Star away from the small Sunshine fleet. There was a first-class row going on between the two couples on board. I assumed that they were American because one of the women was wearing stars and stripes shorts.

It was obvious they were having real difficulty in anchoring, and this was because the man at the wheel ordered the anchor dropped and then went astern at full speed without giving it time to catch. After the umpteenth time, tempers were such that the man on the bow dumped the anchor unceremoniously on the deck and went down below with one of the women following him. This left the man at the wheel with both jobs to do, which rather compounded his problem. Remembering that we'd had help anchoring previously in Union Island, I thought I'd repay the debt, albeit to another sailor and I jumped into the dinghy and quickly motored over to the Morgan. As I went alongside, I yelled, "can I help?" The man behind the wheel glowered. "What I suggest," I said, without awaiting an answer and as tactfully

143

as I could, "when you've dropped your anchor, don't use your engine to reverse, but let the wind do it and when it has caught, then reverse at about quarter speed." I knew that the Morgan's had an extremely powerful engine for the size of the yacht.

'THE SNORKELLERS'

"Fuck off you Limey bastard. I know what I'm doin'."

The woman who was sitting on the top deck and hadn't lifted a hand to help rushed to the side of the boat nearest to me. "Edgar was in the US Navy for twenny years, he knows how to put down an anchor." I was so astonished that I laughed, which didn't endear me to either of them, so I beat a hasty retreat to Silver Star and watched the continued struggle. In the end, the man did as I had suggested. About to turn away from the late afternoon's entertainment, I was surprised when the man on the Morgan pulled a second anchor from the depths of his boat, dumped it into his dinghy and rowed it out at forty-five degrees to where the first one lay.

He then threw it overboard.

One of the things I'd learned in my short time of sailing was that if you're throwing something overboard with lines attached make sure the line is free from fouling. The man hadn't done so and as the heavy anchor plunged towards the sea bed taking the line with it, the American found himself lassoed around his ankles. There was a moment when it looked as though his weight would be enough to halt the anchor's momentum, but his dinghy tipped in the same direction of the falling line.

As the American's feet were now well and truly lashed together, the angle of the dinghy could mean only one thing. His expression was one of complete surprise as he disappeared over the side with a yell. I was at first concerned, but I needn't have been as the large man surfaced some seconds later. It then became obvious that the other end of the weighted line hadn't been tied to anything in the dinghy either and so the spectacle of the American diving like a large killer whale for it, proved to be a fitting end to the afternoon.

Eventually, the big man retrieved what he'd lost but because he was far too large to climb back into his dinghy from the water, he swam back to the Morgan with the end of the anchor rode in his teeth. The woman on board took it and cleated it while he set off in pursuit of his dinghy, which had drifted some hundred yards away from its original position. It was just getting dark when I saw the man, now very red-faced, laboriously climbing the yacht's aft ladder. I noticed the name of the vessel with some amusement it was 'First Time Ever.'

By 7 p.m., we'd all showered, except Wayne. Liz and I tried

145

to keep our distance from him, which was quite a feat in the enclosed confines of a yacht cabin

"Thank God, they're only on board for a couple of days," sniffed Liz as she wrinkled her nose.

When planning to take our guests to shore, I considered the combined weights of everyone plus Liz and would be too much for the dinghy, so I took the men first, and then went back for the women. Wayne had pulled a muscle getting out of the dinghy near the nude beach and remarked that he was feeling stiff.

I just happened to pass this information on to Margo as we were heading for the boat dock that led into Club Med. I noticed she was showing rather more of her very ample bosom than was quite decent.

"Stiff," she snorted. "Wayne's not had anything stiff since 1953," Liz got a fit of giggles.

The meal was good, and the show excellent, the latter run entirely by the staff. Margo sat on one side of me, and she seemed to tip back the Piña Coladas with gay abandon and without much apparent effect. After the show, Liz said she was going to turn in, but Margo persuaded me to stay for one more drink.

Liz told me not to worry about the dinghy; she said she would swim back to the boat.

Budgie said that she would join Liz, and they disappeared. I said that I'd follow shortly.

We all moved to a bigger table, to allow everyone from the Sunshine yachts who were present, to sit together.

I was embarrassed when Margo grabbed my hand and squeezed it.

I gently pulled it away. Wayne sat directly opposite his arm around a pretty Martinique girl from the show and seemingly taking no notice whatsoever of Margo, who shifted her ample bottom nearer to me and whispered something in my ear. The background music drowned her words.

I smiled and raised my eyebrows questioningly.

She leaned over again, and I smelled her heavy perfume mixed with the scent of alcohol.

"I said, I feel like a good FUCK." My face must have registered complete astonishment. I hesitated, but although

146

genuinely shocked, I congratulated myself on my quick recovery. I smiled at her, recognizing that a bad word from Margo to Willum may not be in our best interests. "Well, there are a lot of good-looking Frenchman around Margo," I added lightly.

"Ah don't want a fucking effeminate Frenchy Jamesy, I want you," she said none too quietly and poked me in the chest with an expensively ringed finger.

I started to feel trapped and thought fast, trying to find the right words to meet this situation.

"I'm really very flattered, Margo but, as you've seen, I'm a happily married man and besides, Liz will be expecting me back shortly."

Her face crumpled "Crap. Fucking crap, you Limeys are all the same; smooth bastards, that guy on the boat was right," she said. I shrugged my shoulders and tried to suppress the aggressive feelings she had stirred in me. Her make-up was melting in the heat, her lipstick and eye shadow had smudged, and she was sweating, damp patches showing under her arms.

She manoeuvred herself round to face me.

"Look," she said, poking me in the chest again, "I book more than thirty per cent of Sunshine's goddamned charters, I expect to be looked after and looked after well."

I realised then that a wrong move by me could prove disastrous to our new found living, but the alternative was arguably much worse.

Aggressiveness was my usual method of dealing with problems, but this required subtlety. I shrugged my shoulders in mock resignation.

"Today, you're the boss," I smiled acquiescently into her eyes, inwardly shuddering. "Yea, that's better," She smiled like a hungry shark. "Now we 'unnerstand each other,'" I noticed, with a glimmer of hope that the effect of drink was starting to show. This wasn't entirely surprising considering the amount she had already consumed. Margo shifted back to her original position and made another grab for my hand. Before she managed to grasp it, I made a lunge for her glass. "Margo," I said smoothly with what I hoped sounded like genuine concern, "your glass is empty. You're quite right. I'm clearly not taking proper care of such an important client," I jumped to get her another drink.

"One more only," she wagged her finger at me, "and then we go."

"Sure," I smiled, picking up a bunch of Margo's beads and heading for the bar, undoing the whole string, and removing enough to buy several drinks.

"I need a strong drink," I said to the bartender, looking at him knowingly.

"Hah, hah, so you 'av found a lady you wish to . . . how shall I say it?" His evil grin completed the sentence.

"Put the bugger to sleep," I answered.

The French barman looked at me as though I was slightly out of my mind. He shook his head in disbelief. "Bah, you Americans, I'll never understand you." I didn't enlighten him as to my nationality, but watched him throw rum, cointreau, vodka and Tia Maria into the one Piña Colada. He handed it carefully to me, as though it contained nitro-glycerine.

"Zis is called Knock Out, 'eet can't fail." I ordered a non-alcoholic fruit punch for myself and was rewarded with an enigmatic shrug and a sad smile.

As I walked back with the two drinks, I noticed that Margo was no longer in her chair and for a split second of euphoria, I thought she had gone. My spirits began to rise.

"HEY Jamsey," she caught me up on the way back to the table, stuffing her credit card back in her purse.

"I've jus' booked a room, thought it would be easier that way."

She giggled, stirring the whole of her body into motion like a large jelly.

We sat down again, and I put the two drinks on the table. Margo made a lunge for my fruit punch, but I was faster and got to it first. She took her own drink and quaffed it in two gulps. I breathed a sigh of relief until she said, "you ready Jamsey?" I held up my full glass and tried to look as though I couldn't wait to get my hands on her. I thought to myself that Laurence Olivier would have been proud of me. However, silently I was worried, Margo had downed her drink much faster than I'd thought she would, and time wasn't my side. I then had an awful thought, "My God, what if she can actually handle the booze."

"I'll just finish this, then I need to go over there," I pointed to the Gentleman's toilet near the entrance to the hall.

Margo shook her head, "no need, I got an en suite room, an' there's a john in there."

Shit, I thought, there goes plan B and I hadn't got a plan C. If the drink failed to work, I'd planned to exit through the window in the men's room. The music was now very loud, and

I noticed that the rest of the Sunshine charterers were getting quite drunk.

Judith had one of the travel agents all over her and Gerald was giving rather a lot of attention to the man's wife. The Martinique girl had switched her attentions to Bill, one of the guys from Geoff's boat, who was part of the group who'd gone snorkelling.

Margo slipped her arm into mine and applied a vice like grip. I did my best to ignore her and started a conversation with a girl called Minnie, sitting on the other side of me. I found out that she was Bill's wife. Her eyes appeared glazed. I wasn't sure how long we were chatting, but I was suddenly aware that the vice like grip had slackened, and I took a quick look. Margo was slouched on her chair, her mouth wide open, making a raucous sound that could have passed for a rendition of a sleeping cow with a stomach disorder. Not a pretty sight, I thought. She was though, totally unconscious.

I carefully extracted her arm from mine and with everyone else concentrating on what they were doing; I slowly got up and slunk towards the entrance. I felt like running but curbed the instinct until I was the other side of the door. Once there, I ran like hell down the passageway as though my life depended on it, which in a sense it did. I reached the dinghy dock in record time.

"Jesus that was a near thing," I groaned to myself.

I decided not to take the dinghy, the others would probably need it as they were in no state to swim, so I jumped into the water fully clothed and felt the warm liquid envelop me. It felt good.

When I reached Silver Star, I climbed the ladder and as I knew there was no one else on the boat but Liz, I took off all my wet clothes before going below. A sixth sense told me not to leave them around, so I bundled them up and took them with me. Just as I was going down the galley steps, I heard the distinctive sound of an outboard coming out from the dock. With my head just above the deck, but the rest of my body hidden inside the boat, I peered into the darkness from the galley steps. There was no moon that night, but the lights from the shore provided some illumination. I saw the dinghy was heading for Geoff's yacht, in it was Bill with the

Martinique girl. They were laughing and shouting, and she was hanging on to his neck. They tied the dinghy to the yacht and with some difficulty scrambled on board; I wondered what Budgie would think of the proceedings. I went on down into the main cabin, sighing with relief, opened our cabin door and switched on the light.

Liz raised her tousled head from the lower berth.

"Where on earth have you been? Its past 2 am," I told her in gruesome detail what had happened.

She listened attentively and then grinned.

"It's just your natural sex appeal," she said sarcastically.

"Yes, I know, but why is it always the big fat ones that are attracted to me?" I complained.

"Probably because you're so skinny," answered Liz, laughing.

I took the pillow off the top berth and threw it at her.

Liz suddenly became serious and lifted her finger to her lips. "Shush! I think there's someone coming on board."

My heart skipped a beat. I stood motionless and listened. Sure enough, there was the thud of heavy feet on the deck above us.

"Oh, no," I whispered. "If it's her, tell her I haven't returned."

Liz sniggered.

"Are you sure?" She swung her shapely legs from the berth to the cabin floor, "wouldn't you like a night of hot sex?" She giggled.

"Is that an invitation?" I asked and got the pillow back with some force.

I switched out the cabin lights and put out my tongue in the darkness.

"Anyway, she won't come in here," Liz's voice trailed off.

There was a scuffling sound as someone unsteadily manoeuvred down the galley steps; the next second there was a loud banging at the cabin door.

"Liz."

"Wait a minute," Liz called back. Then to me, in hushed tones "what are you going to do?" I pushed her towards the door.

"Commit hara-kiri, if necessary, but for God's sake, don't

151

let her in," I whispered.

Liz opened the door.

There was really no contest, Liz said afterwards, 'my one hundred and thirty pounds holding the door slightly ajar, and Margo's two hundred plus leaning on it from the other side was a foregone conclusion.' Margo burst into the cabin. She was sweaty and dishevelled.

"I'm looking for Jamesy," she said with urgency in her tone.

Liz looked behind her, expecting to see me standing there and was amazed that the cabin was empty.

Quickly assessing the situation, Liz put on a worried look. "I thought James was with you guys. He hasn't come back here."

"Oh Jeez, he must be looking fer me on shore." Margo said unsteadily.

Liz nodded.

There was a huge expelling of air as Margo sighed. Without another word, she waddled out and we heard her climbing the galley stairs, breathing heavily.

Liz whispered. "James, James, where are you?" she said after opening the head door and not finding me. I unfolded myself from the mini cupboard in the cabin.

"How on earth did you get in there?" asked Liz amazed that I'd been able to compact myself into such a small space. I'd chosen the cupboard rather than the head or engine compartment just in case Margo had insisted on looking there.

I could hardly believe it myself and the extraction procedure was quite painful, as I tried to un-wrap my scrunched-up legs from the bottom of the cupboard.

"With extreme bloody difficultly, but at least there's some compensation in being skinny, as you call it," I groaned and tried to straighten up. "But thank you for the timely lies," I gave Liz a kiss.

She pulled away; a trifle breathless.

"I should think so too, I just saved you from a fate worse than death."

There came the sound of a heavy splash from outside the yacht.

"Oh no," I said, with a sinking heart.

"Do you think that was Margo?" inquired Liz.

"I sincerely hope not," I could imagine me diving in to try and save her from drowning and the thought was too horrible to contemplate, particularly as it would be akin to trying to save a small elephant.

Liz was concerned. "She was a little the worse for wear, she could have fallen in and hit her head or something."

I knew Liz was right,

"Bloody woman."

"You must check James, just to make sure."

Liz opened the cabin door.

I was still naked, so I hurriedly pulled on some shorts and reluctantly went out creeping noiselessly up the galley steps. At the top, I heard a shout from Geoff's boat. Bill was on deck, shaking his fist at someone in the water. I just caught a glance of the Martinique girl swimming powerfully towards the shore, with something clamped firmly between her teeth. Bill hadn't seen me, so I ducked out of sight.

Looking over the top of the cockpit, I saw the unmistakable chunky figure of Margo, rowing back to shore, obviously oblivious to the commotion and I breathed a sigh of relief, not for the first time that night.

The next morning, I was up bright and early and was astonished to see Margo was the first guest to appear on deck, clad in a bright yellow T-shirt and Bermuda shorts, looking surprisingly fresh considering what she'd put away the night before. She averted her eyes when I called a cheery, "Good morning, Margo," then she sidled up to me.

"Oh shit," I thought.

"Jamsey, Jeez, I jus' wanna apologise fer my behaviour last night. I guess I'd drunk too much," I shook my head, not knowing whether to be relieved or thankful or both.

"Oh, I don't remember too much Margo," I lied. "I think we all drank rather a lot."

She grabbed my hand before I had a chance to draw it away, and I felt something thrust into it.

"Yea, well I'm real embarrassed, so say sorry to Liz fer me too, an' don't let's mention it to anyone." She raised her eyebrows, winked, gave my hand a squeeze, turned around and waddled off down into the cabin. I looked in my hand and discovered a $100-dollar bill there.

After breakfast, which was a light affair with all the guests excluding Madge feeling a little the worse for wear, Geoff came over with Bill in the dinghy. When they'd climbed on board Geoff indicated that Bill wanted to speak to me confidentially, so I suggested we walk up to the bow area away from the other guests. Geoff looked around to make sure we were alone. "Bill was robbed last night," he said, looking serious.

"*Of his virginity,*" I muttered under my breath.

I raised my eyebrows, "oh."

Bill took up the story.

"I got this little doll back on the boat," he grinned sheepishly like a naughty boy. "And I'd jus' got undressed, an' I'd this hard on that you couldn't believe. Well, while my back was turned, she grabbed my wallet out of my pants and when I looked around, she'd gone. By the time I'd found somethin' else to put on, an' got up on deck the bitch had jumped overboard with my wallet."

I took a deep breath. "How much did you lose?"

"About $1,500 bucks give or take," answered Bill.

"HOW MUCH," I asked incredulously.

Bill shrugged. "It's not the dough I'm worried about, it's stopping that dishonest little bitch from doin' it agin' that I'm concerned with," he said untruthfully.

Geoff interrupted. "Bill felt that as you're the oldest one here James, he'd like to discuss it with you before going to the police."

I nodded and smiled. The last thing Sunshine would want was for the other travel agents to go home with the idea that yachting in the Caribbean was unsafe. In any case, in my view, Bill had asked for it.

"I'm flattered Bill," I said, "but if you go to the police have you considered the repercussions?"

Bill looked puzzled.

"First," I said, "they'll want a statement from you AND may want one from each member of your boat crew, including your wife," I laboured the point.

"Then," I continued, "they may well interview the hotel

staff and then they'll put two and two together.

"Frankly Bill, I'd keep quiet about this if I were you. Don't forget, you're not dealing with local police here, they're all gendarmes imported from the French mainland in Europe."

"Yea, I guess you're right," Bill said slowly.

"And . . ." I interrupted, "don't forget that some local girls have a bad reputation for nasty diseases, I lied. You may well have got off lightly," I smiled at him.

Bill was convinced. "Yea, you are right James, I guess I'll jus' put it down to experience."

"Very wise," I said, patting him on the back.

We had decided to leave our anchorage at about 10 a.m. and sail via Diamond Rock, situated at the south westernmost part of Martinique. This would give them all a pleasant downwind sail in excellent conditions and introduce them to a bit of Anglo-French History.

Gerald was the first away and then Geoff. I was just about to pull up the anchor, when I heard a commotion coming from the Morgan 47 of the previous day. It was obvious that no one was going to help the rude skipper of First Time Ever to lift his anchors so, stupidly, the large man simply slammed the engine lever to forward at maximum revs and turned to port at full speed, the problem was that this happened to be in the direction of Silver Star.

I had never seen a yacht sailed with two anchors streaming out behind it and was amazed it could move at all.

I quickly realised that First Time Ever wasn't going to turn away and I rather uselessly started to put down fenders on the starboard side of Silver Star. Wayne however had sized up the situation and rushed to the side of the boat.

"God dammit," he shouted. "No wonder you Limeys lost the war." At the top of his voice, Wayne yelled at the Morgan now rapidly bearing down on us.

"GET YOUR FUCKING ARSE OUT OF THE WAY YOU STUPID BASTARD."

Even people on shore heard and stared.

The Morgan skipper certainly understood the shout and desperately turned his wheel. Through his rage, he obviously hadn't seen the Nautilus at anchor, he missed our stern by less than a foot and without even glancing at us, the large man

155

turned his yacht out to sea. When last seen, he was still sailing with both anchors trailing behind. I learned something from Wayne's direct approach. Fenders would have been useless in those circumstances, although afterwards I firmly but gently put him right about his interpretation of history.

Diamond Rock is about an hour's sail due west from St. Anne. Shaped like the top of a bullet, it lifts sheer out of the sea to a height of about 500 feet. The distance between the south end of Martinique and the rock is only a few hundred yards, but the water between is deep enough to sail through safely.

While Silver Star was passing the rock to the port side, before turning south towards St. Lucia, I told the guests that some hundreds of British troops had captured the rock during the Napoleonic wars, and it had been a severe embarrassment to the French. The main reason for the capture was because some British military wag had decided that as there were no mosquitoes on the rock, it would be an ideal site for a hospital for sick troops based in St. Lucia. It was correct that there were no mosquitoes there, but the place was, and still is, infested with the deadly fer-de-lance snake. More British troops died from snake bites than they would've done from yellow fever.

Viewed from the sea it was difficult to imagine how they landed, never mind lived on the place and impossible to imagine them pulling heavy cannon up to the top, but they did. It was the only rock in the world at that time commissioned as a ship and it became HMS Diamond Rock. This annoyed Napoleon no end as his darling Josephine came from Martinique. To redress French honour Napoleon sent the French fleet under Admiral Villeneuve to remove the Brits.

Despite Nelson chasing him all the way there, he completed the job, and the occupation of Diamond Rock came to an inglorious end after only eighteen months of annexation.

Because Villeneuve had wisely chosen not to fight Nelson, Napoleon ordered him to return to France in disgrace. This stinging rebuke encouraged him to put to sea again rather earlier than he'd contemplated and before the fleet was ready, the result was the Battle of Trafalgar.

The funnier story, which I enjoyed telling about the rock, came much later, however. In 1978, just before St Lucia became an independent country, some Brits and South Africans had been celebrating the New Year. The story of Diamond Rock had come up and for a dare, a dozen or so men set out from St. Lucia before first light in a fast motor boat. Their equipment included climbing gear and a huge Union Jack. By 10 in the morning, the British flag flew from the top of Diamond Rock for all to see.

Had that been all there was to it, a rather headstrong prank, it would have passed by without becoming an International incident. What the Brits and South Africans didn't know was that the senior admiral of the French navy had chosen that day to visit Fort de France, the capital of Martinique and was sailing in from the Atlantic just as the British flag was raised.

There are stories that the poor man almost had an apoplectic fit and he immediately ordered the marines to go in and remove the invaders. Unfortunately, the French marines had no climbing gear, so could only glower from the sea at the jeering throng on top, who were making unkind suggestions about the efficiency of the French Navy.

Now, of course, the whole thing had got out of hand, with a French cruiser and destroyer standing by at vast cost while twelve cold, hungry, and now worried Brits and South Africans stood their ground, afraid to go down amongst the tough marines at whom they had been hurling insults. In the end, the French sent in armed police paratroopers in helicopters. The offenders were slung in jail and subsequently deported. The French had the last laugh, because by the time the deported pranksters had bought their tickets to travel back to St. Lucia, the island had become independent, and they were denied entry into the new country.

The charter guests had another little history lesson when they neared the northern shore of St. Lucia. I told the unbelieving Americans that one of the main reasons for General Cornwallis's defeat at the hands of George Washington was because half his army sailed away to protect, of all places, St. Lucia.

"I always knew the Limeys were mad," muttered Wayne with some justification. We got back to the dock in Rodney Bay just before 4 p.m. and as the guests disembarked from Silver Star, Margo gave me a hug and full-frontal kiss that left me feeling as though my teeth were under attack, and my body crushed by a vice. The guests said their goodbyes and disappeared towards the office, from where they and a mound of luggage piled up to return them to their hotel by taxi.

The crews decided to have a well-earned drink and I invited them all to come aboard Silver Star. Each brought a bottle, and we began swapping stories about our recent experiences. During the celebrations, Wayne's face appeared above the free-board. He asked if I could step on shore for a second, he looked a trifle uncomfortable.

I climbed down uneasily. When we were out of earshot of the boat, Wayne handed me a cheque drawn on a New York bank. It was for $150. I looked surprised.

"I know Margo gave you a hard time last night, so I guess I jus' wanted you to know we sure appreciated everything you arranged for us." It was kind of him, and I appreciated it and I told him so. We came to learn that the American charter guest was by far the most appreciative of any nationality, and certainly the most generous.

Liz and I were pleased to have passed our first real test in chartering for Sunshine without a major disaster, and I was relieved to have retained my 'virginity'. My feeling of exuberance wasn't to last. On our return, we learned that on the next charter, our guests were to be Italian. We were soon to notice a major difference between the two nationalities.

SILVER STAR

8 - THE HURRICANE

And How I Stole a French Boat

On returning from Martinique and saying our goodbyes to the travel agents, we had under a week to get ready for our first full charter.

I spent some time checking the electrical system because the engine had been sluggish to start. There was also a problem with furling the mainsail and this was now well and truly jammed inside the mast. When I mentioned these matters to John Peachcombe, he told me to talk to George, the dock master and to Wince who oversaw the rigging. He was called that because he winced whenever asked to do anything. St. Lucian's are generally a happy people, but the crews said that Wince had been known to only smile once, when one of the South African skippers unfurled a newly repaired jib sail, only to find that it was covered on both sides with the design of the ANC flag. When the skipper, in a rage, unpicked it, the sail fell to bits.

I was surprised to find so many South African yachtsmen around the Caribbean but one of them said that it was because one of the few ways people could get money out of South Africa was to buy a yacht there and sail it to some area that dealt largely in US currency and then sell it. The US

160

currency back home was worth a huge premium and many youngsters were able to buy their first house by this method. Of course, none of them had South African passports; they had English, Zimbabwean or Dutch,

There was an amusing story going the rounds at the time. Certain people were denied access to most countries in the Caribbean, and these were predominately South Africans. This was no problem for most, as they had dual nationality.

However, one man travelled to Trinidad and presented his South African passport at immigration.

"You can't come in here man, you're South African."

"But I'm a BLACK South African; it's the whites that you're banning." The immigration officer sought the opinion of a higher authority, who confirmed that the ban was against all South African nationals and the poor man was to be deported the next day. I understand however that this decision was eventually secretly overturned.

It was after 11 a.m. on Monday before I traced George in the bowels of another yacht. Its new engine had arrived and there were three of them fitting it in. I told George of the battery-charging problem and George said he'd get someone to check out the generator.

"In de meantime, get th' batteries out and tek 'em up to th' shed," George pointed at the parts store. "Get" 'em charged up really well." The batteries were under the lower berth in the crew cabin and a cursory look indicated that there were about twelve of them. I decided that I could do with some assistance.

"Any chance of some help George," I asked.

"Noo man, we're all too busy," he looked at my arms, put an oily hand on my biceps and grimaced. "Yer need some serious work man, der be nothin' der." I pulled my arm rapidly away and went back to Silver Star. I removed the cushion from the lower berth, lifted the board covering the batteries and was shocked to find not twelve batteries as expected, but four, each of which was four times bigger than a normal car battery. There was only a quarter of an inch lip near the top of each, so there was little to grip. I decided to have a coffee while I thought about the problem and afterwards, I asked Liz for some help.

161

Liz told me she'd quite enough to do without helping me with my jobs, but when she saw the nature of the problem, she realised that even the two of us would find it difficult to lift the batteries out and get them on deck.

I suggested that both of us stood on the lower berth, which meant that we had to bend almost double because of the upper berth, and after several tries, we managed to heave out the first battery as far as the cabin floor.

"We'll never get this up the galley steps," Liz said, breathing heavily.

"We've no choice," I said, wiping the sweat off my forehead, which left an oily mark there.

"But how,"

"I don't know, but let's get the bloody thing to the bottom of the steps and then we'll think again," I wiped the same dirty hand unthinkingly on my white shorts that produced the same result as it had on my forehead.

Liz was furious and made me change into some dark blue swimming shorts.

When I returned, I measured the distance between the crew's cabin and the galley steps with my eyes and decided it was only about fifteen feet. It turned out to be the longest fifteen feet of our lives, because of the weight and the fact that our grip kept slipping, we had to constantly put the battery down and take a breather.

Liz broke a nail and cursed me even more.

After fifteen minutes, we had reached the foot of the steps. Liz made yet another coffee and I again pondered the problem. We were by now both sweating profusely.

"We'll have to do it one step at a time," I suggested tiredly. I didn't even dare to think about the three remaining batteries that still needed moving after we'd dealt with the one at my feet.

"Assuming we can get it onto the deck," said Liz, "just how are we going to get it off the boat?"

I thought of the distance between the deck and the dock. My mind wandered back to the days when my chauffeur used to carry my light briefcase into the office for me. I'd never been used to manual work.

I was aware of Liz talking. "And then, we've got to get it

from the dock to the shed."

"That's no problem," I answered confidently. "We can use the provisioning trolley." I remembered the trolley kept in the office, which was used to carry provisions to the boats.

Liz looked doubtful. "I don't think the trolley is going to be man enough."

I stopped her short and added irritably, "let's deal with getting the bloody thing off the boat and when we've solved that problem, we can think about the next stage. Now, heave." There were eight steps altogether and so we started up, Liz first and me following her. "In case the thing falls back," I had said gallantly.

It took us another full fifteen minutes to get the battery on to the step below the top one and we were just about to give it one final heave to clear it over the lip of the door frame and onto the deck, when my sweaty hand slipped.

The battery started to slide back down the steps, spilling acid all over me as it went. I managed to stop it before it hit the floor and yelled to Liz to come and help me, because I was now jammed between the galley steps and the cabin floor with the battery at a forty-five-degree angle, on top of me.

Gradually, we lowered it to the floor, and I became aware that my hands and other parts of my anatomy were starting to sting.

"You'd better get those clothes off, so I can get them into soak quickly, they're covered in acid," said Liz. "To say nothing of me," I grumbled, looking hurt.

"You can always wash it off," she retorted un-sympathetically.

I was going to respond but thought better of it when the acid started to create pain in an area where I certainly didn't want to burn. Rushing into the cabin and shooting under the shower fully clothed, I undressed and felt the coolness of the water soothe away the pain. Soaping myself liberally and emerging naked into the main cabin looking for some clean clothes I was aware of George peering down from the top of the steps.

I heard a loud guffaw.

"What's dat little 'ting,"

I looked up at him irritably, but also puzzled.

163

"What?"

George pointed at a certain part of my anatomy.

He was grinning like some huge ape.

I felt my face go red and quickly turned sideways on, away from him.

"Don't know how honkeys get it up enough fer yer to have chilun," he slid down the galley steps into the cabin.

I rapidly pulled on some shorts.

"Well, we've managed quite well to have three children, thank you George," I said huffily. "How many do you have?" George looked up at the cabin overhead, "Uh, four in the house an' eleven out."

"What, you've got fifteen children?"

I couldn't believe my ears, particularly as I estimated that George couldn't be much over thirty years of age. Now it was George's turn to look embarrassed.

"Well, there be two on the way, but I'm only tirty." he confirmed, making it sound like an excuse.

"Jesus," was all I could find to say.

Liz had overheard this conversation and emerged from the cabin, grinning.

I glowered at her.

She, who had assimilated a deal of local culture, told me later that in the house and out of the house, meant that the children in the house lived with him, probably with his 'wife,' and the rest were from various liaisons that West Indians seemed to accept as a normal way of life. I was to learn later that a politician without at least two families wasn't worth a vote.

"How you fellow's gettin' on?" asked George.

He saw the solitary battery on the cabin floor. "That the last one?"

I gritted my teeth and shook my head irritably.

I told George what had just happened. He looked at me pityingly, as one might look at a lame dog. At that moment, two of George's men got on the boat and he called them down.

"Let's get dese batteries out," he called, "dey need chargin'." The first man lifted the battery from the floor as though it were an empty cardboard box and almost ran up the steps.

164

I saw the admiration on Liz's face and found myself adding clenched fists to gritted teeth.

It was, nevertheless, a huge relief to get the batteries out of the way as it meant I could concentrate on the jammed mainsail. Eventually, I had to get into a boson's chair and go up the mast, where I spent most of the afternoon thirty feet above the deck. By 4 p.m., I'd managed to release the strained pulley wheel, the cause of the jamming and the sail pulled free.

On Tuesday morning George had the batteries put back and a reconditioned generator put in place of the faulty one. He was tightening up the fan belt when he mentioned the latest weather report.

"Hurricane is headed straight fer us."

"Oh?"

"Yea man, it's a big un', be here by T'ursday."

Liz asked what was going to happen to the Italian charter guests who would be arriving on Saturday.

"The boss wants to see all crews in his office at 12," he said, as he put a final twist to the bolt he was tightening.

"'Spect you'll hear then," he said in a matter-of-fact way.

To a yacht charter company, the very thought of a hurricane spoils their day. Although all yachts had radios, many bareboat charterers didn't switch them on and thus might miss weather warnings. There was also disruption on the dock, where all boats moored out had to have double anchors fixed; boats on the dock needed extra lines to keep them in place.

We had never experienced a hurricane, but I remembered one just missing Jamaica when we lived there in the early 1970's. Even the fringe of the storm was most unpleasant. The biggest danger is from flying objects, particularly corrugated iron roofs, which most poor West Indian dwellings had.

Liz and I walked up to the office at 12 noon and met there by Geoff, Budgie, Gerald, and Judith. John came into the office with George. They both looked worried.

"This looks to be a really bad one, so we'll give the preparation top priority, as if we haven't enough to do," John said. "Thankfully, most of the boats are out now and we've put a general call down island to try and warn all our bare boaters. The Sunshine crews call in every morning, so they're all aware of the problem."

"Is there anything we can do to help on the dock?" I clearly earned some brownie points with George for making the offer.

John shook his head.

"No, all three of you have charters to pick up on Saturday. You must concentrate on getting your boats ready, but I suggest you sail down to Hurricane Hole at Marigot, where you'll be less exposed."

"Except for the mozzies," I complained.

"Rather a mosquito bite than being turned upside down in a 120 mile an hour wind," said John grimly.

John turned to Gerald.

"Gerald, you've been through one of these before. Can you show James and Liz the ropes when you get down there? Back up your sterns to the mangrove and get in as far as you can. Make sure you tie yourselves down well and truly, use both anchors, and DON'T leave anything loose on the deck." John wished us all good luck and I got the distinct impression that the dock crew, with fifteen boats on the dock and three or four anchored out, would be glad to see the crewed yachts moving away as soon as possible.

We all sailed within the hour and arrived at the now familiar Marigot Bay by 3 p.m. Gerald arrived first and when I was motoring in around the spit, I saw a problem looming up ahead. A large boat had anchored in the north-east corner of the little enclosed bay and its skipper had spread his lines attached to trees to such an extent that it was taking up the room of about six boats. I noticed that it was a large catamaran called Je T'aime.

Marigot isn't a large area, but it's the only safe anchorage in a hurricane in St. Lucia and it was already quite crowded. Gerald and another man were trying to persuade the skipper of Je T'aime to move his lines and let others get in beside him, but it was clear he wasn't going to do so.

Liz pointed out that the man had what appeared to be a baseball bat in his hand, presumably for use if anyone decided to climb on board without his authority. Gerald had already anchored in the bay, I took Silver Star alongside, and

I tied up to his yacht.

"Bloody selfish frogs," Gerald pointed at Je T'aime. "They anchor all over you in normal times, but when there's a hurricane warning, they take up half the fucking bay to themselves."

I looked at the Frenchman, who was standing on deck, fending off some Anglo-Saxon abuse with a good Latin exchange.

"We'll fix the bugger, but after sundown," Gerald muttered darkly, stooping to grab a line from Geoff, who had just come in on the other side of our yacht.

After dark, there was a distinct party atmosphere. All the boat crews, save the Frenchman, were necessarily close together and had decided to indulge in a pre-hurricane party, which involved moving from one boat to the other and drinking it dry before moving on. I could see the skipper of Je T'aime sitting on the deck of his boat scowling, still with the baseball bat close by his side. There was no way he could join the festivities and still protect his position.

It was about 11.30 p.m. when Gerald called a group of the crews together.

"Right, what are we going to do about that bastard over there?" He pointed in the direction of Je T'aime.

I looked across and saw that the skipper had disappeared below.

"We could cut his lines," someone offered.

"I've got a better idea," Gerald said, "why don't we move the bloody thing altogether?"

I frowned. "How can we do that? Apart from half a dozen lines, he's got two anchors out and they're both on chain."

Gerald grinned. "That's no problem. I've got my diving gear on board. I'll go down with my wrench and unscrew the chain from the shackle on the anchors."

Someone from a yacht further out in the bay interrupted. "Untying his lines is no problem, but how the hell can we move him without banging into someone and waking the bastard up?"

Gerald had all the answers and I wondered if he'd met a similar circumstance before.

He turned to two of the other skipper's present.

167

"David, Jumbo, you both have rubber inflatables. Your job will be to keep hold of the sides of the catamaran, one of you each side, to provide a sort of super fender, just in case. I'll help James tow the bugger into the outer bay, and we'll let him off just before we hit the sea proper. The current will do the rest."

"Hope he wakes up before he hits Venezuela," someone muttered.

David looked thoughtful.

"But how are you going to tow him? Surely the noise of the outboard will wake him?"

"I know this guy from my days in Martinique, he's a heavy drinker and unless we make too much clatter, he'll probably sleep through it and I noticed he's already had several beers," Jumbo said.

"Yes, but David has a point" I said, with a vivid vision of the baseball bat crashing down on my head. "I suggest we pull him out with one of his own lines and we stay about thirty feet in front. If we go slowly, I doubt if anyone could hear the outboard at that distance."

"And don't forget," said Gerald, who was already getting his equipment together on the deck, "A Cat is pretty light to tow, so we shouldn't have any problems."

The SAS School in Herefordshire would have been proud of us. The lines on the catamaran were swiftly untied; the anchors parted from their chains and left on the bottom of Marigot Bay. Gerald took one of Je T'aime's lines, already tied to the bow of the Frenchman's boat and rowed towards the sand spit and entrance to the bay. I carefully paid out the line, then about thirty feet out Gerald started the outboard, but there was so much merriment going on with parties on various boats, that it was doubtful if it was audible above the din.

We had some initial difficulty in pulling the catamaran out of the confined space and I thought at one stage that we'd run Je T'aime aground on the sand spit, but fortunately catamarans don't have much of a keel and it was pulled across the shallows with ease.

When we reached the opening to the bay, I just let the line go and we made a wide detour because of the noise of the dinghy's outboard motor, and we puttered back to Gerald's yacht. Once there, we moved the sterns of the Sunshine yachts and, along with a couple of other boats, tied stern first to the shore, taking up all the space previously occupied by Je T'aime. This allowed some other boats in the bay to move into a safer area.

I expected to see the Frenchman motoring back into the bay at any minute, but as the parties broke up around 4 a.m. there was still no sign of him. Liz said she'd love to have been a fly on the wall of his cabin when he awoke.

The skipper of Je T'aime apparently slept until well after dawn the next day, when his boat was some four miles off the coast. He returned to Marigot the following week, made an official complaint to the police about his boat being stolen and he kidnapped. The police thought the whole thing hilarious, but made the man laboriously write out his statement in English, that took him most of a morning. He then hired Peterkin to dive for his anchors. As it had almost certainly been Peterkin who, on hearing the story the day after the incident, had removed them, he was, nevertheless, quite happy to relieve the Frenchman of $100 per day for the search, which was called off after the Frenchman realised, he was being done.

The hurricane never came. There'd been one puff of wind, and everyone cheered, but for whatever reason it had turned north-west, just east of Barbados and went hurtling towards the Virgin Islands.

We all sailed back to Rodney Bay and the Sunshine dock on Friday, ready to pick up our charter guests on the following day. Geoff and Budgie were also picking up some Italians, as were Gerald and Judith.

It was up to the charter guests to decide where the yachts went. Some decided to go north to Martinique and beyond, but most wanted to visit the Grenadines, which Liz and I thoroughly encouraged because the anchorages were nicer and easier to manage. The three crews agreed that we would try and stick reasonably close together, assuming the Italians would be happier to have their own kind around them.

I had permission from Sunshine for our schoolboy son Robert, who had come out for his summer holidays to join us on the trip. We planned to leave him in Union with Anne for a couple of weeks and collect him again on our next trip to the Grenadines. Jessica, our second daughter, preferred to stay in the UK with a friend. When I went up to the Sunshine office on the Friday, I looked at the charter board and saw that Silver Star was going to be quite busy. The Italians were to be with us for the next two weeks. After that, a same day turnaround and we were to pick up members of the Rocky Mountain Horticultural Club, whose members wanted to visit the various rain forests within the island chain. They were to be with us for ten days. The third charter was booked for a threesome for a whole month. I learned that the party consisted of a woman with her 'boyfriend,' an oil millionaire from Texas and her young daughter and his young daughter. The man's daughter was only going to stay with us for a week.

Liz, ever practical realised that we would have only three days to re-provision after dropping off the horticultural club members. Then we would have to sail immediately to St. Maarten, a two-day trip.

On Friday night, Liz and I went up to the office to phone for a registered taxi driver to fetch Robert from the airport. John saw us and called us in to his office.

"Just wanted you guys to know we've heard from head office regarding your charter last week."

He looked serious.

I held my breath.

"Margo Feldman was VERY happy," smiled John. "I don't know what you did, but obviously it was the right thing, well done."

Liz giggled.

"Think of what the reference could have been," she whispered.

"Oh, just one other thing," John wagged his finger in warning. "I know the weather looks great, but the hurricane that missed us has left some very nasty seas. I'd try and persuade your charter guests to stay around the St. Lucia shores at least until Tuesday. I understand that only one of them has sailed before."

Liz thought his advice made good sense, but it was down to the Italians, who might think otherwise.

9 - THE ITALIANS

And How Bebe Tried to Walk on Water

The Charter guests hadn't arrived when they were due, so just after 11 a.m. I walked up to the Sunshine office to investigate. Laura put the telephone down as I entered.

"That was the agent at Hewannora airport. Your guests were delayed three hours in Barbados, something to do with the Air Italia flight not connecting." She smiled and shrugged her shoulders. I thanked her and was just walking out of the office when a taxi drew up followed by a pick-up stacked full of luggage. I grinned at the thought of the poor crew who would have to stow all the cases away.

I was half way back to the boat when Laura ran out of the office and called after me.

"James, your charter guests have arrived." She looked apologetic and held her hands out, as if to say don't blame me.

When I walked back to her, she explained that it was Geoff's party of Italians who were delayed, not mine. "Your guests apparently flew via the States."

I went across to meet the four people who were getting out of the taxi. A stocky well-dressed man came up and introduced himself. He spoke perfect English, but with a slight American accent.

"My name is Victor. I'm afraid I'm the only one who really speaks English, although Bebe speaks a little and understands more." Victor introduced me to an attractive woman with long blond hair and a bosom that could have graced any page three.

"This is Bebe," Victor said genially. She smiled and looked me straight in the eyes as she shook hands. Bebe had an

171

infectious twinkle.

"And this is Boris," I tore my eyes away from Bebe. Boris held out his hand, and as I was shaking it, I felt Bebe's eyes sizing me up. It wasn't an unpleasant experience. Boris was the only one of the four who fitted the English perception of a typical Italian. He was quite portly, running to fat and reminded me of a giant panda. His gold teeth matched the gold rings on his fingers, and he wore tinted glasses with very thick lenses. Victor half turned towards a slim woman, who stood with her back to us.

"And this is Francesca," he said looking a little embarrassed. She didn't appear to hear, because she was busy berating the driver of the taxi and the pick–up in non-stop Italian. I sympathised when they started to throw the bags off the back of the pick-up on to the dusty ground. The bags were all Gucci, hand-tooled matching luggage, and the rough treatment they were getting wasn't conducive to the continued expensive look that all Gucci products display.

Francesca turned to Victor with a scowl on her face, giving him a string of Italian verbiage. She pointed to the now harassed drivers, who were trying to off load even more quickly to escape her haranguing. She stamped her foot on the ground and started to approach the drivers, her hands waving in the air. Bebe went after her to console her. Victor rolled his eyes at me.

"Poor Francesca, she's tired after the trip," he turned and looked at her as another string of now quite hysterical screaming came from her lips. The drivers, having had enough, threw the last piece of luggage on the ground and dived for their respective vehicles. In true St. Lucian fashion, they skidded off from a standing start, splattering gravel all over us and the bags, while at the same time creating a minor dust storm.

Francesca shook her fist after them in rage.

I made some innocuous comment about St. Lucian's and their driving capabilities and suggested that I take everyone down to the boat. I said I'd return to get the luggage.

"No, no, we can help carry them," Victor said kindly. So, everyone, except Francesca, who carried only her handbag, loaded themselves with as many bags as they could carry, and we walked down the dock towards Silver Star.

During this short time, I learned that Victor was a carpet manufacturer from Turin and Boris was the editor of a left-wing newspaper in Milan. When they arrived at the side of the yacht, Liz was waiting to welcome everyone on board.

I'd constructed a special box step, which I'd placed on the dock to make it easier for those not so familiar with boats to climb onto Silver Star.

I introduced everyone to Liz.

Francesca, who seemed by now to have calmed down, headed straight for a cockpit seat, crossed her legs, and lit a cigarette.

I studied her out of the corner of my eye and decided that she wasn't the most attractive of people. She was devoid of a chin, but that didn't hinder her haughty attitude. She was about five feet eight inches tall and the direct opposite of Bebe in that there was no sign of any mammary glands whatsoever.

To describe her as skinny, I decided, would have been an understatement. I had to admit though that she and her companions were all extremely well dressed, but more for a Royal garden party than a yachting holiday in the Caribbean.

They stowed the first lot of luggage in the main cabin, and I walked back with Victor for the rest. When I looked at the bags still sitting on the ground, I realised there was no hope of stowing them all on board and I told Victor that there simply wouldn't be room.

"Francesca will NOT be happy," he groaned.

"Tough shit for Francesca," I muttered silently.

We walked back to the boat again with as many bags as we could carry, and Victor told the others the bad news. Francesca spilled out a stream of Italian. She was not happy.

After several minutes of haggling, Victor turned to me.

"Francesca wants to see the cabins; she doesn't believe us." I knew that Victor had added the 'us' on the end to save my feelings.

"Yes, of course, follow me, but watch the steps. Oh," I said, "would you mind asking the 'girls' to take off their high heels, as they damage the deck and in any case are dangerous to the wearer." Victor translated and Bebe and Francesca slipped off their shoes, but I felt that Francesca had done so with bad

173

grace.

Liz pointed out that there was a spare cabin, but even that was too small for all their bags. Francesca spotted the door to our cabin, and I knew she was asking Victor what was on the other side.

"That's our cabin," I said, not waiting for Victor to translate. The charter crews on the '60's christened the crew cabin the coffin, because it was so small. I could guess what Francesca was saying. It was words to the effect that they were only staff, and they could sleep anywhere, on top if necessary, providing her bags were somewhere dry.

Victor had some trouble with the translation because he didn't want to tell me what Francesca had said.

Liz stopped him. "Tell Francesca that we'd gladly give up our cabin for her luggage." Victor looked at Liz in amazement and I was speechless.

"Unfortunately," she carried on without a pause, "we've only just taken this boat over and we found a really bad leak in the porthole that James hasn't had time to repair."

I caught on fast.

"Yes," I said sorrowfully from behind, "when we're sailing, the sea water seeps through, and it's already completely ruined two pairs of Liz's expensive shoes, of course it's quite safe I added hastily, but salt water does play havoc with leather. However, if Francesca insists, we can certainly sleep in the main cabin. Of course, that would also mean that we'd have to share your toilet facilities too," I added, almost as an afterthought. "You see our shower unit is at the back of our cabin and we'd not be able to reach it if the space was piled high with bags."

Victor grinned. Whether he'd rumbled us or not, I couldn't tell, but when he turned to Francesca, he looked very serious. Liz could see that it was the thought of the crew using her bathroom that finally persuaded her, as the look of horror on Francesca's face was all too apparent and further string of Italian followed, which eventually finished in a sob.

Victor comforted her and winked at me.

"We'll store the surplus luggage in the marina offices, can you arrange that?" asked Victor.

"Yes of course," I said, "I'll ensure that's done

immediately." Having overcome that incident, Francesca and Bebe picked their cabins. Francesca picked the main aft cabin with the king-sized bed, and they moved the luggage they'd brought on board into their respective cabins. Victor and I then walked up to the offices to arrange with John Peachcombe to store what had to be left behind. John suggested the sail loft would be the cleanest and most secure area and so we moved the surplus bags in there, much to the disgust of Wince, who regarded this as an invasion of his territory.

I took the opportunity to mention the recent weather problems to Victor and suggested that we sail down to Marigot Bay that afternoon and then perhaps to Soufriere the following day where we could anchor until the following Tuesday, by that time the sea should be calm enough for a normal crossing. Victor seemed quite amenable and accepted the plan.

Liz had prepared a light lunch, but Francesca left most of hers. She particularly irritated Liz by disdainfully picking her way through the food. Conscious that Francesca might have some eating disorder, Liz asked Victor if there was anything she didn't like.

"Liz, if I were to write you a list it would not be finished by the end of the two weeks." Liz smiled at his humour.

"What about spaghetti and pasta?" she asked. "Ah, we've brought our own and the girls will cook it when they want it. Don't worry, just carry on normally."

Liz wasn't particularly happy about Francesca taking over her galley, even for one meal, but she shrugged her shoulders in compliance.

After lunch, Francesca went below and changed, not into anything more casual, just into another designer dress. She lit another cigarette and continued to look thoroughly unhappy.

Bebe in the meantime had changed into white tennis shorts and a revealing green blouse; she looked much more like someone having a holiday on a yacht. With the lunch dishes washed up and stowed and the guests settled I went to start the engine.

It was then I realised that Boris wasn't on deck.

"Where's Boris?" I asked.

"He's asleepa," answered Bebe, looking wide-eyed. "He sleeps all day AND all night."

"Do you want to wake him before we get under way?" asked Liz.

Bebe nodded and went down below. She came back up after a couple of minutes and shook her head.

"He sleeps still," she shrugged.

"He's probably tired from the trip," said Victor.

I saw Bebe scowling.

Silver Star swung away from the dock at just after 2 p.m. I'd already negotiated the channel between the lagoon and Rodney Bay proper and Liz had just finished raising and adjusting the main in preparation for the sail to Marigot when a sound of a commotion came from the rear of the cockpit. I'd invited Victor to take the wheel once we were out of the channel while Liz and I finalised the setting of the sails. I walked back along the deck to the cockpit. Something was amiss. It was Francesca.

"Mama Mia, mama mia," she cried sobbing intermittently. Victor had his arm around her in a comforting way that wasn't improving the steering. I quickly took the helm so that Victor could concentrate more fully on the subject matter in hand.

The sea was calm, but Liz wondered if Francesca was already feeling ill.

"What's the problem?" she asked.

Victor looked at her resignedly. "Francesca has left her makeup–case. Apparently, we stored it in the sail loft. She insists we go back for it. I'm very sorry." he added.

I groaned inwardly and tried, unsuccessfully, to instil some humour into the proceedings by suggesting that Francesca didn't need any make–up, that she'd be even more beautiful without it.

I probably overdid it a bit. Victor passed on my untruthful compliment. Francesca screeched like a cockatoo in pain and started sobbing again.

"Don't worry Victor," I said hastily, "we'll turn around and go back. It's no problem," I said as I turned the wheel 180 degrees.

"This is going to be two weeks of sheer fun," muttered Liz so that only I could her.

We pulled the sails down and motored back into the lagoon towards the dock we'd just left. Unfortunately, there was another yacht berthed where Silver Star had been and I had to anchor out in the lagoon, which meant fixing the outboard to the dinghy to enable us to get ashore. Fortunately, I hadn't winched the dinghy on board, so this was accomplished quite quickly. Next, I ferried Victor and Francesca back to the dock. There was a look of pain on Francesca's face. When we landed, she headed straight for the office lavatory.

Victor tried to clarify things with me while Francesca was absent. 'Francesca,' he explained, 'was his girlfriend, not his wife, the latter was with her bambino in Turin. Francesca had visited the doctor before embarking on the trip. She explained to him that she wanted something to stop her bowel movement because she disliked using 'ships' lavatories. The doctor decided that because Francesca was one of his best clients, he wasn't going to argue. He knew it would do her no permanent harm, so he wrote her a prescription.'

Victor and I went up to the sail loft to find her make-up case, but it wasn't there. Afterwards, we found a disgruntled Francesca coming out of the toilet. When Victor told her that her case was nowhere to be found, she insisted on going up herself to look. I went back to the boat and when Francesca arrived at the dock, I went across in the dinghy to fetch them. Victor said that Francesca had accused Wince of stealing her case, which didn't endear her to him or the dock crew generally. Some fifteen minutes later Victor found the make-up case on board. Francesca had stuffed it under some other bags in her cabin.

Silver Star eventually got under way for the second time around 4 p.m. and we reached Marigot by 6 p.m. The bay was almost deserted, which was a far cry from the day before. Our son Robert had been in Castries with the 13-year-old son of another charter couple and Liz and I were pleased that he'd found someone of his own age. He arrived by taxi at Marigot Bay about an hour before Silver Star showed up and he became worried when no boat arrived. When he came on board, he met everyone and soon became a great favourite because of his ability to run errands, including going below for a constant supply of drinks.

I warned Victor about the mosquitoes, and he passed on the warning to Francesca and Bebe. Francesca couldn't find her anti-bite cream and another bout of hysterics ensued, until Bebe offered hers.

About half an hour after mooring in Marigot there was shouting and screaming coming from Boris and Bebe's cabin, Bebe came out with large sunglasses covering her eyes. It was obvious to everyone she'd been crying, though no reason was given for her sad demeanour.

The next day, Sunday, was warm and sunny and despite Francesca's complaints about Marigot, it was difficult for me to get them back on the boat in time to sail to Soufriere. Because it was later than I'd intended when we set out, it was after sundown by the time we arrived. The trade winds invariably blow from the east, and it was only in the most unusual circumstances, such as a large weather system, that the wind blew from another direction. The westerly we were currently experiencing had produced a wave surge onto the beach. Although this didn't affect anyone on the boat, I was relieved when the Italians decided that they didn't wish to go ashore. There was no boat dock at Soufriere, and I knew that landing a party from a dinghy would have been tricky, to say the least.

Bebe and Francesca decided to cook spaghetti for dinner, and they used the pasta strands they'd brought with them that were much thinner than we were used to.

Apart from the fracas emanating from their cabin earlier Boris had been asleep most of the day and when Bebe went to waken him for dinner, there'd been another row. Bebe came out of the cabin and slammed the door on poor Boris, just as he put his hand on the doorjamb. He gave a yell of pain, and Liz had to apply first aid to his bruised fingers.

Despite the silence that ensued, the meal was delicious.

The next morning was Monday, and I'd assumed that the Italians may want to go to mass that they missed on Sunday. There was still no suggestion of them moving off the boat however, and I certainly didn't suggest it. We had just finished breakfast, during which Boris drank two bottles of beer, a breakfast diet he stuck to religiously throughout the trip, when I heard Francesca shouting from below. Victor gobbled up the last piece of toast and went down the galley steps. He was up again within a couple of minutes. I could hear Francesca screaming.

"James, Francesca says the toilet isn't working," I groaned inwardly. There are several jobs on a boat that aren't very pleasant. The worst is freeing a head that some cretin has blocked. Of course, in the initial introduction given to charter guests, it's made it very clear just what could go down a boat head, and what couldn't.

I resignedly went below and dug out my tools. I found that the head handle was seized, and I knew that I'd have to take the whole contraption apart. I told Liz about it afterwards.

"I'd to work through Gods' knows what and after an hour, I discovered the culprit: a sanitary towel, which by then had been shredded. I'd a quiet word with Victor afterwards, but while Victor was tactfully explaining to Francesca that she shouldn't put sanitary towels down the pan, I saw her shrug. My Scorpio personality started to consider ways of getting even.

I finished rebuilding the toilet and took a long shower.

When I appeared on deck, I was met by Victor. "Francesca doesn't want to stay in Soufriere Bay,

I knew that Silver Star, even in a rough sea, would be perfectly safe, just bloody uncomfortable. However, I was becoming less and less concerned about Francesca's comfort, so I told Victor that we'd sail. When I told Liz we were moving, she was most unhappy, mainly because she had already started to cook the lunch.

"Never mind," I said, "Do 'em peanut butter sandwiches instead, it'll be cheaper." We left the anchorage at 11 am. I knew we wouldn't reach Bequia before sundown, but now that we knew the Bequia area so well, arriving after dark wasn't a problem. It did make difficulties for Liz, however, as she would have to prepare the evening meal, which she wouldn't be able to do until we anchored

Boris had gone back down below just after breakfast, but just in case, I insisted that everyone on top put on life jackets. Bebe asked me to tie hers for her and when I finished, she brushed my cheek with her open mouth.

"You're so kinda," she said in broken English and smiled with her green eyes flashing. I felt my blood pressure raise a touch.

The weather was beautiful in the lee, and I began to think that the seas would be okay. Liz provided coffee just before we hit the channel, and I pulled in the main so that we'd an equivalent of one reef.

My feeling of well-being was shortly to be rudely shaken. Moving from the lee of the island to the channel proper was akin to opening the door of a warm house and stepping into a gale outside. I quickly realised that despite the reef in the sail, Silver Star was still over-sailed. The wind blew at thirty-five knots, with gusts up to fifty. To prevent the boat from broaching, I sailed further off the wind, but the sea was coming towards us in a westerly direction, which meant that even though the yacht had a Plexiglas windscreen and a canvas cover in the cockpit, it didn't prevent everyone from being soaked every few minutes.

I waited for a howl from Francesca, and sure enough, after fifteen minutes of sailing almost on our side I was aware of hysterical sobbing behind me.

Victor touched me on the shoulder.

"Francesca can't carry on, James, we must return," I smiled grimly.

"I did warn you," I wiped the salt water from my nose.

Victor agreed.

"Well at least she now knows that she should listen to your advice in the future." I doubted very much whether Francesca listened to anyone but herself but said nothing. I brought the boat about, and Liz expertly moved the jib line to the other side.

After some more adjustments to the main, we sailed back to Soufriere, where we arrived just after 2.30 p.m. Francesca immediately complained that Liz had only prepared peanut butter sandwiches for lunch and asked why she couldn't have something cooked.

Liz, usually a person of the most even temperament, told me she felt like pushing the bloody woman over the side.

Once Silver Star had anchored, Boris decided to emerge, like some long hibernating creature taking his first step outside after the long winter.

Once he joined the other Italians in the cockpit an earnest discussion ensued, that developed into quite a fierce argument.

Victor told me afterwards that Francesca and Boris wanted to sleep ashore for the night, whereas he and Bebe were quite happy to stay on the boat.

Francesca had another sobbing fit and that really decided the issue. I radioed a small hotel above Soufriere called Dasheen and asked if they'd any rooms available. They had, so I booked the Italians in. With that organised they all disappeared below to get ready. Liz and I were amazed when, a quarter of an hour later, they arrived back on deck, dressed in clothes that would have been appropriate for a Royal Regatta Evening in Cowes. Francesca had on yet another long designer dress, one which, Liz said later, she'd have given her eye-teeth for. Bebe wore a leather outfit, with a brightly coloured blouse, liberally studded with ethnic jewels. Victor and Boris sported long, light-coloured slacks and smart open-necked shirts, Victor also wore a smart blue blazer and Boris had put on what looked like an Armani casual jacket, everything colour coordinated. None of them would have looked out of place walking along the Champs Elysees.

In preparation for going ashore, I attached the outboard engine to the dinghy and dropped it into the water with the winch. Liz dropped the aluminium ladder and Victor went down it first and when he was in the dinghy, I pointed out the surf breaking on the shore, and said that I was seriously worried about how to land the party safely. Victor cupped his hand to his forehead and studied the beach.

"It's no problem. I'm well used to this, from my days in the Italian navy. As we get close to shore, I'll be on the bow, holding the line. If you let the surge carry you as far as possible towards the beach and lift your outboard at the last moment, I'll jump off on to the sand and pull in the boat."

I'd read stories about the Italian navy and must have

looked dubious.

"Trust me I know what I'm doing," said Victor smiling.

I told him untruthfully, that of course I did trust him, but as there was a very strong swell and the dinghy wasn't a very stable craft, it would certainly be better if I took them in two separate parties.

Victor was just agreeing, as Francesca was standing at the top of the ladder. I politely held up my hand to help her. She took it until she stepped in the dinghy. Then, she threw it off, as though the mere touch had offended her. I could again feel my teeth grinding. So preoccupied was I with Francesca's insulting behaviour, that I realised with a start that Bebe was also coming down the ladder. I was about to say something when Victor got in first. "It is okay James we'll manage." What I hadn't bargained for was the deluge of luggage that Boris handed me. There was barely any room left for him, but he managed somehow to perch himself on top of all the gear. Once I was in, I saw that the dinghy was now very low in the water, with about an inch to spare.

Liz peered over the guard-rail and looked distinctly worried.

I started up the outboard and very slowly motored towards the shore. I felt and saw a couple of surges pass under us and I knew that we would have to get it right if the guests were going to get ashore without wet bottoms, or worse. It was going well and by the halfway point, I'd got the feel of the heavily loaded craft and felt sure I could get in okay. We were about thirty feet from the shore when Victor got up to grab the painter as planned. He stood up and held it with both hands his right foot on the forward seat and his left foot wedged on a seemingly secure position amongst the luggage. I spotted a big surge coming in behind us and I thought it would be possible to ride it on to the beach. I shouted to Victor, who had also seen it and agreed.

Everything would probably have gone without a hitch, had it not been for Francesca. She suddenly let out a howl of rage and made a snatch for whatever Victor was standing on.

This was, it transpired, her patent leather handbag. The result of her precipitant action was that for a split second,

Victor had nothing under his left foot, and he started to fall backwards and towards his left. As a result, his weight on the already overloaded boat now transferred to the port side, which forced the boat sideways, precisely as the surge hit us.

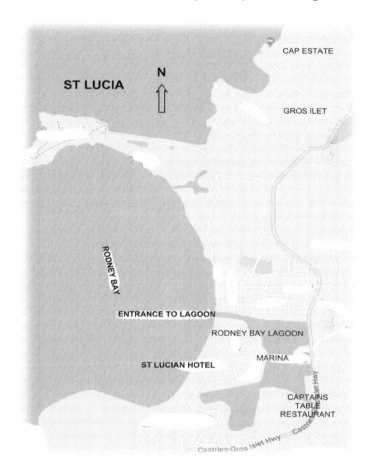

As the surge went through and underneath, the dinghy sailed sideways. Victor, now bent almost double, was desperately trying to keep his balance, when Boris decided to lend a hand, by standing up abruptly and making a lunge at Victor's blazer. The rest was a foregone conclusion. Victor went over the side with a large splash, shortly followed by Boris. Boris's weight on the side of the dinghy when he fell, tipped the freeboard below the water. A following surge caught the boat and the next thing I knew was that I was under water with Gucci luggage raining on top of me.

I surfaced, to find the boat had somehow inexplicably righted and only Bebe was clinging to its side. I was at first pleased to see that the outboard engine had stopped, until I realised that it had been doused in sea water. This reminded me of the mechanical problems I'd with the engine on Shady Lady and it was ironic that it had happened again, in almost the same spot.

Whilst treading water, I looked around. Victor was already on shore, and I could see Boris just climbing on to the beach, both looked like newly dipped, fat sheep.

Francesca was shouting hysterically, but it was obvious that she was okay, as she was doing a strong breast stroke towards where Victor stood. In any case, he was looking unconcerned, so I turned my attention to Bebe, and swam over to the dinghy.

"Can you swim, Bebe?" She shook her head.

"Okay, you keep hold of the dinghy and I'll tow you to the shore. She looked a bit pathetic and unexpectedly let go and moved towards me, splashing wildly. I caught her and suggested she turn on her back. Surprisingly, she seemed completely relaxed and she certainly had plenty of buoyancy as with my arm around her, I swam slowly to the shore.

As she got out of the water, she turned and smiled at me, showing her perfectly aligned teeth.

"Gracias, James," she said.

As I was swimming ashore with her, I'd realised she'd nothing on under her blouse and my gaze now travelled down her legs. The leather skirt was up around her thighs, and she'd lost her shoes. My attention was rudely diverted by the now familiar hysterics from Francesca. Victor walked over to me and Bebe.

"Francesca is worried about our bags."

I laughed, which produced yet another howl of anguish from Francesca. For the first time, Victor looked at her irritably.

"She says it was your fault, but I've told her that it was hers," that was the only time Victor contradicted her.

I shook my head in disbelief and looked across at Francesca who sat on the beach, her head down on her knees.

The designer dress had a rip right up the side.

Boris had lost or thrown off his jacket and was squeezing surplus water out of his trousers. Worse still, his glasses had gone. Without them he could see no more than a yard in front of him. I asked Victor what else was lost.

After a brief discussion, I went back in to the water and dived down to the seabed. Although most of the stuff was only about ten feet down, the surge was moving the lighter items away from the shore. I came back to the surface and found Victor swimming by my side. I shouted to make myself heard above the breaking of the surf, "I suggest we get the light things first, like handbags and shoes. Then I'm going to need a line to loop around the heavier bags."

Victor looked behind me. The dinghy was still floating on the surface nearby.

"I'll get the dinghy," and with that he swam towards it. It took us the better part of an hour to get most of the things up, but we never did find Bebe's shoes, Boris's glasses, or Francesca's handbag, the cause of all the trouble. I was sure she believed that I'd stolen it. The final dripping collection was placed on the beach, and I engaged a taxi to take them all up the hotel. Liz and Robert swam over to help me sort out the salvage and, after the Italians had gone, we all swam back to the yacht with the dinghy in tow. I tried unsuccessfully to start its engine, spending the rest of the evening dismantling, and cleaning it.

The engine wasn't reassembled by the time the Italians joined the boat the next morning and I was relieved that they were brought out to Silver Star by the hotel's own motor launch, which had been brought over from an adjoining bay. Somehow, they didn't look quite so well dressed and Francesca still looked totally unhappy with the world.

We sailed Silver Star out of Soufriere for the second time in twenty-four hours and it was surprising how quickly the sea and wind had dropped. We had a fast, exhilarating sail to Bequia, arriving just after sundown. Rodney and Wilbur, the boat boys, assumed I'd gained promotion now I was the skipper of a bigger yacht and they paid due deference to me.

They offered to take the charter guests ashore the next day and Liz was grateful for that. Robert was fast becoming a real asset acting as gopher, particularly for Francesca, who kept him quite busy with her constant needs.

On Wednesday, the weather was perfect, with the wind speed around 18 knots. The pure blue sky matched the water where the yacht was anchored. Liz hoped the Italians would like Bequia and decide to stay in the area for a couple of days.

After the guests had gone ashore, I reassembled all the outboard engine parts, but as I feared, it didn't start. To be on one's own without an engine was one thing, but it was different when one had guests on board. Also, an inflatable, even if larger than a fibre-glass dinghy, is much lighter and isn't made for rowing particularly if there's a strong wind. Robert had been watching me closely, "what about the fuel Dad, is there water in that?" I looked at him blankly for a moment, and then closed my eyes. The fuel tank for this outboard, unlike the one on Shady Lady, was in a separate container. I'd completely forgotten it. The story of the mishap would have been common knowledge in the town of Soufriere before we'd pulled anchor. I knew that the moment we left the Bay, there'd have been an immediate throng of local divers looking for anything that had been missed. I realised that the petrol container would never be seen again.

I'd just radioed one of the boat yards in Port Elizabeth to arrange for a replacement petrol tank when Rodney returned with the Italians. Liz, who met them at the side of the yacht, could see from Francesca's face that there was trouble brewing.

Victor came on board first.

"Is there a problem?" I asked.

Francesca was just about to climb up the side of the boat.

Victor nodded. "She doesn't like Bequia," he said resignedly.

"She thinks it's dirty and the people unkempt. She wants to go to Mustique straight away, I'm very sorry James."

Bebe was beginning to climb the ladder.

"That's no problem for us," I said, tearing my gaze away from Bebe. "The only thing is that Mustique isn't an ideal anchorage. The swell can be uncomfortable for an overnight

186

stay."

Francesca interjected. In Italian, she asked when we could sail. She wanted to leave as quickly as possible.

A livid Liz went down to make some coffee, while Bebe and Boris came on board. Another long discussion took place between the Italians. Francesca quickly dissolved into tears, but this time Bebe was also sobbing. It transpired that it was only Francesca who wanted to go to Mustique. The argument lasted for more than an hour and Robert, who had been supplying drinks on a demand basis, suggested an end to the impasse.

"Why don't you toss for it?" Victor, Boris and Bebe thought this a great idea.

Francesca was vehemently against it, until she realised, she'd won the toss. Suddenly, she showed a rare smile.

"I don't ever remember seeing her teeth
before," I told Liz afterwards.

The length of time Francesca spent in the shower put Anne to shame, but I knew it would be pointless to suggest she conserve water. Instead, I decided to fill up our water tanks when I picked up a new petrol tank. With that on board and with full water tanks, we sailed placidly towards Mustique after we'd had lunch.

Liz pointed out the strange houses at the end of Bequia and the wrecked ship on the northern end of Mustique. We dawdled a bit and arrived at our anchorage in Mustique just after 4 p.m.

Victor offered to take everyone out to dinner at Basil's bar and that mollified Liz somewhat. The offer was withdrawn an hour later, when Francesca said she'd nothing suitable to wear and couldn't possibly go out to eat. I tried to persuade her, through Victor that it was quite normal to go to dinner in a T-shirt and shorts, but she wouldn't hear of it.

I said to Liz that I was going to put Milk of Magnesia into Francesca's food that night, but she discouraged me.

"Knowing that wretched woman, she wouldn't reach the loo in time, and I'd be the one to clean it up." In the evening, Bebe appeared at dinner again with her sunglasses and puffy cheeks, but it had not the slightest effect on her appetite, which was voracious.

"Surprise, surprise," muttered Liz, when, next morning, Francesca said she didn't like Mustique and wanted to move on south.

I had not put out a kedge anchor, because the swell hadn't been too pronounced when we turned in, but from about 3 a.m. in the morning, the yacht had rolled incessantly. During breakfast, the boat was inundated with birds and there were many more than usual mainly due to some British bird lovers on a boat nearby, who were feeding them.

Francesca lost her cool. She dug a mace spray out of one of her bags and went around spraying the stuff.

It did the birds no harm whatsoever, because it disappeared with the wind, fortunately aft of the boat. One extremely annoyed bird left its mark plumb in the middle of Francesca's day dress, one of the few she claimed she could still wear.

Liz was not sorry to move, and we sailed down towards Salt Whistle Bay at the northern end of Mayreau. As we were passing the island of Canouan, just before reaching Salt Whistle, Francesca went into raptures about the golden beaches she could see in the main bay.

"Bella, bella," she repeated and insisted in Italian that we should anchor there for the night. Victor translated for me.

"Tell her no," I said firmly, "we're going to Salt Whistle Bay, which is nicer, and we can all get a good night's sleep," Victor looked a bit taken aback, but Bebe clapped and nodded her head enthusiastically. There was the usual sobbing, of course, and Victor asked me if I'd reconsider.

"No Victor, we'd roll even more at Canouan, Salt Whistle Bay is very calm and is great for swimming."

I now knew enough about Francesca to be certain she wouldn't like Canouan. The message was passed back and although the sobbing dried up immediately, Francesca sulked for the remainder of the sail.

The small anchorage at Salt Whistle Bay is protected from the sea on the north and east side by a mere sliver of land. It's possible to walk from the west beach to the east beach in under ten strides. Because the bay is seventy-five per cent enclosed by land, it's very calm inside, and as I'd told Victor it's quite perfect for swimming.

There's a little hotel on the island, a two-minute walk from the beach and in the evening one can enjoy dinner there in the open. The biggest problem in the season is that the bay is popular as it is a favourite stop-off for yachts. It tends therefore, to get a bit crowded, which is why it's advisable to get there early in the day to ensure a choice spot.

We arrived at about 3 p.m. and found only one other yacht there, crewed by Geoff and Budgie.

I thought it would be good for the Italians to meet their countrymen from Tiger Lilly. Francesca did not wish to socialise with her countrymen either because she thought them beneath her in social standing or Victor and Boris didn't wish to advertise that they were on a trip with their mistresses. I never found out which. Liz and I had the opportunity to have a drink with Geoff and Budgie that night, and it was obvious that they were having a very rough time with their guests. Robert was amused to see that Budgie, who was a former art student, was chiselling and carving what appeared to be a replica of an automatic pistol.

"I'm going to get the buggers with this," she held up the unfinished block of wood. We all knew how she felt, but none of us could have guessed that she might be serious and what she'd be able to accomplish with a wooden shaped gun.

The next day I indicated that the sail from Salt Whistle to Tobago Cays was a short one and we were about to set off, when Francesca decided she wanted to stay. I stood down and turned the engine off and then she changed her mind, so we eventually sailed, arriving at Tobago Cays a little later than planned. Geoff and Budgie's Gulf Star was already there, as was the yacht of another crew, Pinky and Perky. The latter had American charter guests on board.

When we anchored, I put the outboard on the dinghy and went to start it. It fired the first time, and I was delighted and relieved. I hadn't relished rowing the charter guests to the reef some 600 yards away, particularly as I'd be rowing against a twenty-five-knot wind and a strong current. Because of the exposed position at Tobago Cays, the wind was always quite fierce, and this created a strong current away from the reef in front of us.

When Liz and I led flotillas down to the islands, we used to take our guests out in a dinghy, leave them on the reef and usually they'd have an easy swim back. I'd mentioned this to Victor.

Bebe, Francesca and Victor wanted to go snorkelling, but Boris had gone back to bed.

"You can leave us out there. We'll swim back when we're ready," Victor said.

"But what about Bebe, she can't swim?" I said, perplexed.

Victor looked at me in surprise and then grinned.

"Bebe is an excellent swimmer, she has many medals, so I wouldn't worry about her if I were you," he saw I was looking puzzled. "The incident at Soufriere, well, maybe she was in shock, or maybe she just wanted a ..." He shrugged.

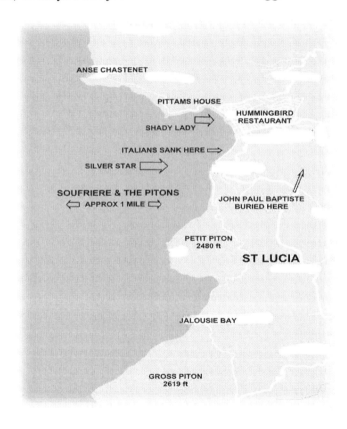

ANSE CHASTENET

PITTAMS HOUSE

HUMMINGBIRD
RESTAURANT

SHADY LADY

ITALIANS SANK HERE

SILVER STAR

SOUFRIERE & THE PITONS
APPROX 1 MILE

JOHN PAUL BAPTISTE
BURIED HERE

PETIT PITON
2480 ft

ST LUCIA

JALOUSIE BAY

GROSS PITON
2619 ft

Bebe had not been in shock.

Perky had auburn hair and freckles and a figure that was the envy of most of the women crews, including Liz. I remembered Liz saying, "I just don't understand it, Perky eats like a horse and doesn't seem to put on a flaming pound."

Pinky and Perky came from Massachusetts and had the rather refined accent that people from that area have.

I accepted some coffee and the talk got around to the respective charter guests. Geoff and Budgie's guests had gone off early in the morning on a fishing trip that had been arranged from Union Island. "Hope the buggers drown," she said with feeling.

Perky handed around the brownies and I took one. It was delicious and I complimented her on her cooking.

Normally, I wasn't particularly keen on chocolate cakes, but this one had a bite to it. She kindly offered seven more pieces for me to take back to Liz, Robert and the Italians, an offer I gladly accepted. I asked what ingredients she'd used. To my surprise, there was general laughter all round. "Oh, I get most of them from Bequia," more laughter.

I motored out with the three of them on board along with Robert, who had decided to go too. On the way back with the empty dinghy I stopped off at Geoff and Budgie's yacht and they invited me on board for a coffee. I noticed Gerald had his diving gear spread around and his wind surfer tied to the back of the yacht, alongside the boat's dinghy. Pinky and Perky came on board. Perky, a young attractive American girl had made some chocolate brownies and she brought a whole pile across with her.

Pinky and Perky were well named. He was a sandy–haired young man, already thinning on top even though he couldn't have been much more than twenty-five. Because of his fair skin he looked perpetually bright pink, rather like an albino rat. He was a vague sort of character and seemed spaced out most of the time. Perky was just the opposite, a bubbling 28-year-old with a ready smile.

"Bequia?" I queried.

Knowing the dearth of produce in the so-called supermarkets in Bequia, I was surprised. Judith chipped in, "one thing though Perky always has happy charter guests."

191

I realised that I wasn't going to get to the bottom of the joke, so I changed the subject and asked where their charter guests were. I enquired more from politeness than anything else. Perky looked at the island behind them.

"They've taken a picnic to the island over there," she pointed.

I noticed an apparently very happy bunch of people playing with a ball on the beach.

It was then I also noticed that Francesca had already swum back to Silver Star and was climbing aboard. Victor was close behind her but there was no sign of Bebe. I looked at the reef and could just see her silhouette. She wasn't difficult to spot in outline. Robert had stayed with her, and they were obviously enjoying themselves.

Nevertheless, I excused myself, saying that I ought to get back. I balanced the brownies on a plate borrowed from Budgie and carefully transported them back to Silver Star.

When I reached the yacht, Victor and Francesca were on deck, and I handed the plate up to Victor, who placed it on the little folding table in front of the binnacle. By the time I'd climbed on board Francesca was already wolfing down a large Brownie. Victor looked a little embarrassed, but I assured him that there was a piece for all of them.

Victor then took one and his face changed when he bit in to it.

"These are VERY GOOD."

I agreed.

A few minutes went by, and I noticed that Bebe and Robert were also swimming back, so I went below to see how the preparation for lunch was progressing.

While I was there, I radioed Sunshine and was given a general weather report, which was good. There were no other messages.

On hearing Bebe and Robert climbing on deck, I went back up to ask how they'd all enjoyed the reef. "Stupendous," said Bebe, throwing her hands out wide for maximum effect. "Even Francesca enjoyed it," she added mischievously.

I turned to Victor.

"Absolutely wonderful" Victor exclaimed. "We could stay here forever."

"Just to stay anywhere for more than one night would be nice," Liz growled from below.

I remembered the brownies and was amazed to find that there were only two pieces left on the plate.

Francisca's mouth was bulging, and little bits of chocolate were dropping on to her designer swimming costume.

I knew exactly where they'd all gone; I was just in time to rescue the last two pieces. I offered the plate to Bebe, who took one.

"The other one is for Boris. You'd better put it away somewhere, before it gets eaten," I looked at Bebe knowingly.

She laughed, "ah, Boris doesn't deserva de cake. I'll eat his. It's 'very good,'" she said in her stilted English.

I took the empty plate down to Liz who had just put some snapper fish in the oven for lunch. I told her that, thanks to Francesca, there was no cake left for her.

SALT WHISTLE BAY
MAYREAU

Budgie carved her guns here

Restaurant

Liz shrugged, "the last thing my figure needs right now is chocolate cake," she said.

I thought her answer hilariously funny, and Liz looked at me strangely. At Liz's request, I started to set the table for lunch and had put all the knives and forks out, when I saw her frowning at what I'd done.

"Is there a problem?" I asked, without caring whether there was or not.

What a strange effect the Caribbean air has on one, I thought. I felt very relaxed.

"The knives go on the right side of a setting, not the left," Liz was irritably moving the cutlery.

I frowned.

"Where did you get it?" Liz asked without interest.

"What?"

"the cake,"

"Oh, those, I dropped off for coffee on Geoff and Budgie's boat and Pinky and Perky came over. Apparently, Perky is a past master at baking them and told me that she got all her ingredients

from Bequia, I can't imagine how, but she must have found a shop that we haven't."

I was suddenly aware that I was going on a bit, but I was feeling particularly silly.

"Oh no," 'Liz looked at me as though I was mad.

"What?"

"Oh, James, you idiot," she hissed.

"Why? I don't understand." Liz took a deep breath.

"Perky has a reputation for having VERY happy charter guests on board."

Now I was really puzzled, "so . . .?"

Liz sighed. "What is the easiest thing to buy in Bequia?" She looked at me.

I scowled. "Pizza, Rum," I stopped, "Ganja."

Liz nodded.

"But what's that got to do with anything?"

"Because the main ingredient in her brownies is ganja, you fool. I thought everyone knew that."

"Oh shit, I've just eaten one."

"That's obvious, but I can't really think that one will do you any harm, particularly as we're not sailing today, but how many did you say Francesca had eaten?"

I gulped. "She must've had at least three large chunks."

We were suddenly aware of much merriment from above. I rushed up the galley steps.

Victor and Bebe were obviously in a playful mood, giggling at something on the fore-deck. I turned to look. Liz had also come up from below and smiled at the apparition that confronted her.

There was a trail of bits of designer swim-wear and accessories, which Francesca had thrown off one by one and she was carefully laying out her towel on the deck, completely oblivious of her audience. She lay down on her back, legs spread-eagled towards us, completely naked, showing all and quietly humming.

There were more giggles from Bebe and Victor.

Victor asked if there was any problem with Francesca sunbathing in the nude.

I shook my head.

"Not really," I laughed. I didn't seem to care.

Liz spoke. "There's no problem out here Victor, but I'd make sure she's a good covering of sun cream," she said sensibly, "this is the hottest part of the day." Victor nodded and went to get up, but Bebe pushed him back playfully.

"I'll see to it." She grabbed the sun cream and took off her own top.

Robert's eyes nearly popped out of his head.

"Coulda, you help me," Bebe offered the cream to me. I was about to accept the tube when I felt a hefty thud from behind and Liz grabbed it before my brain engaged. She put a liberal amount on Bebe's back and when she'd finished, Bebe took the tube of cream and walked unsteadily towards me.

She looked at me with a cheeky grin.

"You come to helpa' me with her, James?" She pointed to Fransesca laid out on the deck...

"No, he doesn't," Liz almost yelped. "I need help with the lunch," she added quickly as she grabbed hold of my arm fiercely and steered me down below. As I was being pulled down into the galley, I saw Victor, fast asleep in the cockpit.

Liz very wisely abandoned lunch and prepared a salad in case anyone was hungry. Boris emerged from his cabin and ate most of it, washed down with more beer. He took absolutely no notice of the half-naked Bebe and the totally naked Francesca. After lunch he disappeared again. It's almost as though he were food–hibernating, I thought vaguely. Whenever there was anything to eat, Boris always seemed to sense it and would appear. He ate and drank everything put before him and when it was clear there was nothing more to be had, he disappeared again.

Anne came over in a motor launch in the afternoon and took a now rather reluctant Robert back to Union. I was asleep when she arrived and still asleep when they left. I awoke about 4 p.m. to find a yacht anchored quite near us. There was only one person on deck, a rather heavy-set man, who was some way up the mast, apparently fiddling with the sail. He'd been there some time, when a small, wispy woman emerged. I guessed she'd been asleep down below. Although I couldn't hear what they said, I supposed the woman was asking what the man was doing up the mast.

The answer must have satisfied her, because she turned away to look towards Silver Star, stretching her arms as she did so. Her arms suddenly became frozen in mid-air when she spotted Bebe and Francesca.

She let out a shriek, turned towards the unfortunate man still up the mast and shouted something unintelligible picking up a boat hook as she advanced towards him.

It was obvious she was livid. She took a swipe at him as he scrambled down. It was very funny. She was five feet nothing and the man quite large.

He ran towards the bow, with the boat hook catching him at least once on the back. I knew from experience that doing anything quickly on a boat can be painful. I winced when the man caught his big toe on something protruding from the deck; he was hopping on one foot, while still trying to escape the wrath of the little lady. They shortly disappeared below and within five minutes, the man was out again pulling up the anchor.

I looked at the flag on the halyard. It was the Stars and Stripes.

Francesca had woken up before Bebe and was clearly mortified that she'd been naked. She turned over onto her stomach and yelled for Victor to bring her some clothes. When she was well and truly covered, she came back to the cockpit giving me a filthy look. I smiled at her as benignly as I could. Victor must have told her what she'd done, because she didn't emerge for dinner or for the whole of the next day, until the evening.

"She's too ill," stated Victor, grinning all over his face. When Bebe awoke, she wasn't at all embarrassed and walked to her cabin without covering herself. We heard the usual contretemps from down below and noticed the usual puffy eyes at dinner. The next day Bebe was on deck without her top, much to the delight of various males on boats anchored nearby.

Despite Francesca's 'illness' she wasn't too sick to eat, and

197

Victor took her meals into their cabin. The following evening, when Francesca did appear just before dinner, she was in a bathing costume and announced she was going for a swim.

I immediately counselled her against swimming as it was dark. I preferred to be able to see charter guests in case they got into trouble. Francesca gave me a disdainful wave and jumped in from the deck. I knew that she was a strong swimmer and even if the current proved too strong for her, she'd only end up on Jamesby, the island behind Silver Star, so I wasn't too worried about her safety.

Liz was a bit annoyed because it meant she'd to hold dinner until Francesca's return. We didn't have to wait too long.

I heard Francesca splashing around between the two boats and she went out of earshot when she swam around to the other side of Geoff's boat. The next thing we heard was a piercing scream of absolute terror. There was now considerable splashing, and Francesca was obviously heading for Silver Star as though her life depended on it. Every time she tried to scream something in her panic, she took in a mouthful of water.

I realised that something must be seriously wrong and jumped from the deck into the dinghy and started the engine.

I could see Geoff and Budgie on the deck of their boat, silhouetted against the cockpit lights.

Liz threw the end of the painter into the dinghy, and I set off at full speed. I reached Francesca in less than thirty seconds, and she tried desperately to get on board. I had to grab the top of her swimsuit and one of her legs and roll her in.

I was immediately aware of a dreadful smell,

I'd read that people who were really frightened evacuated their bowels, but this was the first time I'd experienced it at first hand.

Francesca tried to recover her breath.

"SHARK," she said breathlessly. "shark," she sobbed uncontrollably.

I had never seen a shark in the Caribbean, but that didn't mean there were none; whatever it was she'd seen, I felt quite sorry for her, as she was now shaking with shock. I quickly motored back to Silver Star and helped her up the steps. Victor met her at the top and covered her with a blanket, which Liz had brought up to keep her warm. Victor then took her below, as she was in quite a mess. Obviously, her doctor hadn't considered such a situation when giving out the prescription.

Liz was extremely worried about the thought of there being sharks around, and once Francesca was safe on board, I motored over to Geoff's boat and told him what had happened. He didn't believe it.

"Sharks are generally deep-water fish. They wouldn't swim this side of the reef. It's too shallow. Besides," he said jokingly, "they've all read the tourist brochures that says that there are no sharks in the Caribbean."

I smiled, but agreed in principle, because everything I'd heard about sharks suggested that one would be unlikely to be in this area. I then remembered a story I'd read in Jamaica about a rogue shark coming close in and attacking humans.

"Unless it was a rogue," I suggested.

Geoff shook his head, "No, if that had been a shark and it had been hungry, Francesca wouldn't have had a ghost of a chance. I reckon she just saw a large fish."

I grinned; I had another theory.

"Perhaps, when the shark looked at her, it realised that there was no flesh there and buggered off to look for a better meal elsewhere?" I said unkindly. We all laughed at that, and Geoff said "If that's the case, you'd better keep Bebe well away from the water."

Surprisingly, Francesca recovered in time for dinner, but she'd clearly been very frightened and was rather more talkative than usual. Later, in the evening, having settled her down with a large brandy, Victor quite reasonably suggested we move on to the next anchorage.

I was up early the next day, which was Monday and discovered unsurprisingly that we were getting short of water, so I suggested to Liz that we should take a sail over to Union and fill up, have lunch at Palm Island and anchor at PSV in the evening.

Liz agreed. Before moving off and still with the thought of a possible shark in the area, I took binoculars up on deck with me and scanned the area. I realised of course, that had there been a shark it would have been long gone, or would it? Out of the corner of my eye I caught a movement at the rear of Geoff's boat, and I focused the glasses on what had attracted my attention. I was reasonably sure that I'd found Francesca's shark. Geoff was an ardent wind surfer and his surfboard had been floating on the surface attached to the stern of the yacht, linked by a fairly long line. No doubt either the wind or the current had turned it upside down and the only thing visible was a dark blue surface shaped just like a large fish, with a fin sticking out of the middle.

I admitted to Liz later that I was relieved, as was Victor, when I called him up on deck and pointed out the offending object.

Victor smiled. "I think it would be wise to leave the story as it is," he advised. "Francesca believes you saved her life by your quick action and who knows, perhaps you did."

I was certain though, that the windsurfer had been the problem. However, one could never be certain about sharks and so I accepted Victor's suggestion.

When we reached Union Island, the Italians went for a walk while I refilled the water tanks. Francesca soon discovered the pool in front of the French hotel. The owner, no doubt trying to disprove what it said about sharks in the tourist brochures, kept several basking sharks there, I heard hysterical shrieks coming from the direction of the hotel and shortly afterwards, I saw Victor carrying a distraught Francesca back to the yacht.

"She's seen the sharks," Victor jerked his head back towards the hotel. He struggled to climb on board with his clinging burden.

"Sharks," I'd forgotten about the pool. I smiled. "Tell Francesca, they won't do her any harm. They've had their teeth removed," I lied.

When Victor translated this, Francesca leapt from his arms and scuttled down below to reappear only after we'd left the island well behind.

After watering at Union, we had lunch as planned at Palm Island. Liz noticed with interest that the hotel owner was putting down some moorings so that visiting yachts would find it easier to moor there. I readily agreed that next time we were in the area we'd pick up a mooring instead of anchoring. After lunch, we moved to PSV where we stayed until the following Wednesday.

Francesca loved the luxury hotel and spent most of her time in the expensive boutique there. In the evening Anne and Robert came aboard for dinner. During the dessert Anne announced that she'd fallen in love with a man from Petit Martinique and she was going to move in and live with him. This shocked Liz so much that she put her pudding spoon into her coffee.

She realised her mistake and withdrew the spoon at such an angle that the hot coffee landed squarely on Anne's bare thighs.

After cleaning up the mess and putting cold cream on the burned legs, Liz asked if Anne had considered the ramifications of what she was doing.

"Do you realise that Petit Martinique has no electricity and no piped water," Liz said in horror.

"Oh mummy," Anne added mischievously, "Jack and I make up for it when we're in bed."

"I don't want to know what you do in bed," yelped Liz. "I'm simply pointing out the difficulties of such an arrangement. Don't forget, Jack is a local, and they're notorious for having more than one woman."

"How do you know that" Anne asked defiantly.

"Because I do," answered Liz, crossly "and what if you have children."

"Well, I guess you'll be a granny," said Anne.

Liz was angry at what she saw as stupidity, "as long as you don't bring them home to me to be looked after," she scowled, desperately trying to find an argument that would convince Anne the error of her ways. She looked at me pleadingly.

"I don't actually think that we're in any position to stop her," I said. "She's well over the age of consent and has already left home, so to speak. I guess Anne must learn by her own mistakes."

Anne rounded on me. "I'm not making a mistake," she

snapped.

Liz scowled at me, "it's your fault."

"Yes," added Anne triumphantly pleased that the attention had passed from her, "it's your fault."

I knew when I was beaten and retreated up to the cockpit, just in time to see the Italians returning from having dinner on PSV Island. I could hear Anne and Liz crying, Robert emerged, grinning. "They're getting all emotional down there," he said. "I think I'd better stay up on top."

THE 'BITE' OF THE BROWNIE'S

The Italians were helped on board and sat in the cockpit for an after-dinner drink. Anne and Liz emerged; with the sort of puffy eyes, we were used to seeing on Bebe.

Robert mentioned to me that he'd noticed a definite change in Francesca's attitude. She certainly was less demanding than previously, and she took my advice on where and when to swim rather more seriously than she'd done at the Cays.

On Wednesday, we set off for St. Lucia, planning to spend that night in Bequia, and Thursday at Young Island, on the southern end of the island of St. Vincent. Victor wanted to visit the hotel on Young Island, because he'd been recommended to it by a fellow Italian.

The current there moved with the tide, from east to west and then west to east. This meant laying two anchors in, and I was never completely happy with the holding. The water was quite deep, even though Young Island is only a few hundred yards off the mainland.

It was late on Thursday afternoon when we arrived there from Bequia.

It took us over an hour to anchor. After which, I arranged to run the Italians over to the hotel dock. Francesca had miraculously found some clothes she could dine in and in fact, they were all looking almost as smart as before the Soufriere disaster. The water was calm. When the dinghy reached the dock, I swung it alongside and grabbed hold of a cleat on the dock to keep the aft of the dinghy close in so everyone could get off safely. Bebe was first to climb up from the dinghy, which was quite a step up, the top of the dinghy being about a foot lower than the dock surface.

She had to pull her short skirt right up to her upper thighs to get the leverage she needed and what she showed left very little for the imagination, particularly as she wore nothing under her skirt. Once she was on the dock, I asked her to hold the painter line, so that the bow of the dinghy held fast while the others climbed up. Victor was the second to get off.

He helped Francesca and it only remained for Boris to disembark. I saw him moving towards the dock side when something behind Bebe caught Boris's attention. I looked in the same direction and saw a woman walking away from the hotel towards us. As she came into view from behind Bebe, she looked at Boris and smiled.

She was stunning and from pictures I'd seen of Raquel Welch, I believed it to be her. I knew she owned a house on Mustique only a few miles away. Boris was completely captivated, and his jaw dropped open when this gorgeous apparition strolled past. Bebe turned to look and let out a howl of rage. She threw the painter back into the boat at the precise second Boris put his foot on the dock. When climbing up from something, a person tends to push with whatever is available to give oneself a lift. This would have worked fine if Bebe had still been holding the line, but she wasn't. Boris was now stranded between the boat and the dock, rapidly doing the splits. He might just have made it, if Bebe hadn't rushed to the dock side and stamped her high heel down hard on his foot. I never found out what the word bastard was in Italian, but I suspected that what Bebe said was close.

"Yeowwww," Boris yelled in pain. A heavy splash swallowed up the noise, as Bebe walked huffily away towards the hotel, with Francesca following. Poor Boris surfaced without his reserve pair of glasses and was clearly in some distress. It was left to Victor and me to get him into the boat, that wasn't an easy matter with such a big man.

Victor was soaked in the process, and I had to take them both back to Silver Star to change. I gathered, upon their return from dinner, that the meal hadn't been a great success. Victor led the now almost blind Boris down to his cabin, and Francesca followed.

Victor called up to say goodnight and he and Francesca turned in. Bebe was still very much awake, however, and sat in the cockpit. We talked for half an hour, and I noticed that her English was improving

measurably. Liz asked Bebe if she wanted anything else before she went to bed and Bebe confirmed she didn't. Liz yawned, looked at me rather pointedly, suggesting that I shouldn't too be too long before joining her.

I nodded.

When Liz had gone below, I poured Bebe and myself another brandy and intended, when I'd finished it to turn in too. It was a very clear night, the lights on the shore were twinkling, the stars were bright and there was a reggae band playing somewhere in the distance. It was a beautiful Caribbean evening. We could hear fish jumping in the water and I got up to investigate a particularly loud splash.

While I was looking over the side, Bebe joined me winding her arm around my waist. I put a comradely arm around her shoulder.

"He says eet is me."

"Who does," I asked surprised.

"Zat man," Bebe threw her spare arm out in the general direction of the cabin where Boris was sleeping. I was very aware of her hand creeping further down my waist, then my hip and then to the top of my leg. I grabbed it, to stop any further movement.

"Eet isn't fair. Do you zinc it ees me?"

"Of course not," I didn't know what she was talking about but couldn't think of a better answer.

I was then vaguely aware of her moving in front of me, more by the smell of her perfume, than by her action and then she drew my head down to hers. Her kiss was extraordinarily sensual. I could feel her thighs pressing against my own and then Bebe seemed to melt in my arms.

I'd have been much less of a man, if I hadn't felt a sudden and urgent desire overcome me, but by some superhuman effort, I broke away. We were both slightly breathless, but she looked triumphant.

"I knew it was notta me," she howled and stamped her foot, "I'm VERY grateful for you," she said in her bad English and kissed me again, but quickly this time.

With that, she turned and rushed down the galley steps, crashing into the cabin where Boris slept. I heard a frightful row going on and Liz and Victor came out of their respective cabins

To investigate. They took one look at the closed cabin door where the noise was coming from and came up on deck.

"What on earth?" said Liz.

"What's happening?" asked Victor.

I shrugged, feeling vaguely uneasy, not knowing what Bebe was saying. As we were talking, Boris shot out of their cabin, with a high heeled shoe narrowly missing his head. Victor, who'd come up from the cabin, went back down below and brought Boris up to the cockpit. Liz was amused to see that he was wearing a night-shirt. The lock on the cabin door clicked, and then there was a loud and continuous banging of drawers. Victor went down below and tapped lightly on the cabin door. There was some hysterical shouting, until Bebe realised it was Victor and not Boris.

Victor came back up.

"She says that she's leaving tonight and wants us to call a taxi."

"There are no aircraft flying until tomorrow morning. It's now," I looked at my watch, "twenty minutes past midnight. She can't go ashore at this time of night," I said firmly.

Victor looked at me seriously. "James, tonight, she's prepared to walk on water if necessary."

"Let me talk to her," I suggested.

Victor and Boris both nodded vigorously.

I went down below and tapped tentatively on the cabin door.

"Who eez it?" she asked in an irritable voice.

"It's me Bebe, James, may I come in," the door opened, and I went in and sat on the berth with her

She was clearly very upset, but after half an hour, I'd persuaded her to come up and have some coffee and by 1.30 we were all able to get to bed, the crisis averted.

I reckoned it was a day I wouldn't forget.

Bebe slept in the main cabin.

"Eet makes no difference," she'd said meaningfully.

"What took you so long?" asked Liz suspiciously, when she'd got me back to the privacy of our cabin.

"Long," I asked innocently.

Liz frowned, "Yes, why did you have to spend so much time with Bebe in her cabin?"

I switched off the light to hide my expression. I shrugged my shoulders in the dark. "Well, you know how volatile Italian women are," I hoped to appear dismissive as my voice trailed off.

"Hmmm, I've noticed," answered Liz as she climbed into her berth.

SAINT VINCENT

ARNOS VALE ⊏⊐ APPROX QUARTER MILE ⊏⊐
STADIUM

VILLA

THE 'CATHOLIC'
CAME FROM HERE

SILVER STAR ⟵

Calliaqua

BORIS FELL
IN HERE
YOUNG ISLAND

TO BEQUIA ⟵

MOPIAN

PENISE — TO UNION

PETIT ST VINCENT
PSV

278 ft

SILVER STAR

HOTEL

TO CARRIACOU
& GRENADA

310
ft.

PETIT
MARTINIQUE
748
ft

100 ft
ft

FOTA

LITTLE TOBAGO

1 MILE

PSV & PETIT MARTINIQUE

We planned to leave the anchorage by mid-morning on Friday, and sail to Soufriere, where we were to spend another night. I promised to have one last look for Boris's glasses, before taking the Italians back to Rodney Bay at the end of the charter. I was just preparing things on deck for us to pick up anchor, when I noticed a dinghy advancing towards us. The rower was a small older man, with crinkly white hair and black complexion.

He'd a priest's collar on and when he came alongside, he asked if there were any Catholics on board. I called Victor and soon all four Italians were on deck, chatting to the man of God. It appeared he was looking for donations for his church and I saw Francesca open her purse. Considering the matter, no business of mine, I went down below to check that everything was stored properly and was about to check the engine oil, when I heard a scream from above.

To check the engine oil on Silver Star, I had to climb into the engine room from our cabin, so it took a few seconds to get back out. When I'd done so, I catapulted myself up to the deck. Francesca was beside herself with anger, she was waving her second heavy handbag (she'd six with her), and I was to learn from Liz, that the bag had encountered the priest's head.

In his haste to get away, the Holy man dropped an oar in the sea and was desperately rowing towards the shore with the remaining one, not an easy task for someone in a hurry.

"What on earth has happened," I asked.

"That guy took a donation from Francesca, then asked her if she wanted to buy some grass," said Victor, "I guess he's not quite what he appears to be," he said, in a classical understatement.

I looked after the retreating cleric, making sure I'd remember him again. Liz, who'd also come up on deck, smiled.

"That could only happen in the Caribbean," she said.

We sailed back to Soufriere, where Victor kindly took all of us to the Humming Bird for dinner. I failed to find poor Boris's glasses, either at Young Island or Soufriere.

Sadly, we bade the Italians good-bye from Rodney Bay dock the next day.

Out of sight of Liz, Bebe gave me a special send-off.

There's no doubt that their luggage had suffered during the trip, but I felt we'd all learned something from being together.

When Liz opened the visitor's book after they'd gone, there were three envelopes inside, one addressed to Liz and one to me and the third marked confidential to me only. The jointly addressed envelopes both contained $300 in US notes. The third envelope was from Bebe.

I never did divulge exactly what was written in the enclosed letter, but there was also a $100 note, with the cryptic comment: 'For services rendered.' I slipped the letter quickly into my pocket.

10 - LAURIE GOES NUDE

And How He Also Went Hungry

After the Italians had gone, and I relaxed on Silver Star, a sixty-foot yacht belonging to Sunshine Charters, which was tied to the Sunshine dock. We knew that later; the day would be a busy one. The new charter guests would be arriving, and we had to provision for six of them, the most guests we'd ever had on the yacht. Silver Star faced the lagoon, and we could see boats coming in from the bay proper. It was just after 1 p.m. when we sighted Laurie. He didn't look in good shape.

Laurie had obtained a job as a skipper of a fifty-foot Gulf Star at Sunshine, soon after leaving us where we lived in Marigot Bay. He had told us that he had just been sacked from his job as first mate on a large sailing ship.

Because we joined Sunshine later than him, he was senior in service to us and I thought he may be peeved that we'd received a '60-foot yacht, the pride of the fleet, before him.

Unfortunately for Laurie, his ability to keep a cook on board for more than one charter was zero, and it was, therefore highly unlikely he'd ever be considered for one of the top jobs.

We had last met Laurie some weeks before. He had been on holiday to North America, and he proudly showed us some photographs of the vacation he'd taken in the Canadian outback. He had set up the camera to take shots of himself sitting by the camp fire, in his tent, driving his jeep. He was totally alone, and the pictures seemed rather pathetic.

The Gulf Star was heading straight towards us and although some sixty feet away, we could see Laurie behind the wheel, his moustache had an even more pronounced droop than usual. The lines on the front of his boat had been set for docking, but they appeared to droop too.

Liz smiled. "I don't think Laurie is a happy bunny."

It didn't take long for the full story to unfold. Within an hour of docking, he was seated on our yacht with a large beer in his hand. He looked absolutely whacked. His light-coloured hair was matted, his T-shirt and shorts were creased and dirty and his eyes looked as though they'd not seen sleep for some time, which in fact they hadn't.

"Another shitty day in paradise?" Liz asked with a smile.

Laurie glowered and then the story spilled out.

"As you know, I was on standby, because Porky, my last no-good cook, had buggered off with that German creep from the Atlantic Clipper. A call came through to me from the charter manager on Tuesday, saying that a guy who was on holiday on the island with his wife and kid, asked if they could charter a crewed boat for three days and he asked me if I'd be interested.

"Well, the money was okay so, I said yes. What he didn't tell me at the time was, they wanted to visit Tobago Cays in the Grenadines, which as you know is almost a day and a half sail from Saint Lucia."

"You're joking" I said, in genuine amazement.

"In three days," Laurie repeated, "can you fuckin' believe it?" He ran his hand under his nose.

"Anyway, I worked out a plan that meant if I sailed overnight on Wednesday, I could get there by about ten on Thursday. I could then get some sleep an' do the same thing on Thursday night getting 'em back in time for their 4 p.m. flight on Friday.

"They were late cumin' on board, an' I learned none of the three had sailed before. The guy was one of those fuckin' know it all types and the wife was a real whiner. She didn't wanna go, an' they did nothin' but yell at each other for the whole of the fuckin' trip."

They were British," he added sourly, as though that explained it.

"How about the child?" Liz asked.

Laurie stopped, took a long swig of his drink, and handed the empty glass for a refill.

"Jesus, I've come across some real bad Yank kids, but I tell you, this one really got first prize," he snatched his glass back and took another drink.

"She was about ten, I guess, and she thought I was her fuckin' gopher," he altered his voice into a squeaky rendition of the child's. "It was, 'Laurie, please do this, Laurie, please do that, Laurie, I need a drink, Laurie, I don't know how to put my life jacket on, Laurie, can you please come and wipe my. . .' I guess you've got the message," he looked at us wearily.

"We sailed about this time on Wednesday, an' I was getting into the St. Vincent channel. About 6.30 to seven, and the bitch of a mother asked when dinner would be ready.

'I naturally thought they knew that I'd no fuckin' cook and that the wife would look after the galley. I asked the guy to hold the wheel while I went below, and the bastard wasn't a bit happy to take it. I told him, it's the wheel or no fuckin' dinner, an' he could take his choice. He took the wheel an' I went down below and opened a tin of Heinz spaghetti, did some toast an' went up an' told them it was ready. The wife whined that she couldn't eat below an' couldn't we have the table set up in the cockpit," Laurie took a deep breath.

"Bear in mind, we're now in the fuckin' channel with waves

running around six feet, an' the Gulf Star was well heeled to starboard. How the idiot woman thought I could set a table in those conditions, Jesus!

"Anyhow, I brought the food up best I could, an' gave it 'em on a plate. There was a quite a wind blowing, so by the time the stupid bitch got to the stuff, she complained it was cold, an' in any case, this wasn't the standard of cooking she'd been led to believe she'd get. Because she was holding the plate up whilst complainin', a sudden gust spewed most of her dinner into her cleavage." Laurie grinned at the recollection, "she then threw her plate overboard."

"The guy and kid wolfed it down as though they'd never tasted anythin' so good and maybe they hadn't. When I took over the wheel, I noticed the idiot father had changed direction and we'd spent half an hour heading for Venezuela. I shoulda' noticed the sails, of course, but I was too busy doin' the cooking."

"About five minutes went by and the kid suddenly ran down below. A few minutes later she was back and said somethin' to her mother. Her mother leaned across to me and said, "I'm awfully sorry, but Pippa has been sick in one of the cabins, the one directly below us, actually."

"How about that," Laurie had put on a very passable English upper-class accent.

"Guess whose cabin was directly below - yea, my fuckin' cabin. It was obvious that mummy wasn't going to clear up the mess, so I handed over the wheel to the idiot father and told him if I found it off course when I came back up, I'd fuckin' sail to South America and leave 'em there."

"And had she been sick?" I asked.

"Sick, sick! I reckon she'd bin saving it up for three days or more and, of course, she wasn't sick in the heads, was she? Oh no," Laurie took another drink.

"She puked all over my berth. I cleaned up best I could, an' took the mattress up on deck to give it an airing. The fuckin' mother complained that it was smelly and would I please remove it. I did. I took it back down, took the mattress from her berth an' swapped 'em over.

"Soon after that they turned in, an' didn't show their faces 'til we were nearly at the Cays the next morning. I'd just anchored when the guy asked when breakfast would be ready. I gave 'im a fishing line an' told him to go catch his own. I was turning in. Then his fuckin' wife started to cry, so I went below and did some scrambled eggs. The woman complained they were too greasy and threw her lot overboard. From then on, we'd a real fun day with the kid. It was, 'Laurie, can you take me snorkelling, Laurie, can we go an' see the lobster fishermen, Laurie, can we do this, that and all the rest.' The woman complained her mattress smelled of puke, so I gave her own one back. I knew I wasn't goin' to be able to use it anyway.

"It became obvious that they expected me to cook midday dinner, so I did a tuna salad and the wife said she didn't like fish. I told her to scrape it off the lettuce. She said she didn't like the Caribbean lettuce either.

"When they weren't yelling at each other, the guy just slept in the fuckin' sun, the woman read her fuckin' book under the cockpit canopy, and the kid spent her time makin' fuckin' sure I didn't sleep. Can't imagine why they wanted to go down to the fuckin' Grenadines anyway." Laurie waved to another crew who were just arriving.

"I was damn glad when the time came for us to sail, and I pulled the anchor at about 4 p.m. an' set off back. We'd only bin goin' about half 'n hour and the kid puked, down below agin', but because this time it was in her mother's cabin, the bitch went spare. I cleaned that up, but when she puked again, in the galley, I'd had enough. I went below an' got her by her shoulders, an' looked her straight in the eyes. 'I know you can't help puking. If I'd parents like yours, I'd puke too, but if you must puke, puke up on deck, understand?" I gave her a bit of a shake to make sure it went in. She promised she'd do as I asked."

Laurie stretched his legs, and I guessed the best part of the story was to come.

"In the lee of St. Vincent, I went below an' cooked a passable pasta dish, an' took it up on deck, this time in a large bowl, so it wouldn't get cold so quickly. The fuckin' mother didn't like pasta. I don't think she liked anything and come to think of it, I can't think how she'd a bloody kid. Maybe that's why she only had one," he said, almost as an afterthought.

"As soon we hit the channel, the kid, who had bin below, rushed up the galley steps and ran straight towards me. She grabbed the binnacle an' puked, all over my front. The guy was asleep down below, so I asked the mother to get me some fresh clothes from my cabin. She told me that she wasn't a servant, an' to get them myself. I was really pissed off by this time so I jus' lashed the wheel with a piece of line an' took off all my clothes, went aft lowered a bucket into the sea, swilled myself off and went back and stood behind the wheel naked. The kid's eyes nearly ejected. The mother hurried her below n' produced some shorts and T-shirt, which she threw at me.

"I was sailing 'em back to Vieux Fort so they'd be near the airport, and wuz thinkin' that at least I had the use of the provisions Sunshine had put on board for the charter, but about a mile off the land, the woman started takin' 'em all out of the galley an' throwing 'em overboard.

"I asked her what she was doin,' an' she said she'd paid for 'em, so she could do what she liked with 'em.

"I dropped 'em off, didn't get a tip and I've just returned. On my sail up after dropping 'em, the manager called me on the fuckin' radio, He said they'd called from the airport to say they were stopping their cheque in payment fer the trip and, as a result, I wouldn't be paid either."

11 - CREATURES GREAT AND SMALL

And How I Got bitten

After Laurie had gone, Liz went off down town with some of the other crews' cooks to purchase provisions. We'd been told that the charter had been reduced to seven days, because the horticultural society wanted their members to spend more time on land.

They were to be picked up from Marigot Bay that evening, stay there for one day and sail down to Young Island, where we were to be anchored for two days, then down to the Cays for one day only. From there we were to sail straight back to Martinique, where the charter guests would continue their studies of Caribbean flora on land after spending one day in St. Anne.

Liz and I were quite pleased about the change, which would give us more time to prepare for the next charter, which was due to start in St. Maarten, in the north.

The current charter comprised of 3 yachts carrying 18 charter guests plus one hostess. The leader of the horticulturists was to be on our yacht that meant six guests all together on Silver Star. The hostess was booked on to another boat and Liz said that she didn't envy the crew who

217

had to look after seven people, six being a real handful. She arrived back at 3.30 p.m. loaded with goods to be packed away. I'd spent some time on the main, which was again giving trouble and this time I'd to take the sail out completely. Despite that, everything was ready by just after 2 p.m. and we sailed to Marigot as soon as Liz returned to get a good spot to anchor as near to the dock as possible.

The day was overcast, very humid and almost windless, so it was nice to be at sea, but when we arrived at Marigot at 5 p.m. it was very hot and stuffy. The guests were not expected until six, so we spent an hour resting and reading. The two Gulf Stars came in shortly after: one crewed by Chris and Cadbury, so-called for her love of chocolate. They were on Gulf Star Daffodil, he British, she was American.

Pike and Piggy formed the second team. Both had nicknames appropriate to their voracious appetites. Pike and Piggy were Dutch South African, and the name of their boat was Gulf Star Capricia.

The charter guests were late, and it was 6.30 p.m. before I picked up my group from the dock. Because of the numbers of charter guests, I had to ferry them over in two trips. The first surprise we had was that five of them were well over sixty, the second that none of them had sailed before and the third was that there were five women and one man, all of them single. They seemed happy to share cabins however, the women took three of them and the man proposed sleeping in the main cabin. This was to prove a bit of a pain, as he was the only one who didn't like getting up in the morning.

Just as supper was ready, we received a visit from the hostess, who introduced herself as Valerie. Val had done a lot of sailing; at one time she was a cook on a large charter boat in the US Virgins. She was an American from South Carolina and had a pleasant southern accent; she looked rather like a very slightly overweight Bo Derek. I guessed she was about 26 years of age and I noticed that she'd the most innocent looking deep blue eyes, a slightly turned up mouth and pretty, light brown hair. She positively oozed sex appeal and proved to be full of fun. She knew just how to manage her charges, joking with them and teasing them, particularly about the only male guest on board Silver Star.

"Now, there's to be no unfairness, you're to share him around equally," she scolded the women laughingly. Bill Cummings, for that was his name, didn't look as though he could manage a hot breakfast, never mind the female Amazons, as Liz and I were to call the women collectively, but this made Valerie's suggestion all the funnier.

Bill was a retired steel erector and he looked it. A very heavy-set man, he was the only one amongst the guests who was well overweight. Madge and Barbara, who shared a cabin, were sisters, a fact that everyone was in ignorance of at first, for they had booked in their married names. They were similar in build, small and lithe, and while Madge reminded me of the Grandma in the Beverley Hillbillies, Barbara was a little taller and much quieter. Dorothy and Gertrude were two spinster teachers from Oregon, who looked and talked like teachers. Molly, who had a cabin to herself, was quite attractive and younger than the others. She was a US government employee, working for the IRS. (Internal Revenue Service).

Val left when Liz began to serve the meal and I went to help her into her dinghy. She smiled at me as she climbed aboard.

"See you later, I hope," she said and raised her eyebrows.

I nodded. I felt there was something else behind the look she gave me and for some unaccountable reason; I felt a pleasant tingling sensation.

Everything went well, the charter guests were all highly appreciative of Liz's cooking and after dinner they congregated in the cockpit and chatted until the small hours.

Bill Cummings was in bed long before the others, which made it difficult, because everyone had to go through the main cabin to get to their own.

Liz said next day that she'd never had such a disturbed night on a boat. First one person would be up and then another. We heard the heads being flushed at odd intervals all night. The cold box (freezer) was raided at least twice. Two of the women obviously couldn't sleep and they went back on deck and spent the night talking, until a frustrated and short of sleep Liz got up at 6 a.m.

Breakfast was hilarious. Bill liked two eggs boiled for two minutes. Madge wanted scrambled eggs, but runny, whereas

Barbara preferred hers well done with bacon. Molly liked a boiled egg with the white hard inside and the yolk runny. Dorothy requested a fried egg, sunny side up, with lashings of toast and Gertrude made do with a grapefruit and toast, but then was still hungry and asked for eggs Benedict afterwards.

"At least they're staying out for lunch," I answered, ducking a large piece of bread that came whizzing in my direction. I hadn't realised that Liz also had to make up the packed lunches and so I helped her do so. Nevertheless, the positive side of the charter was that the guests all planned to meet up on shore each day by 9-30 a.m. and they'd be away to look at some part of the rain forest and not return until the evening, which gave us hosts some time to recover. "How long did you say they were to be on board?" asked a tired and exhausted Liz, when they'd all gone off for the day.

Several crews had complained of an increase of petty thieving in Marigot, and this had reached the stage where it was getting serious. I'd lost an expensive camera and other items of value had been stolen from other boats. The problem was that although one could lock the boat when leaving it, the padlocks would only deter casual incursions. If anyone was determined enough and had possession of a large hammer and chisel, the locks could be broken in seconds.

The thefts had been reported to the St. Lucian police, but no one was encouraged by their response. Therefore, just before the horticultural charter, the crews scheduled a meeting to discuss what, if anything could be done about it. Some crews weren't present, but there was a long list of items that had all gone missing in Marigot. We decided that the next time there were a few of us in the bay, we'd meet again. Gerald and Geoff had come down to Marigot for a second meeting and Chris and Pike who were on our charter joined us. As soon as the charter guests had left for the day, we used Silver Star as a meeting place and as the elected Chairman, I started the proceedings.

"The point is, we know there are a small number of thieves in Marigot, and we also know that there must be someone on shore watching, because they never tackle a yacht when the crew is on board," everyone agreed.

"I suggest," I went on, "that we set a trap for them, Gerald you've got a couple of walkie-talkies, and some of us are going to be in Marigot on Sunday night, that'll be a busy time, with the maximum number of yachts moored."

"When there are a lot of boats in the bay, that is when most of the stuff goes missing," interrupted Pike.

"That's right," Gerald agreed. "Tomorrow night a big party is being thrown by the owner of Hurricane Hole for his wife's 40th birthday, so that's the time we may catch 'em."

"But how do we set a trap for 'em when they've such a choice of boats to go for and, if we do catch 'em how do we detain 'em? If they're big guys, they could be more than we can handle," Geoff looked worried and that amused Liz, as he was by far the largest there.

"They may also have weapons, like a machete for instance," Pike chirped.

Chris answered, "I reckon we can handle 'em between us, but we'll keep flare guns handy just in case." All the charter yachts carried flare guns, the projectile included phosphorus, which could cause some considerable damage if fired at a human being.

"I agree," I said, a little alarmed at Chris's suggestion, "but the thing is to catch them and hand them over to the police in one piece as a deterrent to others."

"How do we go about it?" asked Geoff.

My suggestion was the one they all adopted. It was agreed that Gerald and Judith, who weren't on charter, would sail their boat down to Marigot Bay in company with Geoff to arrive just before sundown on Sunday night. The inner bay would be crowded, so the yacht should anchor in the outer bay, making it somewhat isolated and thus it was much easier for someone to break in, there being fewer people and boats in that area. "When Gerald arrives, I'll transport Pike and Chris over to Gerald's boat in my dinghy and we'll smuggle them down below, Geoff, Pike and Chris will be hidden below deck to await the break-in. At around 8 p.m. Gerald and Judith will lock up their boat, get in their dinghy, pretend to be more than slightly the worse for drink and head off towards Hurricane Hole. I'll position myself on top of Silver Star and watch Gerald's boat carefully through night glasses," which I knew Gerald also owned. "I'll communicate any threat to Pike, who will have the other walkie-talkie in Gerald's yacht." It was all agreed.

That evening I told the guests what we were up to, and Molly insisted on keeping watch most of the time. No doubt, being in the IRS was good training for her new-found role.

Gerald sailed in as planned, anchored out in the bay and we got Pike and Chris on board and below without any fuss.

When Gerald and Judith left their boat, I thought the display of drunkenness was a little overdone, but in fact there was no acting whatsoever. All concerned were well and truly plastered, including those below.

I kept in touch with Pike via the W/T and by 8-30 p.m. it was becoming obvious that those inside Gerald's boat were getting restless. A quarter to nine came and I got a message that they'd enough of being cooped up below and wanted to go ashore. I reluctantly agreed and was about to fetch Gerald, who of course had the key, when Molly called softly, "there is someone who has just rounded the point in a small dinghy."

I called Pike urgently on the W/T and was concerned at the noise going on in the background; they obviously had the radio on.

"For God's sake turn the radio off they're almost at the boat now," the radio was switched off and I heard Pike saying 'Shh'.

I gave Pike a running commentary.

"They're now at the stern and have stopped. No, they're moving around to the port side. I think one of them is going to look inside. Keep your heads down. Okay, they're now travelling around the bow and now they're on your starboard side. They're probably going to the stern again where Gerald left the ladder. Yes, one is climbing up, the other one's following." Molly was getting extremely excited, as were all the others who had gathered round on the deck and were listening. Pike radioed me back in a whisper.

"I can hear the bastards fiddling with the lock. They've smashed it," that was all I heard. The rest of the story Pike and Chris told me later.

"The buggers broke in and we made a lunge for 'em, but they were too quick." I guess he meant that the crew members were too drunk to act quickly.

"The older guy, who was behind, jumped straight in to the water and struck out for the shore leaving his dinghy behind, the other one turned out to be a youngster of about seventeen, and he dived over the side too. The problem for him was he could not swim, and as he didn't have time to get to the dinghy, used to get there in the first place, we were able to fish him out. We took him back to the dock in his dinghy and asked the manager of Hurricane Hole if we could borrow his office. The manager agreed.

"Gerald met us at the hotel entrance, and we frog-marched the guy right through the main dining room. When we had him in the office, we asked him where we could find his accomplice, but he seemed to have lost his tongue. Gerald got a large pair of scissors from the manager's desk drawer and told us to take down the guy's pants. Gerald said that if he couldn't find out who'd got all the valuables, then he was going to make sure that the man we were holding didn't have the balls to steal again.

"Suddenly, the young man recovered his memory and by the time the police arrived, the information was presented to them on a plate. The police acted quickly for once and caught the other man at his home, with a huge store of cameras, wallets, credit cards and various pieces of boat equipment."

I reflected on the political fallout that could have followed their action. A South African, in a black country, who marched a native through a crowded restaurant threatening to cut off his testicles, would have been manna from heaven for a certain section of the press. Fortunately, the story remained under wraps.

Monday came, and after the excitement of the night before, everyone was cock-a-hoop, justifiably so, as it effectively ended the petty thieving in Marigot. It also sent a strong message to other areas that if crewed yachts were broken into, there'd be retaliation.

The first disaster of the charter came just after breakfast. I noticed that one of the water pumps, which had been working overtime, seemed a bit sluggish. I soon established that there was nothing wrong with the pump, but Silver Star's batteries had run very low, due to the nocturnal goings on of the charter guests. I feared for a moment that the engine wouldn't start, but it eventually fired, and I made a mental note to run it 2 hours a day instead of the normal one hour, to give the batteries an extra charge.

The horticulturists had arrived back on board the evening after all the excitement with loads of cuttings from various plants and trees. I'd ensured that all the foliage went into an external locker on deck. It had taken a considerable amount of work to get rid of the cockroaches we had discovered on board when we took over and I wasn't keen to encourage any further creepy-crawlies gaining entry by subterfuge. The engine had been running for about quarter of an hour when I went below to make my routine radio call to Sunshine. Madge and Gertrude were by the table in the main cabin, holding small boxes in their hands, looking at each other, with an air of naughty children. When I appeared, they quickly shut the boxes.

It was Molly who drew to my attention to what they were doing. She came from her cabin and asked me if I'd seen Madge's and Gertrude's specimens. I could see Madge mouthing something at Molly, but I was intrigued and walked over to them.

"Come on, you two, what have you got in there?" I smiled and looked at the box Madge was holding. I thought they'd probably found a rare example of flora and covered it up for safety. Madge looked embarrassed, but she and Gertrude put their boxes on the table and opened them.

I looked in the first one and froze. I knew immediately what it was. There's a most unpleasant, poisonous centipede that lives on most of the Caribbean islands. It usually grows to about six inches long it's a bright almost a translucent maroon and it's not something a normal person would keep by their bed. I recoiled in revulsion and investigated the other box. There, staring up at me was the most evil-looking spider I'd ever seen.

"I think it's a black widow," said Madge excitedly. I looked at her in absolute amazement.

"Do you realise, Madge, just how deadly a Black Widow spider is?" I was glad to see that the bloody thing hadn't moved. She had just started to close the box when we felt Silver Star shake and heel sharply to starboard. It was so sudden, I thought someone might have hit us and I rushed up the galley steps, only to see Peterkin disappearing around the sand spit. Because I'd been below and the engine had been running, I hadn't heard his approach. In any case, as we'd anchored near to the dock, I probably wouldn't have had time to react.

Liz was furious too, because she'd been taking a shower at the time and was thrown heavily against the bulkhead, hurting her leg. She rushed out, with a towel around her. I went back down below and met her coming out of the cabin, explaining to her what had happened.

Gertrude and Madge landed on the floor and Liz thought for a moment that they were hurt. Molly put him right.

"They've lost their goddamned insects," she said angrily.

"Oh Jesus," I'd temporarily forgotten them.

I told Liz.

"Oh no, I don't believe it," it was Liz who found the centipede.

Madge approached just as it was trying to dive under the oven. She had her box open, ready to catch it and was mortified when Liz picked up one of her shoes and hammered the creature into the floor. In fact, she continued to bash to such an extent that the creature changed from a three-dimensional shape to two-dimensional.

"Jeez," complained Madge, "I was going take that little feller home."

"Well, you can take the little feller home now," answered Liz crossly, "and just think, Madge, you won't have to feed the little pest," I turned around to see Gertrude getting up looking rather shamefaced. She evidently hadn't located her spider. "I guess he's gone for bush," she said sadly.

"What if the bloody thing is a she," I asked angrily, "I can't think of anything I'd rather have on my boat than a family of deadly Black widows," My sarcasm was lost on her. I'd always been paranoid about arachnids of any sort, I hated spiders and scorpions and all other insects together were a close second. The thought of going to bed at night, not knowing whether I'd find it in my bed, or, even worse, in my shoe the next morning didn't help me to present a sunny disposition to Madge, or Gertrude, or indeed anyone on the boat. I

225

immediately gathered everyone on the yacht into the cockpit. "Has ANYONE else brought ANYTHING live on to this boat?" I looked grimly around the assembled charterers.

Everyone shook their heads vigorously.

"What about sleeping?" asked Bill, who looked uncomfortable. Not only did he sleep more than the rest of them, but the deadly creature had disappeared near his berth.

"Okay, this is what I want us to do," I said wearily. "First, Gertrude and Madge, please continue to carry out a thorough search of the area where you last saw the spider. And please, be very careful. In the meantime, I'm going to douse the whole cabin with fly killer, particularly in the crevices. We should have sailed to St. Vincent today. Now, we're not," a look of alarm spread across some of their faces.

"Yes, I know, it's going to muck up some of your holiday, but my responsibility is for your safety and I'm not going anywhere until the little pest is found and dealt with."

"What if we don't find it?" asked Dorothy who was sitting on the galley steps.

"I'm about to call Sunshine. If we haven't found our friend within fifteen minutes, I'll request that bombs be sent down by a launch."

"Surely," Barbara said breathlessly, "isn't it a bit of overkill to blow up the boat."

"No Barbara," I said reassuringly, "we don't blow up the boat." At that moment Val came aboard and I quickly put her in the picture.

She shook her head at Gertrude and Madge.

"The bombs are designed to kill everything that crawls," I added, "and they're extremely effective. The only problem is that no one can be aboard for about five hours while the bombs are active, and you guys will have to leave."

"Should we take our luggage off too?" asked Molly.

"No, it could be housing our friend and that would rather defeat the object, wouldn't it?" I said a trifle sarcastically.

We had another intensive search, but the spider wasn't found. I radioed Sunshine and asked for two bombs to be sent straight down. John radioed back ten minutes later and confirmed that they were on their way in a fast motor boat.

Val gave the charter guests a good talking to and I was impressed with the way she dealt with the situation. "You have to understand that this is someone's home," she said, "and not just a holiday vehicle, would you like it, if someone brought a poisonous snake into your home?" They all shook their heads vigorously. In fairness, Madge and Gertrude were very contrite and told me that they'd dumped overboard a box that Barbara had. I never discovered what it had contained.

Val visited the other boats and established that Silver Star was the only one with charterers remotely interested in live specimens. When she'd completed the rounds, she came back across the bay to see me. Gerald was with her.

"Gee, I'm so awfully sorry James and Liz," she said. "I've made it clear that no one should bring anything on board in future unless it's cleared by the skipper and that includes

227

plant life." I thanked her for her cooperation and complimented her on the way she'd handled the old ladies.

Gerald was spitting fire. Although his boat hadn't caught the full wash from Peterkin's inflatable, it had caused him to slip in the shower as Liz had done, but with more serious consequences, for he'd been badly bruised.

"I'm bloody fed up with that guy," said Gerald. "We've mentioned his recklessness to the manager several times and nothing seems to be done." I agreed with him, remembering my last run in with Peterkin, when I was in Shady Lady.

"I wish we were going to be here tonight," said Gerald.

He added as an afterthought, "Hell, there's no reason why I can't stay, I'm not picking our charterers up till Tuesday," he looked thoughtful.

I told him that we weren't going to sail either and explained why.

Val had proposed that she take the guests on a trip to the drive-in Volcano at the bottom end of the island. "They'll love that and I'm sure we can organise some transport."

I had another good idea, which I outlined to Chris and Pike. "When we sail south, I suggest that we anchor in Bequia rather than Young Island. We then elect one yacht to do the fetching and carrying from St. Vincent daily," I said. "As we only have two days in St. Vincent and there are three boats, we can draw straws for which boat will do the ferrying."

Liz was delighted when I drew the longest straw, which meant that once in Bequia, we would not have to move from our anchorage until the following Thursday.

Val gave me a full kiss on the cheek as she got back into her dinghy.

"I think you're rather nice," she smiled at my obvious embarrassment.

Gerald was just going down the steps. "I think she's got something going for you," he said quietly and winked.

"Don't be bloody silly," I answered irritably. "I'm nearly twice her age."

"You know what they say," said Gerald. I didn't know and I didn't ask.

As Gerald was motoring away, he called back, "James, as I'm staying tonight, leave that bastard to me," he jerked his thumb in the direction of the dock, where the Hurricane Hole boat stayed when Peterkin wasn't beating up the bay.

For the moment, I'd other pressing things to deal with and I forgot about Gerald and his threat.

Val took her charges off; all guests accepted the change without debate, partly due to guilt and partly because of the engaging way she presented the plan. The insecticide bombs arrived just before lunch. Pike and Piggy had invited Liz and me to share their lunch. I set the bombs, closed the boat, so they'd have the maximum effect and motored over to their Gulf Star.

Pike resembled the fish after which he was nicknamed.

When he smiled, his teeth were in evidence right round his mouth and when he ate, he grabbed at the food, as though afraid someone might pull it away. The junk food they invariably consumed hadn't put an inch of extra flesh on his tall frame. Piggy, on the other hand, was quite fat, which was a shame, because she'd have been attractive if she were to lose just a little weight. She ate constantly and all the wrong things. They presented us with hamburgers and French fries, which I thoroughly enjoyed. Liz was much more conscious of a good diet, and I never saw French fries unless we ate out.

Liz put her foot down when Perky's brownies appeared. Obviously, her cooking was in demand throughout the fleet.

We had a lazy afternoon and I opened Silver Star and aired her cabins just before the guests returned. I was pleased to see the remains of several flies and one or two mosquitoes, but the deadly spider was never found.

From that time on, I was never truly comfortable on Silver Star, and I adopted the cautious attitude of looking in my berth at night and tipping my shoes upside down before I put my feet in them, much to the amusement of Liz.

Peterkin came back in to the bay at around 6 p.m. locked his inflatable to the dock and strutted off towards the hotel bar. Sometime later, I glanced across at Gerald's boat and saw him putting on his diving gear. I thought he might have lost something overboard and was going down to look for it.

We sailed early the next day, which was Tuesday, to Bequia. The weather was perfect, and the oldies just loved it.

Despite the nonsense over the insects, which everyone had

229

now forgotten, Liz and I were getting to appreciate our guests' good humour. Liz said she was a little worried about Bill though, as he seemed unwell.

"Perhaps it's all the girls we've got on board," I suggested laughingly and thought no more about it.

They all loved Bequia and had the trip to St. Vincent not been pre-arranged, they'd have been happy to give it a miss. Pike and Piggy had lost the draw, so their yacht moved off with all the charterers on board while the rest of us relaxed for the remainder of the day.

Liz reckoned that she needed until midday to recover from the daily palaver over breakfast.

The guests were still active at night, and all night, but she had become more used to their nocturnal activities, and it didn't disturb her in the same way it had done in Marigot.

On Thursday, there was a change of plan. One or two of the group had heard that English royalty had houses on Mustique, so they decided that seeing Mustique might be more interesting than peering at tropical flora. I arranged over the telephone for them to have the Royal Tour that the Mustique Company was always glad to do. The plan, therefore, was to sail to Mustique on Thursday morning, have lunch there, and go on down to the Cays in the afternoon.

Although they got over to Mustique in good time, the tour took considerably longer than anticipated and the group didn't return to the boat until 4 p.m. Another change of plan was therefore, agreed. None of the crews were particularly comfortable about sailing to the Cays and arriving after dark, so the group decided to stay the night in Mustique.

Basil's Bar had its weekly Bar-B-Q that night and they all decided to have an evening out. The crews were invited to join them. It was always nice to be able to eat out once during a charter and when we were asked to join in, it was very much appreciated by all concerned. There was music afterwards, and we all had great fun. We got back to the respective boats well after 11 pm. Liz made a last coffee, when Bill was violently sick over the side. We all assumed that he had eaten something that didn't agree with him, or perhaps drunk too much.

I had put two anchors down this time and was glad I had,

as it became very turbulent indeed during the night. The next morning the guests were all thrilled to see some particularly interesting birds in large numbers, and the deck of Silver Star was liberally sprinkled with bird droppings before we sailed.

Liz commented on the difference in attitude between Francesca and the current bunch.

Val came over just after 9 a.m. and had a discussion with the group on Silver Star, and yet another new plan was formulated. They'd heard good stories about Tobago Cays and were particularly keen to have plenty of time to see the reef. I was asked if I could sail down there to arrive by lunch time, and then spend the whole of the following day, Saturday, on the Cays. I was told that I could drop the guests off at St. Vincent Airport on Sunday morning and they could fly from there to Martinique. After consultation with the rest of the crews, I offered to make all the necessary arrangements, which Val said she appreciated. I radioed Sunshine and obtained permission to extend the charter for one day, then contacted Air Mustique, who arranged the flights.

By 10.30 a.m. we were all on our way to Tobago Cays. Then, the second disaster struck.

Silver Star was about half an hour out of Mustique when Bill started to develop chest pains. These got steadily worse, to the extent that he was banging his head against a winch to try and knock himself unconscious, the pain was so severe.

Liz was a tower of strength despite never having done any nursing or even first aid. She was constantly with him, massaging his back and chest, which seemed to help.

I immediately radioed the other crews and told them to carry on while I turned Silver Star back to Mustique. When I'd set the sails for the return, I handed the wheel to Molly and went to radio the Mustique Company.

Fortunately, there was an excellent expatriate doctor on the island, and I was able to talk to him.

He came to the same conclusion as me, that Bill was having a heart attack. I told the doctor that we would be anchoring in about twenty minutes, and he promised to meet us in a boat, which he did. We had a bit of a problem getting him on board, because he'd an eye condition that made it

231

difficult for him to climb steps, but we managed. Bill received an injection and with the help of others from Mustique, he was borne away on a stretcher. By that evening, he was in intensive care in Barbados and in a New York hospital the next day.

We all decided, when Bill had gone, that there was nothing else we could do, so Liz made sandwiches and we headed once again straight to the Cays. Bill's illness had dulled the day somewhat, and everyone was quiet. Probably, as most of them were about his age, they were perhaps contemplating their own future.

On the way south, I radioed Sunshine and asked them to contact Bill's relatives in the States.

We arrived in time for everyone to spend an hour on the reef, and great enthusiasm was generated for the next day.

Val came over to the boat in the evening and I introduced her and the others to a game that we had found popular when we were guests on The Atlantic Clipper. The idea was to get a deep tray or bowl and fill it with water.

Each participant had a little paper yacht, which they put on the imaginary start line. A liberal dash of shaving foam was added to the surface to represent islands in the sea, and everyone was told to get ready.

The idea was that all competitors had to blow their yacht across to a designated finish line at the other side of the tray. Obviously, the winner anticipated a prize. I went through the routine, "ready, steady," before I shouted go, I blew as hard as possible from the other end, and thoroughly doused everyone in shaving foam. The anticipation of the silly race and the shock at finding they'd been done always provided a great amount of merriment. This time it was no different and Val, who appeared to be doused more effectively than the others, chased me around the boat with the remaining can of shaving cream. She didn't catch me, but before giving up she said mischievously, "today, I can't get you, but sure as hell I'll get you tomorrow." We all had a good laugh and other games developed during the evening, until the initial sadness of the day was almost forgotten.

The next morning, after a particularly hearty breakfast, we took our charterers to the reef in two boatloads and stayed

232

with them until lunch time. The dinghy had a small anchor, which I used to secure it.

I spent some fifteen minutes ensuring everyone was safe, and then did some snorkelling amongst the coral, which was just below the surface. In fact, so high was some of it that one had to be careful not to get scratched. A scratch from coral, which is mildly poisonous, takes a long time to heal, so I'd warned every one of the dangers. Because the water is so shallow, there are many places where one could stand up so no one became overtired from swimming. I took two of them back to the boat for lunch and the other three swam back. After lunch we all had a bit of a siesta.

Later, I watched Pike's charterers playing a sort of water polo, and some of the guests from Silver Star, including me, joined in, using the side of our respective boats as goals. It was quite exhausting, and eventually individuals went off and did their own thing. I swam lazily back to the Silver Star and, face down, rested my elbows on the stern ladder, my legs floating backwards in the water. I must have dozed off because I woke suddenly when something jerked my body. For a split second I thought of Francesca's shark, but when I looked round, I saw Val some few feet away, with my swimming shorts in her hand. She was grinning.

I realised that I was now naked. Not wishing to draw Liz's attention, or indeed anyone else's, to the fact that I'd lost my shorts, I decided to play along with her for a bit, and then make a lunge and retrieve them. I knew that I was a strong and fast swimmer, so it shouldn't be too difficult, I thought.

"See you on Jamesby," Val yelled at me, holding the shorts up in the air like a bit of bait. I glanced up at the boat where two of the charter guests were sunbathing on the top deck. I knew I couldn't get onto Silver Star without being spotted and if the story got out, I reasoned to myself, I'd never hear the last of it.

I finally decided the best plan was to retrieve what was mine, so I turned to swim after Valerie. It took me a few minutes to realise that she too was a good swimmer, and she was keeping the distance between us constant.

As we came near Jamesby, which was behind the stern of Silver Star, I struck out in earnest to catch her before she could reach the island. I knew it was uninhabited, but I didn't particularly relish chasing her naked along the beach. I started to narrow the gap and, to create a better slipstream; I swam with my head below the water, powering myself along. After about a minute of this I knew I should be close to her. I took a quick look and was chagrined to find that she was already on the beach, her legs crossed and cheekily smiling, holding the swimming shorts aloft. I wasn't to know that Valerie had been an American swimming champion.

As I approached, I saw her run into the trees. I knew there was a beach on the other side, so I quickly left the water and dashed for cover, and I hoped to God that there was no one on any of the boats with binoculars trained on me. Once I'd reached the privacy of the foliage, I crept through to the other side of the island as quietly as I could. This took a little time, and when I reached a small clearing, I detected Valerie lying completely naked on her back. By being on the west of the island, we were completely hidden by the trees from where the yachts were anchored. Feeling a little safer I dropped on all fours and crept forward to see if she'd put my shorts nearby. I couldn't see them, so I bent down to see if she was sleeping on them. She really had a most attractive body, I thought. She was deeply bronzed all over and despite a bit of puppy fat, she had exquisitely rounded breasts. I suddenly felt ashamed to find myself looking at her nakedness that caused a stirring in my own body. At that precise moment she turned lazily onto her stomach. I froze and waited for her to settle again, and then I saw my shorts underneath her legs, I approached from the trees and walked stealthily into the clearing. I managed to get within a few yards of her, and I stopped to take stock of the situation. The islands overlooking the beach were Union and Palm, some eight miles away and I knew the reef prevented anyone from anchoring on western end. I decided to pounce when she abruptly looked up and straight at me. She was smiling a half shy smile, but very engaging. She stretched an arm towards me and raised herself with her other arm on to her elbow.

"Come and lie down beside me for a bit," she patted the ground. "It's gorgeous here, and I promise I won't bite."

She lied.

N
APPROX
QUARTER MILE

WRECK OF
ANTILLES

MUSTIQUE

AIRPORT

DANGEROUS
SHOAL

SILVER STAR

BASIL'S BAR

400
ft

PRINCESS
MARGARET'S
HOUSE

300
ft

APPROX AREA
WHEN PASSENGER
HAD HEART ATTACK

12 - THE GRASS AFFAIR

And How Laurie Nearly Lost It

The rest of the horticultural charter went smoothly, and the charter guests duly arrived at St. Vincent airport as planned on the following Sunday.

I stayed in Young Island overnight, and planned our trip to St. Maarten, where we were due to pick up our new charter guests on the following Saturday. I decided to spend one night on the Sunshine dock to re-stock with water and diesel and then sail directly to Fort de France in Martinique the next day and stay there on the Tuesday night and all Wednesday.

Martinique was a perfect place for provisioning. French cheeses were available and good wine was cheap. The plan for Thursday was to pamper ourselves and stop off at Iles des Saintes, just south of Guadeloupe. We'd then sail directly to Philipsburg, the capital of Dutch St. Maarten on the Friday, giving ourselves just enough time to do any last-minute cleaning and repairs on the Saturday before we picked up the guests in the afternoon.

We left Young Island just before 5 a.m. on Monday morning. It was an eleven-hour sail to Rodney Bay; the conditions were perfect, and we reached the dock just after 4 p.m. in the evening.

It was the tradition among charter boat crews, that the last ones in were always invited to dinner on another yacht.

This was not only nice for the exhausted cook who had just come off charter, but it allowed everyone to get up to date with all the news and gossip, of which there was usually plenty.

When I went up to the office the next morning to see if there was any mail, there was a courier packet from the U.S.A. which intrigued me. Thinking it was a communication from Joan Hargreaves the literary agent, I quickly ripped it open with a surge of anticipation. It contained a short note, which I read with mixed feelings. It wasn't from Joan at all, but from Bill Cummings, who had written from his New York hospital bed to say that because of the prompt attention he had received his heart attack was curtailed, and he was on the mend.

The next day, Tuesday, we set off later than planned for the short four-hour sail to Martinique. Both of us realised just how much more skilled we'd become since our first sail in the O'Day, and we thoroughly enjoyed the trip. I knew that we'd not reach Fort de France before nightfall.

It was too late to book in through customs and immigration, so Liz suggested that it would be more comfortable to overnight in a bay called Anse Mitan, a bay that is opposite the city of Fort de France anchorage, but in rather nicer surroundings. We reached Diamond Rock about 6 p.m. The trip from Diamond Rock to the opening to Fort de France Bay took us a further hour. As we passed the lush foliage of the southern end of the island on the east side, we watched the sinking sun in west, on the port side.

"A perfect end to a perfect day," said Liz. I agreed.

Once we reached Anse Mitan, it was quite dark and we could see a multitude of lights winking in the distance, which told us that we were looking at one of the largest and most advanced cities in the Caribbean. It took us until 8 p.m. to anchor just off a large, modern hotel in the bay and because there was no moon that night, we didn't notice the boats anchored around us. Liz prepared an early supper and after drinking too much wine, we collapsed into our respective berths well before 10 p.m.

The next morning, I rose at 6.30 and went straight into the water for an early morning swim. I returned to the boat, showered, and dressed and went to buy some freshly made French croissants from the shore. As I passed by the bow of the boat next to ours, I thought something looked familiar, but didn't take too much notice of it, particularly when I saw a very attractive young girl coming towards me in a similar dinghy to mine. She had a dog with her, and the wretched animal snarled at me as the boats passed each other, but the girl gave a beaming smile. The name on the dinghy was also familiar and I guessed it belonged to the boat I'd just passed.

It wasn't until I returned with chocolate croissants and French bread, that I recognised the boat I had passed going in to the shore.

As I approached Silver Star, I saw there was another boat's dinghy tied up alongside. It didn't take me long to realise that I was in for a morning's entertainment, at the very least.

Liz had risen just after me and had been doing her exercises on deck. She had just seen me disappear into the small complex by the hotel, when there was a yell from the boat next to Silver Star. She stopped what she was doing and looked across, just in time to see a rather shapely young thing being pushed over the side by a blond man with his arm in a sling. She immediately recognised Laurie. A few minutes later, Laurie appeared on deck again, this time with a mass of struggling white fur in his arms. This was also deposited into the sea shortly followed by two full carrier bags of what looked like clothes.

I handed the purchases up to Liz as I manoeuvred the dinghy around the stern of Silver Star. She raised her eyebrows and inclined her head towards the cockpit, where Laurie was sitting, mournfully holding a beer in his hand.

"I think he's had another shitty day in paradise, in fact he's had a bit of a rough time," Liz whispered.

I was shocked to see the state Laurie was in. He had a bandage round both ankles, another one on his right hand and his other arm was in plaster and held up in a sling.

His moustache was pointing downwards. To say he that looked totally pathetic would be an understatement.

"What on earth happened to you," I asked, as I sat down in the open cockpit and grabbed a coffee Liz had just made for me.

Liz brought up butter and jam from the galley. There was the hint of a smile on her face. She sat beside Laurie and offered to butter some bread for him. To my annoyance Laurie refused the bread and took both the chocolate croissants I'd bought for Liz and myself. "Do you guys really want to hear the story?" he asked gloomily, his mouth full of chocolate. We both nodded enthusiastically. If we'd said no, we knew we'd have heard it anyway.

"Well, it went like this," Laurie took another swig of beer from the bottle, and I shuddered at the mixture of chocolate croissant and beer together.

"I wuz down in Bequia an' I'd dropped some fuckin' weasels off at Young Island and Jesus, was I glad to see the end of them. And this young French doll comes up to my boat, askin' if I needed a cook. Well, as you know, I've bin getting all the shitty charters lately, 'cause I didn't have one."

"What about ...?" I was about to ask where his last cook had gone, but Liz stopped me with a frown.

"Oh, that bitch, well that's another story. Anyway, this girl looked real nice and she'd real great ti..." His bandaged hand tried to illustrate something large and round. He looked at Liz. "Er, she'd a real good figure."

"I noticed," she said.

239

"Yea, well, as I said, she looked a real nice girl," Laurie took another swig of beer and handed the empty bottle to Liz who opened a fresh one for him.

"I asked her to come aboard, and she did, and had a look around the boat. I don't mind tellin' you, I thought, this is the woman fer me. She was obviously well educated, a bit of class," he added, "I guessed she was well travelled, and her swim suit was real good quality, not like some of the bums I've had to put up with.

"She sat down in the cockpit, and I asked her if she could cook, and she asked had I ever come across a French woman who couldn't. Well, I hadn't come across too many French women, so of course I assumed from that she was okay in the galley.

"I asked her if she'd sailed much, and she said she was born in Le Halvar."

"Le Havre," I corrected him.

"Well, wherever, and her father owned a thirty-metre job, so I thought this one's perfect, and I took her on the spot."

"Didn't you ask her how she got to the Caribbean?" I asked.

Liz leaned forward to hear the answer.

Laurie looked a bit uncomfortable.

"Didn't think of it at the time, why should I?" He shrugged his shoulders and winced with pain, "I assumed she'd fallen out with a boyfriend or somethin'." I smiled. The Caribbean was full of young girls wanting free lifts on boats and quite prepared to give any story to get one. "Go on," I said.

"She said she'd to go back to the shore and get her things, and while she was gone, I radioed Sunshine to tell 'em I'd got a cook at last. John was pleased and said I could have a seven-day charter out of Martinique, which comes in today."

Liz looked alarmed. "But how on earth are you going to manage, with your arm in a sling?" she asked incredulously.

Laurie frowned. His moustache twitched. "I wuz hoping I

240

might find someone before 4 o-clock this afternoon. If I can't, I'm snookered," he looked at Liz.

"You're not avail...?"

"No, she's not," I cut in.

"In that case, the charterers' will jus' have to fuckin' manage with me giving 'em advice, they're only Italians anyways."

Liz took a deep breath and looked at me. I shook my head.

"We've to be in St. Maarten by Friday," I reminded her quickly. "So, I can't see how we could help."

She nodded and turned back to Laurie. "But surely, she couldn't have been so bad, wasn't it possible to keep her until the charter was over?" she asked sensibly.

Laurie shifted on his seat and clearly found it painful to move. I couldn't understand why his bottom should be painful, but I was shortly to find out.

"Well, as I was telling you, she came back to the boat with about three bloody large cases, and" he repeated for emphasis, "a bloody dog, a dog," he repeated. "What sort of dog?" I asked, "a bloody white poodle, a vicious little bastard."

"A miniature one, surely?"

"'Bout this high," Laurie bent down and with his free hand indicated the size of the animal from the deck.

"Oh, so it was a small one then," Liz said.

"Yea, I guess the little brute was quite small, but I told her that I couldn't take a dog on board, and she'd have to take it back." Laurie scowled as he remembered the incident.

"She said that was impossible, 'cause the fuckin' thing was in season, and she couldn't leave it. By that time all the cases were on board, and the boat that brought her had gone. I remembered I'd told John that I'd got a cook, so I told her she'd have to keep the dog in her cabin." Laurie leaned back and stared at the sky.

"She agreed, but as soon as she put it in there and closed

241

the door, the fuckin' thing started barkin' and scratchin', she wanted to let it out, but I said no, so she left it howlin' its fuckin' head off.

"It wuz about 10 in the morning by this time, so I said I thought it would be a good idea if we sailed for Martinique to arrive with a day to spare, which would give us time to provision the boat. I took up the anchor an' she handled the wheel, did it real well too," he added. "Once we were in the lee of St. Vincent, she asked me if she could unpack her stuff, and I said she could. I told her the cabin she could sleep in, that just happened to have a communicatin' door with mine," he grimaced. "I'd some great thoughts about the night to come an' when we reached Martinique, she seemed real friendly, and very grateful I'd let her fuckin' dog stay on board.

"I don't mind tellin' you guys, I was planning a small candlelight supper with some low music and plenty of cheap French wine, and, well. . ." Laurie stopped for a minute to savour his thoughts.

"What happened," Liz asked impatiently.

Laurie looked at her and frowned, "we were in the lee of St. Vincent, and I thought she was takin' a long time to unpack her gear. I was goin' to ask her what she'd been doin' all that time, but eventually, when she did arrive on deck she'd put on a very small bikini, and it sort of drove any other thoughts out of my head. Then she asked me if I minded her taking off her top. I said no of course I didn't, and the bitch did it straight in front of me, they jus' fell out like two huge melons." Laurie passed his bandaged hand across his forehead.

"She then went and sunbathed on deck, in full view. After a time, I suddenly realised that the breeze was picking up, and as I knew it shouldn't be doin' that, not in the lee anyhow. I tore my gaze away from her and found we'd been heading for fuckin' Venezuela. I got back on course, but the trip wasn't an easy one, I can tell you. I couldn't wait to reach Martinique."

"I assume you got there without incident?" Liz asked, laughing. "Oh yea, we arrived the night before last, 'bout midnight, and once we'd anchored, we found the fuckin' dog had scratched the hell out of the cabin door and shit all over the floor. I wasn't pleased, as you can imagine. I'd only recently re-varnished the interior and I was even less pleased when she said she couldn't clean the shit up, 'cause it made her feel sick. Jesus! So, I had to do it while she went up above for some air. I was just coming out of her cabin when I noticed the little bastard with its leg up against the cooker."

"I thought bitches weren't supposed to cock their legs up," I queried.

"Anyway, this one did, probably 'cause it wuz French, they're always fuckin' different. I rushed forward, to shove the nasty little bugger out of the way, with my foot. It was then the bastard savaged me."

He felt tenderly down to his ankle with his good hand and grimaced. "It then ran off up the steps and into the arms of the girl."

"Did this girl have a name?" I asked.

"Bloody right she did. I found all sorts of names for her, but the fuckin' broad was called Yvonne. I followed the dog up the steps, with its shit wrapped in a paper towel in one hand, and a bleedin' ankle. Just as I reached the top of the galley steps, the fuckin' thing leapt out of her arms and shot between my legs. I thought it was going for my fuckin' ankle, agin' so I lifted it off the step. There I was, with one hand holding the shit, one hand trying to protect my savaged ankle, and standing on one leg. The dog went straight for the fuckin' ankle it hadn't already savaged and then shot below into her cabin. I teetered on the edge fur a split second, and then followed it down, backwards, all eight steps on my fuckin' arse the shit spillin' out all over me. I knew I'd really hurt myself badly, and I found I couldn't use this arm." He held up the arm in a sling. "It was too late to go to the hospital, so I decided to go the next mornin'. Problem was, I was covered in dog shit and needed a shower. I eventually managed but I hurt my arm even more in the process, and I didn't get any sleep because of the pain.

"There was no way I could carry out any other function either," Laurie looked at us sorrowfully. "I just had to sit on my tail and wait for morning. Yvonne took me to the dock in the dinghy before 8 a.m. an' I got a taxi to the hospital. It took 'em all fuckin' mornin' to do the X-rays, and then half the afternoon to put the thing in plaster. I didn't get back to the boat until after 4 p.m. When I returned, I couldn't catch her attention from the shore, so eventually I got a lift in a small boat that was passing. By the time I got on board, I was well and truly pissed off, particularly when I saw Yvonne sunbathing on the deck again, and she hadn't even washed up the breakfast dishes. She saw I was bloody mad, so she got up and came down into the cockpit and seemed very apologetic. Well one thing led to another, she said she wuz sorry and wuz real attentive, and soon we were getting on famously, we drank nearly a bottle of wine that I'd brought back with me, and she told me that she'd spent a year doin' aroma therapy in France. She offered to give me a healin' massage in her cabin. She said that all I'd have to do was lie on my back, and she'd do the rest."

I noticed Laurie's eyes shining at the thought.

"As we went down to the main cabin, she helped me down the galley steps and when I was at the bottom, she came up real close," Laurie breathed heavily. "Remember, she wore nothing on the top and well, I guess I got a bit overheated, and my shorts couldn't contain what was in there."

Laurie shot Liz a sly glance and seemed upset when he saw she was unimpressed.

"She noticed and helped me get my trousers off, then she gently drew me towards her cabin opened the door and told me to go in first and lie down on the berth. I could feel her breasts pushing my back, and she was holding my hips with both her hands as she steered me where she wanted me to go. I could hear her breathing heavily, and I was getting really twitched up by now."

"Are you sure you want to tell us the rest?" Liz smiled.

"Yea, well, I'd forgotten the fuckin' dog, hadn't I? As I walked in to the cabin, the bloody thing flew for the only piece of my anatomy that was stickin' out." Laurie put his good hand down carefully towards the lower part of his anatomy, a grimace of pain on his face. "Have you ever seen a lacerated pen...?"

"Strangely, no," said Liz, with an intake of breath, "and, I've no interest in seeing one now," she said firmly.

"Well, I'd to get back to fuckin' hospital, and how do you tell a nurse that a fuckin' dog bit your crotch? They thought it was very funny particularly as the bloody thing had swollen to three times its normal size, and then would you believe it, they brought in all the fuckin' medical students to have a look. I asked them if they'd never seen one before, and they answered that they'd once had a guy who'd been bitten by his over enthusiastic mistress, but never one gnawed by a dog. They said I'd go down in their fuckin' record books. The girl students seemed to be very impressed though. The only advantage was that they dealt with me more quickly this time I suppose 'cause there were no X-rays needed. I was back on the boat by 8 in the evenin'. When I finally got back on board, Yvonne seemed a bit agitated and said she'd to go ashore. Before I could say anything to her, she'd taken the fuckin' dinghy and gone with her bloody vampire dog."

"You didn't try and stop her?" Liz asked.

"You're joking. I could hardly walk, I'd a lacerated 'er, thing, both ankles, and a fuckin' broken arm. What could I do, hold her back with my teeth?"

We both grinned at the thought, particularly as we that

knew Laurie's teeth were all false, another result of his Vietnam experience.

"When she'd gone, I'd a sudden thought. I went below to her cabin and opened the door. I half expected to see her stuff gone, but it was all there. She'd one case, which she'd unpacked in her cabin and the other cases were in the cupboard. The thing that surprised me was that two of the cases appeared to be empty. I knew the stuff in her cabin wouldn't fill three, but I'd carried them all below, and I knew they were all full when she came on board. I started to feel a bit uneasy, particularly when I remembered how long she'd taken to unpack, when we were in the lee of St. Vincent. I looked in drawers and other cupboards and found nothin.' I was about to give up, when some sixth bloody sense propelled me to the space underneath the galley berths, you know, where the water tanks are. I'd a feelin' I'd find grass there.

I nodded.

"I pulled up the first cushion and the wooden cover. There was nothin' to see, so I put my hand down underneath the water tank and felt something soft and when I drew it out, it looked like a transparent bag full of fuckin' flour, but it wasn't flour, I reckoned it was heroin. I felt some more and found another six when I heard this bangin' on the hull and a frog voice announcing itself.

"Marine Gendarmerie, monsieur," Laurie inhaled deeply.

"I felt like shittin' myself, I could just imagine the fuckin' conversation as I was being led away."

'So, you say monsieur that you'd a girl on the boat, but she's gone.'

"Yes.'

"You say her name was Yvonne, there are a lot of French girls with that name, Monsieur. Where does she live? I don't fuckin' know . . .' "You get the drift?" We did.

Laurie looked at me, his eyes mournful.

"So, what did you do?" I asked.

246

"I knew the little tart had probably seen the gendarmes checking other boats, which was why she was so eager to fuck off, and she knew I'd been left with the dope, and now my fuckin' fingerprints were all over it too. I'd a faint hope that they'd just come on board to ask some cursory questions and check documents, like they sometimes do, so I quickly stuffed the bags back, closed the lid and put the cushion back into place. By the time I'd done that, they were bangin' again, and I went up above, telling 'em I was injured and couldn't move quickly. That part was bloody true. It's fuckin' painful."

He looked down at his crotch.

"When I got up on deck, I knew that was the end, there were two of them in uniform, both French, with a bloody sniffer dog."

"Jesus," I said.

"Too right," said Laurie. "I knew I was in for ten years at the best, and I thought about how I'd gone to Vietnam to save the fuckin' frogs at Dien-Bien-Phu.

"Now they were going to clap me away in a Martinique jail for the rest of my fuckin' life."

I knew Laurie had been in Vietnam, but his memory of the Americans rushing to save the French didn't quite tie in with the historical facts, I didn't disabuse him.

The French were extremely harsh on drug smugglers and the penalties were severe, including the automatic confiscation of the boat and sometimes, life imprisonment.

"So, then what?" I asked, as Liz fetched him a third bottle of beer.

"They came on board with this fuckin' great animal, and within seconds the dog had dragged its handler down to the main cabin, which it ignored and from there it went straight into the cabin that Yvonne had slept in. I thought this was where the bitch had stored the rest of the stuff and when I saw the dog pawing the berth cushion, I assumed she'd stuffed it underneath, or even in the cushion itself.

"The Gendarmes took the cabin apart, literally. They spent about an hour in there, while I was up on top. I did think of makin' a run for it but swimmin' with a broken arm in plaster was the next best way to suicide. I wasn't quite ready for that yet, but I couldn't understand why they were taking so long, eventually I went down below and saw the dog still sniffin' the berth cushion.

"The cabin was in chaos, but it was obvious there was nothin' hidden there. The Gendarmes were very apologetic at the mess they'd made, and were rough with the dog, who still didn't want to leave Yvonne's cabin. One of the guys sat down in the main cabin, right on top of where the stuff was, and inspected the boat's papers, which of course were in order, and then they left. I gave them about half an hour, then searched the boat myself and found there were ten bags of the stuff under the water tank.

"It took me over three hours to empty it all down the head. I got the empty bags, put them all in one large carrier bag, added some fishing weights, and threw the fuckin' lot over the stern.

"I was bloody exhausted after that, so I turned in, and didn't wake until this morning, when I heard someone climbing on board. I knew who it was from the footsteps, and I got out on deck just as she was tying up the dinghy.

"I told her what I'd done with her stuff, and she became hysterical. I then told her to get off my boat, and she dropped her dog, which rushed back down to the cabin. She went to the side of the boat and started shoutin' that I was trying to rape her. I gave her a shove, and in she went. I then went down to the cabin eventually cornering the bloody dog. I got this for my pains." Laurie held up his bandaged hand. "I eventually got it by its fuckin' collar, whipped it up on deck and threw it in after her. Thinking about it now, I wish I'd tied some fuckin' weights round the little bastard before throwin'

248

it in."

"I don't think you should have done that," Liz said.

"Yea, you're probably right. Anyhow, I reckon that gave me more pleasure than anythin' I've done for a long time. The bloody woman then shouted from the water that she'd no clothes, so I went back down to the cabin and stuffed all the gear she'd unpacked into two plastic shopping bags and went up and threw those over too. I told her that I'd take her cases to the police station, which I will, later this morning."

"But the one thing that puzzles me," said Liz, "is why didn't the sniffer dog find the stuff."

"Yea, I thought about that too," said Laurie, "an' I realised the reason when I saw the animal on the berth cushion, which is where the bloody poodle used to sleep at the girl's feet."

"So, you're saying the smell of the poodle was stronger than. . ." Liz twigged. "Of course, the poodle was in season," Laurie nodded. "Thank God it was, otherwise. . ." He made a cutting sign across his throat with his bandaged hand.

13 - THE GERMANS

And Liz Tossed a Coin

Liz knew Laurie would have some difficulty in preparing food, so in case he didn't get a cook straight away, which was highly unlikely in the circumstances, she prepared a large bowl of bolognaise sauce. Laurie could simply heat it up and add spaghetti. Our Italians had left a substantial amount of their own special spaghetti on board Silver Star, and she gave it to Laurie, with instructions on how to cook it.

"At least Laurie's Italians will appreciate their first meal," said Liz afterwards.

"That's probably all they'll appreciate," I answered.

We were just preparing to leave Martinique when John Peachcombe contacted us by radio.

He told us that the charter we were to pick up in St. Maarten had been postponed for two weeks and he wanted us to come straight back to St. Lucia, to change boats.

I was alarmed, "change boats?"

Liz overheard this and came up to my side. The last thing she wanted was to clean yet another boat.

The speaker on the radio crackled.

"Yes, I want you and Liz to take over Chardonnay." I knew that Chardonnay was another '60, but much better equipped than Silver Star.

MARTINIQUE

ANSE MITAN

N

FERRY TO
FORT DE FRANCE

HOTEL

GERMANS ARRIVED HERE

LAURIE WENT AGROUND HERE

COOK AND DOG   SILVER STAR
DROWN OVERBOARD HERE

"But what about Budgie and Geoff," I knew they were next in line for one of the larger yachts.

There was a brief silence at the other end.

"They've, 'er gone," answered John hesitantly.

"Gone, what, for good?" asked Liz into the microphone. "It was only a few days ago that they were going to sign on for another year."

"Yes, well. I'll tell you the sorry story when you get back, but I need you to take over the yacht tonight as Silver Star is being withdrawn by the owner; he wants it to go back to the American Virgins to be sold. Apparently, he's lost a packet on the stock exchange and needs the cash before the creditors grab it."

John continued, "I've heard from Laurie about his problem and so I'm going to get him to bring his charter guests down and then transfer them to you."

"Oh, yuppy do," said Liz, who knew that after a day with Laurie, particularly in his present condition, the charterers wouldn't be in the best frame of mind.

"At least we can provision in Martinique, so we won't have to do that in St. Lucia," I told Liz, when I'd finished talking to John.

I called up Laurie and told him what was happening.

He sounded relieved. I told Liz that I thought it would have been better to take the charter guests on board straight away, rather than have Laurie sail them down to St. Lucia, but Liz quickly disabused me of that idea.

"What and move boat with a load of guests on board. Are you mad?"

After we checked in and out in Fort de France, we spent an hour at Monoprix, the large supermarket there and sailed straight back to St Lucia. Knowing that Laurie's charter guests were not arriving in Martinique until 4 p.m., and this meant that by the time Laurie reached St. Lucia, it would be late evening. John had explained that he intended to give the charter guests dinner ashore and put them up in a hotel for the night at the company's expense. He felt that the move onto a more luxurious yacht plus an extra day gratis would compensate them for their trouble.

We sailed Silver Star into Rodney Bay for the last time, and we felt sad at leaving her. I mused on how one could get quite attached to a boat; Silver Star had served us well despite all the problems with the main.

Chardonnay was berthed at the end of the dock and looked huge against the other yachts berthed nearby. We sailed round her and docked further down on one of the fingers.

Once we were securely tied up, Liz started to pack; I went up to see John, at the same time picking up some mail and stuffing it into my pocket, not having time to see who it was from.

John beckoned me into his office. He looked grim, "Sorry about the sudden change."

"What happened?" I asked.

John sat down behind his desk and ushered me into a chair opposite.

"Well, you'll remember that Geoff and Budgie had some Italian charterers recently and for whatever reason, they didn't see eye to eye.

"That mad Budgie decided to play a joke on them; she carved two wooden guns, covered them in cooking foil and then apparently sneaked them into the Italians luggage after they'd packed.

"Budgie said she thought they would be going straight back to Italy, where perhaps such matters could have been explained away more easily, if indeed the fake weapons had ever been found. Unfortunately for her and Geoff, they flew to Italy via the USA. There was a terrorist scare on at that time, and the USA immigration didn't take kindly to the items showing up on their x-ray machines. Apparently, the Italians were arrested and spent a most difficult eight hours trying to explain that someone had played a joke on them. When they were released, it didn't take them long to guess who the culprits were, they lodged an official complaint with Sunshine's head office."

I then remembered that I'd seen Budgie carving one of the guns in Salt Whistle Bay in Mayreau, and I couldn't help smiling to myself at the result.

"They were due to take over Chardonnay when Dan and Barbara left," John continued. "Barbara is pregnant and there are complications, so she'd to fly back to the USA a few days ago, and she won't be returning. You guys were the obvious replacements. I had a chat with head office, and they talked to the American oil-man who was to be your next charter. He said he preferred the better yacht anyway, and it would suit him to come down a couple of weeks later."

"So, it all fits into place nicely," I said, "but what about the Italians?"

"Italians?" John Peachcombe looked puzzled.

"Yes, the charter guests coming down on Laurie's yacht."

253

John smiled. "I think Laurie must have misread the charter. They're not Italians, they are Germans."

"Germans?"

"Yes, a family originally from Dresden, I believe," John reached over for a file lying on a small table near his desk. He shook the dust off it and opened it. "Yes, here we are, Herr Heinz Steiner. He's an architect by the way. His wife is called Matilda, their young son Willie, is fifteen and their daughter, Helga, she's nineteen," John looked up.

"Why did they want to get on at Martinique," I asked.

"I expect it's because they've flown from Argentina where they now live and assume that flights from Buenos Aires to this part of the world are restricted." It may be because of the problems hotting up between Argentina and the UK." he shrugged.

I left the office and went back down to the dock and stopped off to tell Liz that we were taking on Germans, not Italians. We both went down the dock to where Chardonnay was berthed. Although it was rated at sixty feet in length, it was in fact 2 feet longer than Silver Star.

We'd been inside Chardonnay but had never had a good look around. We stopped just short of the vessel and took stock of the external view. She was much the same externally as Silver Star but had a very much better dinghy that was slung up on davits behind the ketch sail mast.

I noticed the outboard was much larger and as a result was clamped semi permanently on to the dinghy. The main difference was the that main mast was a fold up type rather than a furling system, for which I was pleased after the trouble I'd with Silver Star.

Standing on the dock, we weren't high enough to see the deck without imitating a giraffe, and it was necessary to use a small step ladder to get onto the yacht, we used the one standing on the dock. I noticed that it could be folded up and stowed on board after being pulled up from the dock by a line attached to them. Chardonnay was a ketch, like Silver Star, which meant that it had two masts, the main mast, and the aft mast. There was a larger and thus more powerful electric windlass to pull up the anchor, which pleased Liz, and I noticed when I climbed on board that the instrument panel had many more gadgets.

I also noticed that most of the other equipment on deck was similar. There were the usual winches, most of those on Chardonnay being self-tailing, but all the fittings were made of stainless steel, which would make it easier to keep them clean.

The big difference in the cockpit area was that it was more luxurious, and the front screen and cockpit cover were much larger and gave almost complete protection from rough seas. The binnacle was in the aft centre of the cockpit, with a huge wheel, and instruments that were duplicated down below.

Wide galley steps in the centre of the forward part of the cockpit, had a rail running down both sides. I went down the steps, followed closely by Liz. All the woodwork was a dark rich mahogany. The main cabin was very spacious, and I no longer felt we were on a boat, it was more like a small apartment. On the right was a built-in desk, with the radios and all the electrical fuses. There were about a dozen different dials, recording everything from water temperature to the amount of water in the bilges. Inside the desk was a full set of waterproof charts for the whole of the Caribbean basin.

In the main cabin on the starboard side, was a plush seating area with a fixed coffee table and seats around it. A sofa covered in a rich cream-coloured fabric gave a startling contrast to the woodwork. On the left was a large dining table with seating enough for ten people.

Liz had gone straight to the galley, which was on the port side of the boat, opposite the desk and navigation area. There were cupboards galore, with fittings that provided stowage for the pots and pans, which meant she was able to put everything away in their proper places before sailing. In fact, there was every conceivable piece of modern equipment, including a food processor, a large freezer, a separate drink cooler, a liquidizer, a large refrigerator, a waste disposal unit even a waste compactor.

I thought Liz was going slightly delirious as she discovered gadget after gadget designed to make her life easier. The galley was partly shut off from the main cabin by a centre screen, which pleased her, because she hadn't enjoyed charter guests looking over her while she was cooking. She felt that she wasn't at her best with sweat dripping off the end of her nose.

Having thoroughly explored the main cabin and galley, we investigated the other cabins. The aft cabin was enormous and took up the about two thirds of the area aft of the cockpit. There was the king-sized bed, a walk-in closet and a bathroom with a bathtub and a shower. Forward of the main cabin were two smaller double cabins, but both had their own showers and lavatory and, although not as large as the aft cabin, they were, nonetheless, luxurious. There remained one more cabin to investigate, the crew's cabin situated behind the navigation area on the starboard side. It was only slightly bigger than the one on Silver Star, but it had a much larger shower and lavatory area, and there were plenty of cupboards. I knew that we'd only have to use this cabin in the unlikely event of there being three couples on board. An internal door from the crew's cabin opened into the engine room, which was directly beneath the fore end of the cockpit.

I was amazed at the size of the engine, which also ran the air-conditioning and the generator, it was clearly a very powerful unit, and was spotless, with chrome parts and pipes gleaming from the top of the cylinder head. It was like a brand-new piece of apparatus on a show stand, there wasn't a scrap of oil or dirt anywhere. I called Liz and showed her the extraordinary sight.

"Huh," she said. "Obviously, the skipper was more particular than the cook." She was right; the engine was by far the cleanest part of the boat.

The dock staff had cleaned the external part of Chardonnay, so while I moved all our personal gear from Silver Star, including all the saved-up provisions; a surprising amount including wines and spirits, Liz got down to cleaning below, muttering about youngsters not been able to clean properly.

One thing she was pleased about, which she remarked on afterwards, was the absence of cockroaches on board. At least, none had shown themselves thus far.

It was just getting dark when we finished, and Liz was at last satisfied with the cleanliness of the interior. She'd spent over an hour on the oven alone, so she was glad to have a long shower. We changed into clean clothes and went up into the cockpit. I opened a cold bottle of white sparkling wine and poured Liz a glass, while she was relaxing in the soft breeze flowing through the cockpit. Just as I sat down with my drink, I noticed a yacht approaching the dock. It was Laurie and his charter guests.

Liz looked up.

"Oh my God, just look at their faces, James."

I'd already seen them; it wasn't a happy party.

Laurie didn't wave as he passed by.

"Thank God, they're staying on shore tonight," said Liz in relief. "I just wouldn't have had the strength to deal with them tonight."

I climbed over the side of Chardonnay, dropped onto the dock, and walked to where I knew Laurie would be berthing; I waited for the yacht to turn in to the slot prepared for him and for someone to throw me a line.

Shortly the Gulf Star turned in towards the dock, I saw Laurie standing on the bow, with a line in his hand. He looked a complete wreck. His hair was still matted and sweaty, his T-shirt still dirty as per usual, his white shorts now had something red and sticky (it turned out to be bolognaise sauce) spilled down them and the bandage on his left hand was flapping in the wind. The moustache, ever the barometer of Laurie's current feelings, was hanging down.

I frowned. One of the charter guests must be at the wheel, that was unusual, but the boat was going far too fast, and it was heading straight for me.

"Cut THE ENGINE. CUT THE," my shout fell on completely deaf ears. Laurie heard, of course, but he was on the bow of the boat, and in his present state he was in no condition to move quickly. The last thing I saw was the almost comical expression on Laurie's face as he realised what was about to happen. I threw myself sideways just as the speeding yacht hit the dock at ten knots.

CRAAAaaassh, there was a noise of splintering wood and fibre glass as the boat heaved itself up, like some huge animal trying to draw itself on to land. I thought for a minute that Laurie would somersault over the top of the bow and onto the dock, but by some superhuman effort, he managed to grab the forestay with his one bandaged hand and stay on deck.

Fortunately, the yacht had hit a floating dock, so although a considerable amount of damage was done to the dock itself, the boat wasn't seriously damaged. John Peachcombe had heard the noise and came running down from the office. As always happens in accidents with boats, people just appeared from nowhere to gawp at the spectacle. John elbowed his way through the throng; his first concern was that no one was hurt. It transpired that, surprisingly, only Helga, the daughter of Heinz Schiller, had banged her shapely ankle, but everyone else was okay. Laurie unwound his body from the foresail; he'd a murderous look in his eyes.

I hastily proposed to John that I take Laurie back to Chardonnay, while he saw to the charter guests. John hesitated only for a moment and then agreed. He knew he had to get the now doubly unhappy clients off the boat and into their hotel as quickly as possible. At that moment, Heinz Steiner appeared on deck, looking rather like Hitler immediately after the attempt on his life. I swiftly steered Laurie away. John called after us that he'd want to see Laurie once he'd got the Germans settled.

Laurie slumped down in the Chardonnay cockpit, and Liz went to fetch him a six-pack of beer. She obviously thought this story would be worth it, but, from experience, she also knew that he would almost certainly drink that amount anyway, so it saved her from continually getting up. She had seen the accident from a better vantage point than anyone else, as she was standing in the Chardonnay cockpit, so she was higher than any other spectator. She told me that a rather pot-bellied, older man had been at the helm, and he'd obviously slammed the engine into forward instead of reverse. When the boat hadn't slowed down, the man, thinking the engine wasn't powerful enough, had compounded the problem by putting the accelerator lever at full power.

I turned to Laurie, "so, what happened," I asked.

Laurie finished his beer and opened the second can. He looked particularly mournful.

"Jesus, with the luck I have, I'm surprised I'm still alive."

"Perhaps that's part of your bad luck." answered Liz philosophically.

Laurie looked at her in surprise, took another swig of beer and then started his story.

"You remember when you left, it was just after midday, so I put the spaghetti sauce in the oven. I thought it best to cook the spaghetti as well, so it was all good and mixed, ready fer 'em when they came on board."

Liz grimaced. "You're not supposed to cook the spaghetti until it's ready to be eaten," she upbraided him. "That's why I left it uncooked."

"Yeah well, I'm not fuckin' Italian, am I? How am I to know such things? An' how was I to know that the stuff would all glue together if it was cooked too early? Anyway, I did it and sort of mixed it up in the big bowl you loaned me. I then did the best I could in cleanin' the boat down below, but the gendarmes had left such a mess, that it was impossible. I didn't worry too much 'cause I knew they weren't sleeping on board. When I'd finished it was after 1 p.m. so I thought I'd better get the dinghy ready to go across and pick 'em up from the dock at 4 p.m., which was the time John had given me.

"Trouble was, the engine wasn't on the dinghy, an' I was in no fit state to put it on," Laurie held up his arm in a sling.

"So, what did you do?" asked Liz.

"I realised I'd a problem, 'cause I couldn't row either, so I decided to take the Gulf Star in as far as possible, an' hope I could get near enough for 'em to get on board. Well, I waited until they appeared on the dinghy dock, wavin' and shoutin,' an' then I took the boat in, but the fucker stuck in the mud just ten yards from the jetty. I yelled to 'em and established they were the right people, an' suggested that the only way they'd get on board was to wade out to me and climb on board via the aft ladder."

"You're not serious, Laurie?" Liz asked incredulously. "You mean you asked charter guests who had just arrived from South America, probably in their good clothes, to wade out in five feet of water?"

"With their luggage?" I added, I couldn't believe my ears either.

Laurie finished his second beer and opened a third.

"It wuz only four foot of water he corrected us. Yeah well, I wuz stressed an' couldn't think of a better way, in any case, what would you've done?"

He looked at us defensively.

Liz and I simply looked at each other.

Liz drew a deep breath, remembering that these were the people who were going on charter with us the next day.

"There you see," said Laurie triumphantly when we didn't answer. "Anyway, the guy shouted that they weren't prepared to jump in the water, and would I take the dinghy over. I told 'em I couldn't, as I'd had an accident, and lifted up my arm in this sling here."

They got into a huddle on the dock and the guy called out that his son, Willie would go to the local hotel and change into his swimmin' costume an' swim out to get the dinghy.

"Well, that was quite sensible of him," said Liz, as she envisaged the Steiner family, wading through the sea to the yacht, with luggage held high above their heads like porters on a safari.

Laurie brightened up. "Yeah, I thought so too, till the fuckin' son swam up to the boat."

"Then what happened?" I asked.

"I told him to climb into the dinghy, an' I'd pass the oars down to him. Well, he did, but as I passed him the oars, he slipped an' they went into the water. As you know, there's quite a current at Anse Mitan, particularly when there's a strong easterly, as there was this afternoon."

I nodded.

"By the time Willie had picked himself up, the oars were long gone, so I told him that he was a fuckin' arse'ole, an' he better swim after them. He told me he wasn't that strong a swimmer, an' if I wanted 'em, I could jump in myself."

"Fine," I said, "now how are you goin' to get everyone on board? Well, as you can imagine, Willie had no fuckin' idea, so I tied a long line to the bow of the Gulf-Star, an' I gave Willie the other end. I knew he was not strong enough to deal with puttin' the engine on the dinghy.

"I told him to tie it onto the dinghy painter an' then jus' doggy-paddle the dinghy back to the shore. Once he was there and everything loaded, I said I'd winch 'em back to the boat.

He asked me what a doggy paddle was, so I said, 'you've no oars, have you?' He shook his head. 'Well, how the fuck will you'll get across to the jetty?' I asked him. 'Blow your way across?' I told him that he should lower himself over the front of the dinghy, paddle with both hands and not lift his head when he got to the jetty.

'Why not lift my head?' he asked.

'Because you'll hit it on the dock and knock some fuckin' sense into your goddamned Italian head'."

"They're not Ital. . . ." Liz protested, but Laurie didn't let her finish.

"Yeah, I know that now. Fuckin' Krauts, but at that time, I thought they were Italians. Willie said something to me in German, which from my time in the US Army there, I knew wasn't polite, so I jerked the line, an' he fell into the bottom of the dinghy. That's how to deal with fuckin' Krauts, show 'em who is boss."

"You got them on board?" asked Liz, tiring of the story.

"Yeah, eventually, but they weren't happy. I told 'em that I was taking 'em straight down to Sunshine in St Lucia, an' that they'd be transferring onto another boat. The mother asked if they'd have to wade through a river to reach it. I asked her how she knew, but I said the alligators were a real friendly bunch, so she should make it without losin' a leg.

"She didn't even smile, typical fuckin' Krauts no sense of humour."

Liz closed her eyes.

"I thought that if I gave 'em lunch, they'd settle down while I figured how to get us off the mud bank. I got 'em seated around the cockpit table and brought up the spaghetti, it looked a bit mushy," Liz closed her eyes again. "But it was edible. I guess, not being Italians, they weren't happy with the stuff, an' the woman complained that it was all stuck together, an' asked who had cooked it. I said you had," Laurie looked slyly at Liz.

"Oh thanks, Laurie, that's great," said Liz tiredly.

Laurie grinned at the recollection. "Well, I guess they were hungry, 'cause they'd soon all got their snouts into their bowls, which was perhaps unfortunate."

"Oh why?" asked Liz.

"'Cause I reckoned the only way to get the boat off the mud bank was to go into full reverse."

"So," I said puzzled.

"It worked a treat. In fact, it worked so well, that the boat sort of rocketed off the mud, sudden like, leaving spaghetti all over the Germans. Willie's went down the inside of his T-shirt and Matilda, that's the mother, had a spaghetti cleavage. I offered to clean her up, but she said she could manage. Heinz got the stuff all over his trousers, an' Helga, who'd bin bending over the basin at the time well, she looked up with a spaghetti face," Laurie grinned. "They were real cross," he added. "An' they swore at me in German, not knowing I'd bin there before Vietnam an' was able to swear back at 'em. I remembered a few words they hadn't thought of an' Matilda placed her hands over Helga's ears, an' got spaghetti all over them too."

Liz groaned remembering the situation when Laurie was sailing charter guests from the Tobago Cays, the difference being that she had now to cope with these unhappy people for another seven days.

Laurie opened another beer can. "Then the fuckin' son threw the dish at me, an' I got it all over my shorts," Laurie looked down at himself. "Bear in mind these are the fucker's that I used to defend agin' the Russians and I put my life on the line fer them," Laurie looked hurt.

"These Germans were originally from Dresden," I said.

Laurie looked at me blankly.

"Dresden was in East Germany, it was under Russian control,"

Laurie shrugged; the information being lost on him.

Liz interrupted, "Dare we ask what happened then?" she asked.

"Well, they went below to shower but I'd forgotten, with all the trouble, that I was low on water. They ran out just washing Helga's hair. They had to come on deck and lift sea water up in buckets to complete the job. You'd think it was the end of the fuckin' world, the way they went on.

"After changing their clothes, they all came up in the cockpit an' sat around lookin' miserable. I couldn't get the sails up on my own, so I asked Matilda to get the sheet up."

'What?' she said.

"I said, 'let's get the main sheet up, otherwise we'll be in Martinique all fuckin' day.'

"She looked at Heinz, an' he shrugged his shoulders, so she went below and came back up with a fuckin' bed sheet, stupid bitch. I told her I was talking about the mainsail, not bed sheets, an' if she didn't know about sailing, what was she doin' on a yacht anyway. Eventually I had to help and gave Heinz the wheel. We got the sails up and they went back to looking miserable and stayed that way right across the channel. When I went to take over from Heinz just before entering Rodney Bay, he said he'd sailed a yacht before and preferred to handle her himself, he said they'd a better chance of arriving alive that way. I knew it would've bin difficult fer me to take her in, so I showed him the engine controls, and got Willie and Helga to bring in the sails. That Helga is quite a dish. You should have quite a..." Laurie was addressing his remarks to me. Then suddenly remembered Liz was listening. "Er, quite a... Well. I was watching her stretch to bring in the sails, an' I reckon she could be a good performer."

Laurie looked at Liz, whose response was frosty.

"I mean, at sailing, of course," he added untruthfully.

"So, if Heinz could use the controls, why the accident?" I asked.

Laurie shrugged his shoulders. "Guess he panicked, 'cause when I was on the bow, waitin' to throw you the line, he called to me and asked how he could get reverse. Well, I turned around to face him and told him to use the left lever. I was talking about my left, wasn't I? Fuckin' idiot took it to mean his left, yer can't help some people, can you."

"No, you certainly can't," interjected Liz, with some feeling. "So, let's sum up. What we've got now are four extremely unhappy Germans who are coming on this boat tomorrow morning. They think my cooking is putrid, and probably have traces of their dinner still on their clothes, if not their bodies, and we've to persuade them that Sunshine isn't a Mickey Mouse outfit and send them off happy within seven days. Thank you very much Laurie."

Laurie shifted uncomfortably. "Yeah, well, I knew ye liked a challenge," he ducked as Liz threw a plastic cup at him.

263

"Guess it's time I went," he said ruefully.

"It might be best," I grinned, "don't worry, we'll manage somehow."

John came onto Chardonnay later and told us that he'd just spent two hours placating the Germans. He thought he had managed at last but warned that their anger was such that it could take a couple of days to settle them down.

"I partially placated them by agreeing for you to take them straight to the Cays tomorrow to arrive by the following morning."

"But that means us doing a night sail," wailed Liz.

John nodded.

"Well, a night sail is one thing, but doing dinner under sail is quite another. We'll take them on tomorrow but stop off in Soufriere for dinner, then we can take them to the Cays to arrive early the following morning," Liz stood with her hands on her hips.

John opened his mouth to argue but thought better of it.

"Yeah, I'm sure that'll be fine," he said smoothly, "I know you guys will sort out the mess." As he got up to leave, he smiled. "I know you like a challenge, Liz."

Fortunately, he didn't stay around to hear Liz's retort.

After John had gone, I thought I'd try to relax Liz a little, and poured her another glass of wine. As I was handing it to her, I remembered that I still had the unopened mail stuffed into my pocket. I sat down and pulled two envelopes out and a hand-written message. The message was a telephone message from Anne in Union, saying that as we were going north (obviously she didn't know the change in plans), she would put Robert on the plane in Union to fly him to St Lucia where he could use his return ticket to get back to his boarding school in the UK. She told us not to worry, she'd organize everything. The first envelope was from Madge from the horticultural charter. She wrote that after she got home, she contacted an expert and gave a description of the spider that had been 'lost' out of the box. It was confirmed that it was not a Black Widow but more likely (and she mentioned a long Latin name) a trapdoor spider, which was completely harmless, unless you happened to be a fly of course. Liz remarked that it would have been nice to know that while they'd been on Silver Star.

The second letter was from New York, and I opened it with some trepidation, as I'd recognised the handwriting of Joan Hargreaves. She wrote that she'd at last tracked down Monica Puesett, the wife of the publisher. She was now in California where she was working for a computer publishing company.

Obviously, Joan wrote, she is no longer interested in your novel. She went on to indicate that she'd no one else interested at that time but would keep trying. She finished up by saying that she would be asking for her expenses.

"Oh," said Liz bitterly, "now what do we do?"

"Do?" I asked.

"Yes, we came out here expressly to give you time and a place to write your novel and obtain a publisher. It's now obvious that it's not going to happen, at least not soon, so why don't we just go home?"

I had to accept her logic but wanted more time to think.

"Yes, we can do that, but that means we've to join the 'rat race' again, whereas we do have a job here that pays reasonably well, so we don't have to dip into our capital," I added, "we're now coming up to the low season, which means we'll have free use of Chardonnay to sail around the Caribbean."

"You call this a job?" said Liz, thinking of the Germans.

"It's better than nothing," I cautioned, "and if we go home now, we've to start all over again."

"Yes," answered Liz, "But you're still young enough to invest in something that doesn't have the strain of employing 6,000 people, and you're in a position to do what you want."

The discussion went on for over an hour, but it was obvious that we would not reach a conclusion, even if we talked all night.

"I know," I said suddenly, "let's toss for it."

"What, toss a coin?" asked Liz.

"Yes, heads we go back, tails we stay with Sunshine at least to the end of this year."

"All right," answered Liz, feeling that at last a final decision was imminent. "I'll get a British coin from my purse," she went down the galley steps, and reappeared holding a ten pence piece. I held out my hand, Liz snatched her hand away. "No, I'll toss it," she said grimly.

I shrugged. "Okay, make sure you spin it."

We watched as the coin went high in the air and then started its downward fall. Suddenly I realised that on this small piece of metal would depend our future. I began to have misgivings and wished I hadn't suggested the idea.

A gust of wind caught the side of the yacht at that very moment.

"Oh no," Liz froze. The coin hit the side rail, teetered there for a moment, and then landed in the water. We both rushed to the side and looked over as it sank slowly to the depths.

We eventually agreed that as the coin hit the water it meant that we should stay on the water, and we did so carrying out another forty odd charters before calling it a day.

The charter with the Steiner's was not a huge success, as it turned out that he was a proud ex SS officer in the German Reich. His views ran close to his Fuhrer who he considered had been unfairly judged. He argued strongly that there was no holocaust and that it had been invented by the Allies. Elizabeth quickly disabused him saying that we had a friend in Nigeria who was Polish, and she had been incarcerated in Auschwitz and she showed us the number tattooed on her arm. Her story was horrific of what went on in the camp.

He asked Liz if she was Jewish because she had almost black hair. I told him that she was a Celt. 'Vat ist Dat,' he frowned.

'I believe they originated two thousand years ago from an area east of northern France,' I said, 'an area that was subsequently infested by low life Barbarians, which is presumably why her ancestors left.' His scowl made my day.

It was not surprising that Laurie was sacked from Sunshine, but the pressure of business for the charter companies who had multiplied during the 12 months, meant there was a shortage of skippers. Most South African crews were returning home, so it meant that he was taken on by another company. We were to meet him many more times in the future and he always had stories of his disastrous life.

14 - THE PREPARATION

Disaster avoided - just

We had been chartering in the Caribbean for just over two years, and despite the difficulties of living on a boat, we had enjoyed the life. Things had been made easier for us because after only a short time with Sunshine Yacht Charters, our employers, had given us command of one of their top yachts. Because of the financial problems of the owner, we had had to change over to a new and slightly larger yacht, but now we were again faced with a situation where the owner needed to sell.

As a result, we sadly decided to bring our chartering experience to an end. The man who owned Chardonnay was a wine grower forced to sell, due to a bad season.

We were at our base in Saint Lucia when the news came through, and we were asked to sail her to Saint Thomas in the US Virgins and hand her over to the new owners.

A smaller yacht had been offered to us on our return, but Liz had refused. She said that she wanted to go back ashore. The main reason was, just before we learnt we were to lose Chardonnay, she was offered a job running a restaurant in Saint Lucia. The owner, and Australian woman called Bess Nesbitt, had decided to go, and visit her sick mother 'down under' and expected to be away for six months or more.

While considering the opportunity, Liz had asked Bess if she would consider selling the restaurant. After some thought, she said she would and after lengthy negotiations, Bess sold her half share in the business. A prominent Saint Lucian businessman, Archibald Cooperson, asked to remain a sleeping partner, with Liz retaining the other half.

For a while, I had considered staying on as a skipper and getting another hostess, but I realized it would not be the same without Liz, so I decided to give up as well, determining to make myself useful and help her set up an accounting system on the word processor I had originally bought for my writing. I reasoned that at least if I handled the accounts and administration for her, it would keep me busy...

We sailed to Martinique and did some shopping there, but regrettably we were restricted to the amount we could buy, because we would be returning from our northern trip by plane.

We sailed out of Fort de France harbour in Martinique the next evening just before 6 p.m. It had been a beautiful day, and now the sun was quickly dropping towards the western horizon, creating a wonderful cacophony of colours in the cirrus sky. The heavens were predominately red, and we remembered the old saying, 'Red Sky at Night, Sailors Delight'. Once out of the harbour we headed out to sea, maintaining a westerly direction until we were well clear of land. We then turned north to sail up the lee side of Martinique. Because we had chosen to sail two or three miles offshore, we picked up a good breeze from the east, and were soon clocking over seven knots. We had never attempted an all-night sail in Chardonnay before, and we were a little nervous as night sailing in the area could be quite hazardous. While Chardonnay was extremely well equipped for chartering among the islands, the navigational equipment on board was sparse. We had no radar, satellite location or other sophisticated gear, just a compass and a depth recorder.

The Leeward Islands were not renowned for sailors' aids at that time, and it was unusual for reefs and rocks to be marked, and if they were, it was rare for them to have lights or beacons. We were aware of most of the principle dangers of night sailing, the main one, is you cannot see unless there is a moon, and there was none on this night. It meant that if the navigation was amiss, you could easily hit land, or worse, stumble across a reef. One of our most experienced yacht captains had done just that only a couple of weeks before.

Justin Cockington had left Rodney Bay, in Saint Lucia. He steered out into the lee of the island heading south. The time was about 10 p.m. (*It gets dark around 6-30 to 7 p.m. all the year round*). Once on course, he knew there was no other land he could 'hit' before reaching Saint Vincent, the next island south. As this was forty miles away, it would take several hours of sailing to reach it. Feeling quite safe, he handed the wheel over to his girlfriend, Marjorie, and told her to keep a course of 206 degrees, which he knew would keep the yacht well away from land. This done, he went down below to get a shower. Marjorie, who happened to be reading a rather raunchy novel, set the wheel with a friction screw supplied for the purpose of locking it, turned on the cockpit light and laid back to enjoy the book.

Justin had taken about twenty minutes to shower and was just about to climb the galley steps to go on deck, when the yacht hit the rocks off Saint Lucia, they were lucky to get away with their lives, but they lost their jobs.

None of the Sunshine yachts had automatic steering, so if sailing, you had to be at the wheel all the time. The friction screw was no compensation for automatic steering gear. The skipper's girlfriend had compounded her problem by switching on a light to read, thus destroying her night vision. She told us afterwards, that she had not seen the danger until the yacht had hit land.

Conscious of this, Liz and I had prepared for our night sail rather more thoroughly, making hot coffee and putting it in a flask, along with the ever-useful peanut butter sandwiches, so that neither of us would have to go below after setting sail. We decided to work two-hour shifts, and to be available in case of problems, thus sleeping in the cockpit when not at the wheel.

Just before 8 p.m. we entered the channel between Martinique and Dominica, and although the waves there were heavier than in the lee of Martinique, and because we could not see, we were occasionally doused with sea water from the odd rogue wave.

There was some quite good foul weather gear on Chardonnay, the cockpit was covered with a canvas roof, the front a plexiglass screen, so the worst of the waves, or rain, could be avoided.

The waterproof apparel not only saved us from the occasional drenching, but surprisingly it can get quite cold sailing in the Caribbean once the sun has gone down, especially in squally weather. We had life jackets at the ready, and in the event of rough seas, we always put them on.

I took the first watch at 10 p.m., and by 11 p.m., I could just see the lights of Roseau the capitol of Dominica.

Dominica is a mountainous island, and in daylight it can be seen from quite a distance.

At midnight, Liz took over. We had some welcome coffee and sandwiches, and I took what I thought would be a light snooze. I must have slept soundly because I did not wake until well past my watch time and I berated Liz for not waking me. We passed the Isle des Saintes, that wonderful little group of islands below Guadeloupe. At about 2-30 a.m., I saw the lights of Guadeloupe on the starboard side, which confirmed we were on the right course. It was shortly afterwards that disaster nearly overcame us.

It was about 4.30 a.m. and because I had been late in taking my watch, I was still at the wheel. Liz, who was awake, had just poured me some more coffee.

We were somewhere off the northern end of Guadeloupe and could still see the lights from the shore, but we were far enough off the land to get the advantage of the wind. Suddenly I noticed the wind dropping. I knew it was not because we had sailed further towards the land, the shore lights confirmed that.

There is normally only one other reason for a sudden drop of wind in the Caribbean Sea, and that was a squall was about to hit us. A squall, as we remembered from our days sailing the O'Day in The Windward Islands, is a band of weather usually quite small, but always containing water and sometimes high winds. Since that experience, we always treated them with considerable respect.

We both felt the sudden rise in humidity as we quickly drained our coffee and swallowed the last bit of sandwich; of course, we could not see the squall, so we had no idea exactly from which direction it would hit us. We assumed it would come from the east, because that is the prevailing wind direction in both the Windward and the Leeward Islands. I felt quite confident, I had put in a double reef in the main to be sure of our safety, and we easily winched in some more jib

270

without having to change course, one of the beauties of roller furling gear. I decided it would be safer to have the engine on, so I started it up, and put it into gear at a slow ahead. In fact, when the squall hit us, there was not so much wind, more torrential rain, if we had been partially blind before, we were now completely so.

As often happens in the middle of a squall, the wind direction changed, and as a result, the sails started flapping, so I bore off to port by about thirty degrees and increased my engine speed to give us some stability. The rain was coming down in torrents now, and while the canvas hood gave protection in normal circumstances, it now started to leak like a sieve, and I felt cold water trickle down the back of my neck, despite the foul weather gear.

I am not sure whether it was a sixth sense that made me realise something was wrong, or whether I had caught a slight movement ahead. I swung the boat further to port and had control of the throttle lever, when out of the squall, a large yacht under sail came hurtling towards us. I slammed the throttle into maximum and twisted the wheel further to port as fast as I could.

As the boat passed us, I could plainly see the deck detail. It had no running lights, and the cockpit was completely empty, the wheel turning as though by some unseen hand. The story of the ghost yacht the Marie Celeste flashed through my mind.

It was under full sail, no engine, so apart from the swoosh of the waves as it slid by us, there was no other sound. I thought for a minute that the heeled over mast would foul our own, so near had the other yacht been to Chardonnay, but fortunately there was no contact. Within seconds it had disappeared as quickly as it had come. It was no ghost.

I realised that if I had not had the engine on at the time, we would have collided, and the combined speeds would have created a major disaster. If that had happened, we would have been much the worse off as the other boat, flying a French flag, was about eighty feet long. If the owner is reading this book, Vous êtes un salaud irresponsable stupide.

Shortly afterwards the squall left us as quickly as the offending yacht had done, and we managed to get back on course. Shaken by the experience, we were to learn from the other crews we spoke to later, that it was known for some skippers to set their automatic steering and go below for a nap. Such a practice was dangerous enough during the day, but at night... Running lights are of course mandatory under International law, but many sailors in the Caribbean simply did not use them. There was at least one documented case when a yacht was cut in two by a coastal tanker, although why no one was looking at the radar screen on the bigger ship at the time, is not known, maybe they were having a snooze too.

In the circumstances, I am not sure we would have had much more warning even if the transgressing yacht had shown running lights. It taught us a salutary lesson, and that was never to sail overnight unless it was necessary.

I felt distinctly uneasy for the next hour and both of us were glad to see the sun rising at about 5.30 a.m. By this time, we were in mid channel between Guadeloupe and Antigua. We aimed to pass Antigua to starboard, and I was glad it was light, because there is a very nasty reef off the southern end of that island, that I was intending to miss.

By 10 a.m., Antigua was well behind us as was Montserrat on the port side, and the hill of Nevis, part of St Kitts and Nevis, was plainly in view. We passed those islands to port and as we came a beam of the island of St Eustatius, we changed course to almost due north, planning to leave St Bart's to starboard and from there it was a short sail to St Maarten, which was to be our first stop.

There is a small rock just north of Montserrat called Rotunda, which one could anchor off on a fine day. We never did, but we were told that there was a British Post box on the island. By posting a letter or card there, would ensure the recipient received a unique postage franking. I never did learn what stamp would be acceptable (presumably British) or who collected the mail from the box, or even, how often it was emptied.

We sailed into Great Bay in front of the Dutch city of Philipsburg arriving just after 3 p.m. on Friday. Carefully negotiating the sand bar that stretches across a large part of the entrance and anchored within an easy dinghy ride to the main dock. We were both quite tired, but after the near collision, our adrenaline was still high and neither of us felt like sleeping. In any case, I still had a few small jobs to do on the boat, which I accomplished before sundown. I took comfort from the fact that we were now in good shape for the forthcoming sail to the United States Virgin Islands.

American maritime law states that if you are flying an American flag, you must have a registered United States skipper on board to enter US territory.

PHILIPSBURG - SINT MAARTEN

Because we had never had cause to sail to a US island before, we did not have the necessary registration certificate. To overcome this, it had been arranged that a US skipper would fly into St Maarten, to accompany us on the final leg. I had asked why the man concerned could not simply take the yacht over in Philipsburg, as it would have been easier for us to fly back to St Lucia from there. I was told that the skipper concerned had not sailed a yacht the size of Chardonnay before, and indeed had never sailed in the Caribbean. The fact that he was to accompany us was simply to assure our easy entry into the US Virgins.

We arranged to collect the man at Juliana Airport at about 3 p.m. the next day. I suggested to Liz, that we have another look at the town of Philipsburg and return for an early night. The next morning, I wanted to take a taxi around the whole island, as previously when on charter, we had not had the

273

opportunity to have a good poke around.

We also had to convert some money to Dutch Guilders, as the EC $ Dollar was not a currency that was viewed with much favour in the non-British Leeward islands.

There may be those of you who have been to one or two islands in either the Leeward or the Windward islands but have not experienced the rest. Here I give you a taste of what you might have missed. In the first part of this book, we were mainly in the Windward Islands. Both are very different from the larger islands such as Jamaica or Trinidad. There are two strings of 'pearls' one called the Leeward in the north, and the Windward Islands in the south, making up the Lower Antilles.

The Leeward Islands consist of (*running north to south*) Anguilla, a lovely little island, quiet and underdeveloped, and still run by the British Crown. St Martin and St Maarten this island is half administered by the French and half by the Dutch, the French side is relatively tranquil, but the Dutch side a veritable powerhouse. Philipsburg, the capital of the Dutch side is a free port, thus shops are stacked with electrical goods and jewellery just waiting to be smuggled into the rest of the islands; the casinos are some of the biggest in the Caribbean. When we chartered in the north, we used St Maarten as our base. The French side of the island is called St Martin and the capital is Marigot.

The next island south, which is only a few miles from St Maarten, is St Bartholomew, St Bart's for short. Originally belonging to Sweden, this small island is now French. The capital port is Gustavia, a little town that sports both Swedish and French colonial architecture. To the west of St Bart's and about four hours sail, is Saba, which is also an ex-Swedish island. Saba is a little roundish piece of rock in the middle of the sea. The anchorages were terrible there, as was the airport. The latter is called Hells Gate and with good reason. Saba is now Dutch, and the houses built in the Dutch colonial style are pretty. There are two main towns, Top and Bottom, and you must go to Top before you can go to Bottom. There is a lovely little story about the roads on the island. Visiting engineers to Saba said roads couldn't be built there because it was so mountainous. One of the inhabitants therefore took it upon himself to go and learn about road building overseas, and when he returned to Saba, he set about building zigzag roads on the island.

SAINT BARTHOLEMEW - GUSTAVIA

These are probably some of the best built and maintained in the Caribbean. Going south again is Eustatius, another Dutch possession, and although quite large, it is sparsely populated. This island had huge importance during the American War of Independence, as it was one of the main conduits for smuggling arms to Washington's army and was the first country in the world to recognise the newly declared United States of America. Landing on St Eustatius is like landing in Holland, only a hundred years ago. Some inhabitants still wear clogs. The next island south is rather better known as an English possession, although it is now an independent country; St Kitts and Nevis has an increasing tourist industry, and St Kitts the most interesting fortification of any of the islands. Montserrat is the next island south, one of the few we never visited.

It has been in the news in the last few years because of the terrible eruption of the volcano there. When we were in the Caribbean its main call to fame was the very sophisticated recording studios, where many of the well-known music groups used to record their albums. Montserrat is British.

Antigua and Barbuda are south of Montserrat, and we spent quite a lot of time in Nelson's old haven, English Harbour, on the South end of Antigua. Antigua is the home

275

of Viv Richards, and other fine cricketers, and although once a British island, is now independent. Barbuda is north of Antigua, and the only way to get there legally, is to go through Antigua customs and immigration, a real pain, because their customs are one of the unfriendliest in the Caribbean. Barbuda was owned by the Codrington's whose principle residence is near Bath in the UK, so far as I know; it was the only island to breed slaves for re sale.

Thirty-eight miles or so south of Antigua is the island of Guadeloupe, very French, and immediately south of that, the Isle des Saintes, a little collection of French islands, which are just out of this world. They are situated just south of Guadeloupe and administered by them. It is a delight to visit overnight as a sailor, as after checking in to the police station the next morning, one can buy hot chocolate croissants from the bakery next door. These islands have a notable history in that this is where the British and French fleet met in the Battle of the Saintes in 1782. The British thrashed the French, capturing four of their main galleons including the flagship containing the French commander. This put an end to a joint French and Spanish threat to invade Jamaica. The importance of this battle, however, was that Admiral Rodney was credited with the tactic of 'breaking the line.' Subsequently this was used by Nelson in the Battle of Trafalgar and even later by Admiral Jellico in the battle of Jutland. Rodney did not deserve the credit, as he was in fact in his cabin below with gout. It was his second in command who was friendly with a man called Sir John Clerk who lived in Edinburgh. Clerk had never been to sea, but despite this he was very interested in naval tactics, and over several dinners with various naval officers, he proved his theory, by war gaming on his small pool in his garden.

Another island off the south-eastern end of Guadeloupe, which we never visited, is called Gallant. We were told it was very flat and uninteresting. Sailing south again from Isle des Saintes one soon comes upon the ex-British island of Dominica perhaps the most primitive in the Caribbean, and certainly one of the most forested and mountainous. The contrast to the next island south has a much greater impact. The French island of Martinique, the first island in the

276

Windward Islands, is very sophisticated, and the capital of Fort de France, is a little Paris. The roads are highways, the hotels are slick and modern and the Martinicans extremely well educated and suave. We used to try to re-provision in Martinique whenever we could, as the wine is inexpensive, and the choice of food is at least as good as any supermarket will offer you in Europe. Apart from Philipsburg, which was our second favourite place for shopping, the rest of the Caribbean was not ideal, and in some cases further south, the choice of provisions was severely limited.

The Caribbean islands has been influenced by British, Dutch, French, Swedish, Spanish, and Danish civilizations, it is a complete history lesson of Europe in the seventeenth and eighteenth centuries. The other fact about these islands and why they are so interesting to sail amongst, is that they are all within five to forty miles or so of each other and the prevailing winds are from the east, the islands running north to south, making for perfect sailing.

We had a light breakfast and took the dinghy into the town dock afterwards.

Philipsburg is an odd town, as on one side, there is Grand Bay where we were anchored, and within about three blocks or so, there is the Great Salt Pond, stretching the whole length of the town on the east side. The town itself is placed on this quite narrow causeway, joining the south-east of the island with the south-west. The shops are mainly for the tourists, and because St Maarten is a free port, there are no duties to be paid on goods purchased there.

In the past, I had always known when we were to have a charter in St Maarten, as the dock staff at Sunshine Yachts would become extraordinarily friendly. It was a good time to obtain maximum cooperation from them for getting jobs done on the boat. The reason was, that a shopping list was produced just before leaving, which included everything from washing powder to radios. (Rasta Blaster's we called them). On our return after such a trip, a fast dinghy would come out to meet us, or sometimes even another yacht and the contraband off loaded with great excitement. I eventually had to stop this when asked to get a full-sized refrigerator. The main shops are electrical and jewellery outlets with a

277

smattering of good restaurants. The largest supermarket is a little out of town, every bit as good as those found in Martinique, but perhaps a shade more expensive. There are several casinos on the island, a good dive shop and several International standard hotels.

We had a good morning, returning with French bread from the Latin side of the island, along with ripe brie and a pound of butter. We had decided to make the best of our swan song.

We took the dinghy back to the yacht, and upon approaching Chardonnay, I noticed another smaller yacht had anchored very close by. It was also flying an American flag. Normally I would be irritated at a boat being so close to us, as often, if the wind changes at night, it means one's boat plays bumps a daisy with the other, not at all conducive to a good night's sleep as we found in the earlier days in Bequia. In this case, however, once we had collected our passenger, we had decided to sail around to Marigot Bay on the French side of the island, and moor there for the night, the reason being that the anchorage there is two hours nearer to the Virgin Islands and would reduce our sailing time the next day.

When we climbed on board, we noticed that there was a rather portly heavyset middle-aged man lounging in the other boat's cockpit. He was somewhat unshaven and was drinking beer; his baseball cap placed squarely on his head back to front. (I have often wondered since if the writers of 'The Simpsons' were around at the time because this man was the spitting image of Homer Simpson, the name I have given to him in this story). There was also a woman who must have been his wife, because I could not imagine even the most sightless of men picking her as a mistress. Neither of them looked particularly happy with life. One of the reasons was shortly to become apparent as Liz and I spread out our feast on the cockpit table.

From down below on the other yacht came a nasal wail, "mommy, I wanna go swimming." The child, who appeared to be female, emerged from the depths like some white blob.

These were bare boaters, (tourist sailors who have hired a yacht without crew).

The mother, a two-hundred-and-fifty-pound ball of obese flesh, yelled back at the 'little' girl, "no, you can't go swimmin."

"Why can't I go swimmin?" She whined.

"'Cause of ... sharks..." answered the mother, triumphantly.

I raised my eyebrows at Liz, who was just about to bite into a huge chunk of bread liberally covered with brie, she grinned.

The girl looked over the side of their boat, her blown up butterfly wings looking like some weird alien attachment fastened to her bleached upper arms, tinged with red from unaccustomed exposure to the sun.

"There ain't no sharks," she scowled at the water, half hanging over the rail at the stern.

"Yea, there are so, real big ones. In any case I gotta' help yer dad do the mast, so I can't watch yer..."

I had noticed the man rather laboriously getting up and going to the mast where he tied the boson's chair to the main halyard (*A boson's chair is usually a fabric chair, which one straps oneself into when being hauled up the mast to carry out repairs*). As they say in the television programme Gladiators, don't try this one at home, as it could be injurious to your health.

"Hey Margo, com'n hold this rope," the big man held one end of the halyard, the other end was already hooked onto the chair, which he had struggled into with great difficulty. The manufacturers never having imagined that a man of his bulk would be involved in shinning up a mast.

Margo waddled onto the upper deck and took the line.

"Now, what yer do, yer wind it round this," he pointed to the mast winch, "and with this handle yer turn it 'til I'm up, yer got it?"

"Yea," she answered, looking worriedly up the mast, which was well over thirty-five feet high. I noticed she stepped well out of the way of his trajectory, a wise precaution in case he fell, not that I blamed her.

"Okay I'm ready..."

She wound the line round the winch and started to turn it.

Now some well-equipped yachts are supplied with what

279

we call self-tailing winches, this meant that when the winch was turned, the spring-loaded sides ensure the line does not slip. In this case, they had no such luxury, so this meant that 'mommy' had to take the slack with one hand while turning the winch handle with the other, no mean feat in normal circumstancing but with 250 lbs or so of male flesh on the other end, the job was not easy.

Liz looked at me. "James, you must offer to help..."

I groaned, as I put down my wine glass, and went over to the side of Chardonnay.

"Hi," I called, "can I give you a hand?" I don't know what it is about the average American, who is normally the most polite and generous of individuals, but when asked if they need help, they appear to take it as some sort of huge affront to their pride, particularly if it comes from an English voice.

The woman now very red faced and showing considerable strain turned and glowered at me. I looked up at the man, now some ten feet off the deck.

"We don't need help," he almost yelped.

Thank you, I said sarcastically, under my breath. I smiled and held my hand up. "Okay, okay," I said, and wandered back, somewhat relieved, towards my wine and French bread.

The woman, as if to prove that she could manage on her own, made an extraordinary effort, and the boson's chair rapidly moved upwards, so rapidly in fact, that the unfortunate man crunched his head with some force on the bottom of the crossbar. "Yeow for Gawds sake Margo..." He yelled down as he moved one of his hands from around the mast to probe for the inevitable lump that must have been forming on top of his head. His baseball cap, spun away from the boat to land with a plop in the water.

She stared up at him. "Well for fucks sake watch what yer doin', this ain't easy yer know..." She was now bathed in sweat, and her breathing was laboured as she continued turning the winch handle, but rather more slowly. He was probably quite near the top when he called down.

"Okay, Margo, jus' hold it...." He didn't finish.

At that precise moment there was a shrill scream from the child, as she disappeared over the side of their boat, the top half of her ample torso having been doubled over the stern rail, had at last given way to the normal forces of nature...Gravity.

Both Liz and I jumped up, and rushed to the side of Chardonnay, but unfortunately for Bart, so did his wife.

Now, a loose line wrapped around a normal winch, may slow down a weight on the other end, but not by very much. This simply meant that our fat American friend had minutely more time to consider his impending dive into the deck than he might otherwise have done.

What had happened was that Margo had simply let go of her end of the line and rushed towards the stern of the yacht where her child had fallen over. She got half way there, when she heard the strangled cry from above as Bart lost his grip on the mast, the line started to slip off the winch, which had the effect of him plunging rapidly downwards.

Realising what she had done, she made a desperate attempt to turn, and at the same time grab the fast-moving line. Unfortunately for her, she did not realise what any sailor knows, that to try to stop a line that is moving with any force or speed, is like trying to hold on to a red-hot poker. Margo did manage to grab the line, and then screamed as she let go. Her weight was still transferred seawards, throwing her backwards against the rail. There was a splinter of over stressed steel as two stanchions gave way, and Margo disappeared over the side with a huge splash, the wash from which, even rocked Chardonnay.

When one is at sea, it is sods law that says any loose line will almost certainly snag on something, just when you don't want it to. The same sods law saved Bart. The line still twisted loosely round the winch, fouled, and Bart hurtling down like some bungee jumper, came so close to the deck I thought he had hit it. I was starting to think in my mind as to how I would call the emergency services on the radio, when the bloated body jumped back skywards by some three feet and hung there. A dark stain appeared in the front of his swimming shorts. I realised, that apart from the embarrassment of wetting himself, Bart had been extraordinarily lucky. The girl who had caused all the trouble, was swimming quite merrily at the stern of the yacht, but rapidly retreated up the aft steps when she saw her mother hurtling towards her like some out-of-control killer whale. Wisely, the girl shot down into the galley, as mother heaved herself up, and for the first time noticed that Bart was not desperately injured.

"You, okay?" She shouted, rather unnecessarily.

"No thanks to you yer fuckin' bitch, get me down," Margo glowered as she moved over to the winch, but she couldn't move the line, it was jammed solid. She disappeared below, and there was a scream and yowl, as no doubt the child was summarily chastised. Margo re-appeared with a very large bread knife. Bart was still cursing and swearing as Margo just cut the line, moving rapidly out of the way, as the unfortunate Bart fell the three feet to the deck with a howl of pain.

Liz and I were by now seeing the funny side of the antics on the nearby boat, and to avoid us been seen laughing, we went below, and watched from a glass-darkened porthole.

Within minutes, Bart was back on deck dressed in another swimsuit. He turned on the engine, picked up their anchor, and we then watched for fifteen minutes as he tried to place the boat as near to his sodden but just floating baseball cap. Approaching it, he cut the engine, then tried to pick it up with a boat hook. Margo who was sitting sulking in the cockpit neither helped with the steering of the boat, nor with the retrieval operation.

Hooking an object from the deck of a moving yacht is not as easy as it looks, and even Liz, who from time to time, attempted to bring in buoys for us to tie up to, had more than once disappeared over the side when she misjudged the line she was aiming for.

Bart was neither experienced in steering the boat nor in using a boat hook, and we were royally entertained as he gunned, the engine so that the hull was near the cap, put it into neutral, grabbed the boat hook, and waddled to the side.

Of course, because he had moved the boat too fast, the force of the wake had long pushed the cap several yards away before he got to it, and so he would try again with precisely the same result.

I could not stand it, I reasoned that if he carried on the way he was, he would almost certainly smash into something, and that something could be us. I jumped into our dinghy, and within thirty seconds, I had handed the wet cap up to him.

He clearly was not happy with this unwarranted interference, and as he snatched it from my hand, he snarled "thanks, but I could've managed..."

"Sure," I smiled, and gunned the engine of the inflatable back to our yacht.

I had just got on board; when I noticed, Bart had the yacht under full engine power headed straight across our bow heading seawards. He was so close I thought for a minute he had fouled our anchor line but thankfully, it remained intact.

"Where is he going?" asked Liz, who had come back on deck, now looking at the retreating trio, *"wherever it is, he's going far too fast,"* I murmured under my breath.

"Presumably, he's going to another anchorage, where he can enjoy his disasters without an audience," grinned Liz.

I watched with dismay. "The idiot is headed straight for the sand bank..."

"HEY, Try Again," (the name of their yacht) I shouted.

Bart turned around and saw me gesticulating.

He then did the most extraordinary thing. He left his wheel and went to the stern of his boat, which was the nearest part to us, and he showed us his middle finger sticking up on his right arm then jerking the same arm upwards while bringing his left hand to clasp his right bicep. I understood the message of course, but his stance was suddenly interrupted when his yacht hit the sand bank at seven knots. He achieved his second flight of the day as he was hurled at the wheel of the yacht, which bent backwards with force of his weight.

They were still stuck when we passed them some hours later, when sailing to Marigot. As we went by, I gave them a cheery wave. The three of them were sitting on the side of the boat next to each other, heads on hands and looking extremely miserable. They did not wave back.

"I hope they are not waiting for the tide," said Liz smiling.

I frowned, "there is no tide in the Caribbean, well none to speak of ..."

"Yes, I know that, but I wonder if they do...?"

I smiled I would miss sailing I thought to myself.

15 - THE FINAL SAIL

The idiot Captain

Half an hour before we were due at the airport, we took the dinghy into the town dock, bought ourselves a delicious ice cream from the cafe nearby, found ourselves a taxi and went to collect the US skipper from Juliana airport.

His name was Chuck, and he reminded me of a University professor. He had thinning hair, a beard just turning grey and a very large pot belly. He seemed jovial enough on the drive back, and I explained to him that we planned to sail for Marigot that evening, and then head for the Virgins first thing in the morning. He agreed to our plan.

The next morning, we woke early, I wanted to get to St Thomas well before nightfall and although the weather reports were normal for the time of year, it was quite windy, and the seas would be heavy. I also knew that the trip to St Thomas would almost certainly be down wind, which in a heavy sea it would be quite tiring just keeping the yacht on course.

At least we had a somewhat lighter yacht, as I remarked to Liz, our total stock of beer had disappeared down Chuck's gullet the night before. I had never seen someone consume such an amount of alcoholic liquid, with no apparent harmful consequences.

There is nothing quite like sailing at dawn in the

Caribbean. The air is fresh, but warm, and the colours of the land and sky create a cacophony of delight with the sharpness, which all too soon tends to drift to haze as the sun rises and heat of the day obscures the definition.

We set our full sails early, and with Chardonnay's motor running to charge the batteries, we made excellent time to Anguilla, the westernmost island of the Leeward's, passing to the north of it.

Just after Anguilla, we set our course for the Virgins, which I reckoned, were about an eight-hour sail. By 10 a.m., we had left all sight of land and were in the open sea. As I had been at the wheel since early morning, Chuck took over, and Liz and I went below, she to prepare lunch and me to write some more pages of the book I was working on. Time went by quite quickly, and although the sea was heavy, I had set the speed of the engine to correspond with the wave speeds making life a little more comfortable, except that the smell of the exhaust tended to waft back into the cockpit. I had just closed off a chapter, shutting the computer down, and was about to take a cup of coffee up for Chuck, when I heard a yell from above.

"Hey, Jaan, (it was how he pronounced my name) get up here quickly," I negotiated the steps as quickly as I could with two cups of coffee in my hand and handed one to him.

"What's the problem?" I asked.

"Look back there," Chuck turned and pointed aft. I could tell there was a trace of anxiety in his voice. I ducked under the canvas canopy we had left up protecting us from any stray wave breaking over the boat and looked.

I must say that I was alarmed at what I saw. The whole sky behind us was black and very menacing, more importantly the weather system I was looking at was catching us up rapidly.

"I've been watching the fucker for the last thirty minutes, looks like a hurricane to me... and a bad one at that," I could see beads of sweat appearing on Chuck's brow.

I frowned, "it can't be, I listened to Radio Antilles this morning, and there was no bad weather forecast." Nevertheless, I was worried. I knew that it could not be a hurricane as they were tracked right from their source in the eastern Atlantic, usually off the coast of Africa, which meant

285

that there was at least seven- or eight-days warning. In any case, I thought to myself, we were out of the hurricane season, which was roughly between September and December.

I looked at Chuck, "don't worry," I said, "I'll go below and call Antilles on the SSB and ask them what we are in for, I'm sure they will be aware of it." (*An SSB was our long-range radio and we had VHF for shorter ranges*).

It took me some five minutes to get through to Antilles, but when I did, the news I got was not reassuring.

"Yea," said the voice at the other end of the ether, "we've bin watching this guy for a few days now, and late last night we had reports of it heading north, which in fact it did, but it now seems to have switched course and is headed south west.

"Fortunately, it's going to miss all the islands, but I guess you couldn't be in a worse spot..."

"Thanks," I glowered at the radio, "any idea of wind speed, wave height?"

"Yea, reports of wind gusting up to sixty knots, could be seventy in places, heavy rain and wave heights reported 'bout twelve feet."

"Size of system?"

"Er, I guess you're looking at something quite small, probably be through you in five, six hours." Oh, great I thought to myself, just about the amount of time it will take us to get to St Thomas.

"Viz?" (Visibility) I asked.

"Er, 'bout five hundred yards," he did not seem too sure, which was indicative of the perils of weather forecasting in the Caribbean.

I called Liz and we both went up on deck. "Okay," I addressed Chuck and Liz together. "It's not a hurricane, but a nasty big squall, it'll take 'bout five, six hours to pass through, so..."

Chuck interrupted me. His breathing appeared laboured, and he was now sweating quite profusely. "Gee, Jaan, I'm very sorry, but I'm just not feeling well, guess I'm gonna hav'ta go below 'n lie down fer a bit." He looked at me sorrowfully, and avoiding Liz's gaze, he passed the wheel to me and was gone.

I had never actually been in a situation before where

someone was visibly afraid, but clearly Chuck was out of his mind with fear. It's a funny feeling because I found his fear to be quite demoralising.

"How bad is it going to be?" asked Liz looking worried.

I looked at her and smiled. "We'll be fine, firstly we're running (sailing downwind) so there will be very little stress on the hull, and we are in between the islands, so not much we can hit, even if visibility is bad. What we must do however, is reduce the main to a double reef again, pull in the jib, stow everything below, get lifejackets, and close off the cabin area so if we are pooped (water coming over the stern), it won't flood below." I looked behind and realised we didn't have much time.

Of course, it would have been hugely helpful if Chuck had at least managed to hold the wheel while we adjusted the main, but after turning Chardonnay into wind, we dropped the large sail to create the necessary slack for reefing. Reefing a large main sail while heading into a high wind in rough water is no easy matter. The boom, even when secured, swings wildly from side to side, the sails flap as though they will tear to pieces any minute, and the water cascades over the bow, drenching everyone near the mast. What with constantly slipping on the deck, getting whipped by stray lines, being bucked in the uneven sea and, while all this was going on, attempting to tie a proper sailor's knot at the four reef points, with fingers that are numb with cold, (yes, even in the Caribbean) was bloody hard work, as anyone who has sailed will vouch for. It can be dangerous too, particularly for us, as Chardonnay had no life lines on board.

(Lines that can be attached to the person and to some solid structure on deck, the theory being that even if you are swept overboard, your dead body can be easily retrieved).

At last, with Liz bravely struggling at the wheel, I managed and then I tackled the jib, which was much easier because of the roller furling gear. Then I double checked that everything was stowed and tied on deck and made my way back to the cockpit in a state of near exhaustion, as Liz turned the Chardonnay back on course. I decided to take the ketch sail down completely and stowed that below. As a last check, I inspected the dinghy to ensure it was hoisted securely on the stern and found our 'professional' sailor had tied a couple of granny knots, which I undid, and re tied.

I only just got my waterproof gear on, and I was tying on my life jacket when the first deluge hit us. I took over the wheel as Liz quickly closed off the cabin area and sat down as far forward into the cockpit as she could. Unfortunately, the canvas top had been designed for rain and sea water coming over the bow. Now it came in the other way, that is, over the stern, and we were both soon drenched by both sea water and the rain, with water running down our necks where the foul weather gear did not cover us. It soon became even colder, and we were to spend the next few hours in complete misery. Having no radar or Satellite equipment, meant we could only rely on our compass to steer and thus we had only an approximate idea of where we were, not a happy thought, when the pointer of the compass was jumping around all over the place each time a wave shot under us.

It was by far the worst sustained weather I had been subjected to, but I felt the boat was comfortable, and so it was going to be more a matter of endurance than anything else. One of the problems with a heavy following sea is that as each wave goes underneath the boat, the aft part of the vessel tries to follow it. Thus, unless you correct the situation quickly, you find yourself thrown sideways to the wind and sea, which is not to be recommended. I used the engine to balance us, and tried as best I could, to keep up our speed.

It was only after four or five hours that I noticed some definite easing of the squall (which would have been called a gale in Europe), and I sighed with relief. The visibility started to clear, and the sky lightened, although the sea itself was still rough.

I thankfully handed over the wheel to Liz, and gratefully sat down on the now soaking cushions in the cockpit, which oozed with water every time I moved.

Chuck must have noticed that the weather was lessening, and he took the precise moment to open the cabin door into the cockpit area, as an especially large wave hit us with some force on the stern. The water came straight through the cockpit, hit Chuck in the chest, and he disappeared below, amid the deluge. Liz, caught off guard, had allowed the yacht to 'screw' so I jumped up and took the wheel again, getting us back on course.

I shouted to her to check if Chuck was all right, and if so to turn on the bilge pumps. (Chardonnay had automatic bilge pumps which came on if the water height went past a certain depth. There were subsidiary pumps also, which helped move a larger mass of water out of the boat more quickly, but these had to be switched on manually).

Bilge pumps get rid of any excess water in the bilge, the area between the cabin floor and the bottom of the hull. I also yelled to Liz to tell Chuck tactfully, that he should consider staying below until we told him it was safe to come on deck.

She did, but not too tactfully, and in fact Chuck did not emerge again until we were about a mile off St Thomas, when he took the wheel as though he had been sailing since Marigot. Liz was furious with him, because the water had made a real mess below and she was particularly keen that the boat be turned over to the new owners in tip top condition. Chuck's previous premature arrival on deck now meant that we had a major clean up job to do when we arrived.

Once Chuck had taken over in US waters, the boat was technically his responsibility. I knew of course that he was not used to sailing a yacht (or anything else for that matter) and thought it prudent to offer to berth the boat in the marina we were headed for. He refused, perhaps because Liz had stung his pride, and he said he could manage fine.

Either because he was nervous or simply did not know what he was doing, he motored in far too fast. Realising he had done so, he slammed the gear into reverse at high revs, and I heard a very nasty hissing sound coming from the engine room down below. We hit another yacht that was moored nearby, with a splintering crash, which stowed in Chardonnay's forecastle, (the steel rail on the bow of the yacht) and he also managed to gouge out a six-foot gash in the side of the other yacht before I took over and brought Chardonnay under control.

After we had tied up, I went down into the engine rooms and was horrified to see the whole area was simply covered in oil. By Chuck over revving the engine, he had burst a main oil seal. I could have cried, as I had kept the engine so highly polished, that it could have easily been lifted and put onto an exhibition stand. Now it looked like Kuwait oil wells after the Gulf War disaster.

Chuck collected his gear and bade his farewell's quickly, leaving us to face the new owners. Fortunately, I had got Chuck to sign a transfer document in St Maarten, that showed that he was the skipper, and thus responsible for the boat. As events were to turn out, it was a very wise move indeed.

Our plan was to spend the night on Chardonnay and catch the plane from St Thomas back to Philipsburg the next day. From there we had arranged to hitch a ride on a St Lucia Airways charter flight, leaving for St Lucia in the late afternoon.

By 7 p.m. we were getting very worried as the new owners had not turned up, it had also been agreed that they would pay us for the trip, and provide us with return tickets... When they had not shown by 9 p.m. I knew that they were not coming that night, so we turned in early, wondering what problems we might face in the morning...

The problems came early, being hailed from the dock by a grainy accented American voice at just after 7 a.m.

"Hey anyone aboard?" Someone thumped the side of the hull.

I bounded out of bed, slipped on some shorts, and went up into the cockpit, to meet a heavy-set man, who I guessed was in his late fifties. He somehow did not fit my caricature of an owner.

He did not hold out his hand and his manner was gruff and unfriendly.

"You the guys that sailed this tub up from St Lucia?" He scowled as he looked towards the buckled forecastle.

"A bit of a mess, isn't it?" His head jerked in the direction of the forecastle. "And you've damaged the boat next to you..."

I shook my head, "no, we didn't do either, but may I know who we are talking to?" He looked at me, as though trying to size me up. "Yea, my name's Bill Crudding, I'm the manager of this outfit," he turned and spread his left hand out which indicated the substantial marina we were moored in and the boat yard and offices on the shore.

"Good to meet you Bill," I said, holding my hand out over the side rail. He took it grudgingly.

"Yea I got a call from a James Tanner, the new owner of this yacht, and he said he couldn't make it down here and asked me to take it over from you'se guys, but someone's gotta be responsible for that damage..."

I told him what had happened and showed him the document signed by Chuck. "I assume Chuck was employed by the owners, so they will have to talk to him," I suggested.

Bill Crudding glowered, "how do I know that you didn't do it?" He asked belligerently. "I don't know this guy. Now you tell me he's gone, and anyway I have no authority to pay you guys anything, and I ain't got no tickets, no siree," I had that familiar sinking feeling in my stomach. "I guess you guys better just beat it..." Added Crudding.

Liz, who had joined me on deck, stopped him. "We're not just beating anywhere, until we are properly paid."

"That's right," I confirmed.

He screwed up his face.

"Guess I'll just hav'ta call the cops..." He started to walk away.

I nodded and called after him. "You just do that, and while you do, I will be going to the nearest lawyer in St Thomas and asking him to get an immediate court order to have this boat seized. I will also sue the owners for substantial compensation. In the meantime, one of us will remain on this boat until we get what is due to us." I did not know whether I could do all these things, but it attracted Crudding's attention, as he turned and walked back towards me.

He gave me a long hard look and I trusted my expression told him I was certainly prepared to carry through what I'd said.

"Okay, I'm gonna call the owner an' get instructions, I'll be back." He turned and walked towards the office.

In fact, Bill Crudding was back so quickly I had serious doubts that he had called anyone. He climbed on board. "Okay, I have been authorised to pay your fares back to St Lucia, but that's it," his face had the look of grim finality.

I shook my head, "no deal, it's all or nothing." Liz took our case back into the cabin and made a big show of unpacking it.

He shrugged his shoulders and disappeared over the side onto the dock. "Well, I'm gonna talk to 'em agin, but I don't hold out much hope..."

I shrugged, "then we stay..."

As he was walking away, he turned around, "How much did you say they owed you?" I told him and indicated that if we could not get away within half an hour, we would miss our connection in St Maarten, which would involve the owners in further expense.

Ten minutes later, he was back with the money. Subsequently, when I spoke to the new owners on the telephone from St Lucia, they assured me that they had transferred all the funds and instructions days before. Bill Crudding had never contacted them once while we were in St Thomas.

We were sad to leave Chardonnay, and it was a shame to leave her in such bad state, as the yacht had been our home for almost two years. Fortunately, we did not have too much time to grieve, as thanks to Bill Crudding's shenanigans we were late and indeed we only just caught the only aircraft going to St Maarten that day.

We were both feeling happier when the island of St Thomas appeared several thousand feet below us as we headed west. We saw the island of St Croix just afterwards, belching out thick smoke from its oil refinery, the major employer on the island. Then we passed over St James's, part of the British Virgins, before heading out to sea. The weather was quite beautiful, with hardly a cloud in the sky, a complete contrast from the previous day.

We arrived at Juliana airport just after 12.30 p.m., so we looked around the area for a small restaurant and had a light lunch returning to the small airport and buying some magazines to read while we awaited our flight some three hours hence.

It was a boring wait, and I was pleased to see the St Lucia Airways aircraft in its distinctive colours, land just after 4 p.m. I watched as the plane, a small Islander, taxied to the apron, and shortly afterwards the pilot appeared walking on the tarmac towards the terminal where we were sitting. I strained my eyes to see who it was, and then my heart sank. Instead of the pilot friend we had been expecting, it was a man all the other pilots nicknamed 'Freddie the Flying Fart'. It was generally considered that Freddie had some extraordinary hold over the management, as no one could comprehend why he should still hold a job flying with the airline (any airline). There were the remains of one of his mistakes just off the end of the runway at Vigie, the smaller airport at the northern end of St Lucia. Freddie had tried to land in poor weather and had gone straight off the runway into the sea.

Fortunately, there had been no fatalities. His other claim to fame was landing on Union Island (a small island in the Grenadines) with his landing gear up. The result was, the propellers on the twin prop he was flying, became somewhat bent.

Although I did not know it at the time St Lucia Airways was a CIA (Central Intelligence Agency) financed project. The reason for their interest in running the small airline was not to support or subsidise the inhabitants of St Lucia or the other Caribbean states although they did so by default. It was because each sovereign country has automatic landing rights in other countries. They needed those reciprocal rights to use in Belgium, where they ran their Hercules cargo planes stacked with weapons to the government forces being supported in Angola. Such flights turned out to be quite hazardous, and a friend of mine was to be killed while on a flying mission.

Whether Freddie had found out about this supposedly covert operation and had threatened to blow the story, I never did find out. Even then, because of his dubious flying abilities, Freddie was no longer allowed on commercial flights, only on charters, which is no doubt, why we had him.

He saw me as he came into the airport building. "Hi James," he waved and came across. I took a deep breath and smiled. "How many do you have to pick up?" I asked.

"Oh, just six or seven, plus you and Liz of course," I looked behind him. "No second pilot?" My heart took another plummet.

"No, Jonathan was feeling a bit sick, and we don't have to

have two pilots on charters, so why don't you join me in the number two seat. You're a pilot, aren't you?" I nodded, although I'd been trained as a helicopter pilot, not on a fixed winged aircraft. Nevertheless, I reasoned to myself that I would certainly prefer to be in front with Freddie at least I would have some pre-knowledge of any impending disaster.

It was with these rather unhappy thoughts that I saw Liz into the jump seat, the third seat in the cockpit, checked that the unsuspecting passengers were in their seats and their seat belts firmly attached before sitting next to Freddie. I could fly a fixed wing aircraft of course, I simply was not qualified to do so, and my take offs and landings were not too numerous. Still, I thought to myself, if anything happened to Freddie, I could probably get the plane down safely, providing I could find a runway big enough...

As we took off, my mind wandered back through the last few months.

Chartering had been full of incidents, some hilarious, some downright dangerous, and the last few days had been no exception. We had met some delightful people, and some downright miseries. I had been subjected to numerous sexual proposals, most of them unwelcome but we had received the opportunity to sail at someone else's expense in what is arguably one of the most beautiful areas in the world.

I then thought about the future. Liz was about to be thrown into the 'deep end' as Bess had left the island of St Lucia two days before. This meant that the next day, which was Monday, was to be Liz's first working day. One thing that would help our settling in however was that Bess had kindly offered to rent her house out to us while she was away, and as it was fully furnished, we could simply get our luggage from the marina where we had left it and move in. This arrangement was of some benefit to Bess too, as we were in effect babysitting her house which would otherwise have remained empty.

We had been flying for well over an hour, when I had put the earphones on and was listening in to the 'traffic.' Our position was midway between Dominica and Martinique, and I could see the sun clearly disappearing under the horizon. Within ten minutes or so it would be dark. As I was

294

marvelling at the sight of the vanishing sun and all the attendant colours in the sky at the time, I was suddenly alerted by a conversation between a pilot landing in St Lucia and the Vigie control tower.

"Jus' made it son, before the shit hits..." It was the controller speaking.

"Yea man, I wouldn't like to land in that lot, no sir," I turned to Freddy, "did you hear that, Freddy?" I could clearly hear reggae coming out of his earphones.

I shook him hard by his shoulder and he turned and looked at me surprised.

He switched onto intercom.

"Did you hear that?"

"What?" I took a deep breath.

"The pilot landing in St Lucia, there seems to be some sort of problem down there..."

"Oh."

"Well, don't you think you had better contact them" I said as gently as I could, but with apprehension mounting.

He smiled and spoke into the microphone. "Vigie, Vigie, this is Hotel Victor ETA you at nineteen ten, any problems?"

A deep West Indian accent answered. "Hotel Victor, yea, we have a minor tropical wave at this time, ground visibility 'bout quarter of a mile, recommend you land in Martinique until the wave is through, over."

"Are you shutting down?" Asked Freddie.

"'Noo, man, landing is possible jus' not advisable."

"You want me to call Martinique?" I asked, reaching forward to the switch on the front console.

Freddie thought for a minute. "Naw, we'll go on down and have a look, I got a date tonight."

"Fuck your date," I blurted out.

Freddie turned to me and grinned. "Well, that was the general idea..."

I sighed.

"Don't worry James," Freddie added in a jovial way, we've enough juice to get us back to Martinique, if we can't get down."

"I'm not worried about running out of fuel," I growled, as my eyes flicked over to the fuel gauges showing well under a quarter full. I found my mouth had gone dry. Oh, shit I thought to myself, why the hell we should be landed with Freddie at a time like this.

I looked out of the cockpit window. It was now quite dark, and as we approached the northern end of St Lucia. The rain hit us with a blast. Freddie turned on the windscreen wipers, but they were totally ineffectual. He then put into effect the procedure for landing in bad weather (ILA) which took some extra ten minutes or more to get into position. The aircraft bucked and swayed as he lined up on some imaginary line.

"Right here we go," Freddie pushed his stick forward. I knew because of the wind direction that we were landing from the sea, so I consoled myself with the thought that providing we did not land short of the runway, we would hit dry land. The problem was which piece of dry land we would hit. The word HIT suddenly took on a new meaning. I stared out through the cockpit window, straining to see something, anything on the ground below. I could see nothing. I looked at the altimeter it was showing under five hundred feet. I wondered how far away from the hill at the end of the runway we were. When I looked again, we were at two hundred feet and falling quickly. I gripped the side of the aircraft as I waited for the crash. Beads of sweat started to form on my forehead, and I inexplicably thought of Chuck. Could I see the runway lights ahead? I knew that the Vigie runway lights were notoriously poor (They've changed them now). Suddenly Freddie pulled out the throttle, and we went rapidly skywards banking sharply to the left as we did so. I felt a sigh of relief, "Martinique?" I asked.

"Naw, I think I'll take another run at it," Freddie looked at me. "Not worried are you, James?"

I scowled at him as a gust of wind and more torrential rain threw the aircraft further to the left, and Freddie shoved his joy stick further to the right to straighten out.

My mind was racing now. Perhaps if I reason with him, I thought.

"Freddy, I know your date is important to you. However, my life and Liz's life are important to us too, surely it would be prudent to run up to Martinique just until the weather blows over," I could see a frown cloud Freddy's face.

Then an idea hit me, if reason doesn't work, why not try bribery. I told myself...

"And, when we return, you and your girlfriend can have a free meal at Captain's Table with champagne." I felt a dig in the ribs from Liz behind me. "well, free wine anyway..." I smiled at him with what I hoped was my most engaging and persuasive manner.

Freddie was clearly delighted at the offer. "That's real nice of you brother," he turned to smile at Liz, banking the aircraft wildly as he did so. "All the more reason for me to get her down, besides," he rubbed the glass of the fuel gauges, "I'm not sure we now have enough fuel to get us to Martinique..."

If anything, the weather had worsened, and on the second run I was barely able to see any lights at all. Again, Freddie pulled out the throttle, and again we banked but even more sharply this time. I could have sworn that we just missed the hill, which is placed strategically and immediately after the runway, but it could have been a darker patch of weather.

I was now getting annoyed, as Freddie had no right to risk all our lives, and I told him so. For the first time I could see he was also worried. He looked at the fuel gauges, they were near empty. I realised he had told the truth, and that we would not reach Martinique. I suggested we should consider flying down to Hewannora, the International airport at the southern end of the island.

Freddie looked at the fuel gauges again and shook his head. I then knew that if we did not land on the next run, it was the sea or worse.

I groaned inwardly, and I looked at Freddie with resignation. "I'd better go to the passengers in the back, and give them an emergency drill," Freddie nodded in assent and started to concentrate on his third attempt.

I knew it would be a good five minutes before Freddie could get the plane into position to land again, so I struggled out of my seat, and went back into the cabin. I told the extremely worried passengers that we were attempting to land the aircraft at Vigie, but if the weather conditions were too bad, we would take them back to Martinique until the system had passed over. I wondered how many lies had been told to me by the cabin staff of aircraft I had flown in previously.

I also told them that it was mandatory in these circumstances to put their life jackets on, as we were approaching the runway from the sea. One woman started sobbing and was comforted by her husband.

"Please don't worry," I said, "this is just normal procedure in these circumstances, and you are fortunate to have the best possible pilot in the whole of the airline." I hoped God would forgive me for lying again, and then the thought hit me that maybe I would not have to wait too long to find out.

Because these aircraft spend most of their time flying over water, there was a life raft stowed aft. The last emergency procedure I showed to the two passengers sitting in the rear. This contraption was a long circular canvas object, rolled up so it would be easy to eject out of the cabin door. I explained to them how the compressed air was operated "But for God's sake, don't pull the cord until the thing is outside the aircraft, I cautioned them." They all nodded grimly.

I could feel the aircraft dropping again, so I tried to appear casual in getting back to my seat, although how one appears casual while running, I am not sure. It didn't take me long to get there. As I strapped myself in, I looked out of the window into the murk. Was it my imagination, or had the weather cleared imperceptibly? As I tightened the straps round me, I was sure I could see some lights, but were they the right ones? Freddie banked the aircraft to the right and headed directly for them. I knew we were near the runway level now, and that we would shortly be committed. I still could not be sure that the lights we could see were the runway lights. Suddenly I knew where we were. We were headed straight for a large hanger at the sea end of the runway on the eastern side.

I flung my left arm out. "GO LEFT, GO LEFT" I shouted. Freddie threw his stick to the left, and the plane banked steeply. I waited for the port wing to hit the ground, as I knew it must be within feet of it. I turned quickly to Liz and told her to brace herself.

I heard a loud bang from the back of the aircraft, waited for the inevitable ball of fire, and was surprised when there was none. I could not tell whether we had hit something or not. I prayed as my life displayed itself in Technicolor in front of me.

Now I could see the runway lights, to our left and as Freddie straightened the aircraft up, we landed first on our port wheel and then it seemed ages before our starboard wheel touched down. We were still not safe, as in order to have enough speed to take off again, Freddie had made the approach with more speed than normal.

Now we had to stop before the end of the runway fast approaching out of the murk.

The brakes squealed as we hurtled the last few yards, and at the last-minute Freddie turned the aircraft to the left, so we did a sort of sideways skid, coming to rest only feet from the perimeter fence. I let out a sigh of relief, as Freddie pulled out the throttle to taxi in to the offloading area.

There had not been a sound from the rear, which was surprising, as I would have thought we would have heard some expression of relief if nothing else. I got out of my seat, and went back to the cabin, holding my shaking hands behind my back.

As I walked through the bulkhead, I couldn't believe my eyes. Someone had pulled the compressed air cord on the life raft, which must have been the bang I had heard, and it had blown up inside the cabin. This meant that all the passengers were firmly jammed in their seats. If someone had been looking in from outside, they would have seen people's faces oddly pressed against the windows from the pressure of the inflated raft. I had to smile, it just looked so ridiculous.

Several minutes later, with the help of the ground staff and a couple of sharp knives, the entombed passengers were led shakily into the airport lounge, with a story they could no doubt tell their grandchildren, who probably wouldn't believe a word of it.

When we eventually got into Bess's house that night, we decided that sailing and flying were low on our priority list for the immediate future. There is no doubt that we had a very narrow escape.

PART II

AND BEYOND

16 - THE TAKE OVER

The owners rejoice

The next morning, we had to be up early. Liz had spent a few days with Bess before we left for the Virgin Islands, so she was familiar with all the staff, and the buying procedures. I was not, so Liz suggested I accompany her that morning. The restaurant owned a small van, and this had been parked in the parking area allotted to the house. We eventually found the key and set off on our new adventure.

The house we were living in was a 'town house' in an area called Panorama Villas, a stone's throw from the St Lucian Hotel. In fact, the back of the houses looked over the grounds of the St Lucian, there only being a road in between.

The front of the house had a small, enclosed garden and just over the fence was a small patch of green before the Rodney Bay Lagoon. Several years before, Rodney Bay had been just a bay at the northern end of the island, which had a strip of nice sand. The British, under the auspices of the Caribbean Development Corporation, had carried out a huge tourist development. They financed the building of a causeway between Pigeon Island, and the mainland at the northern end of the bay. This project effectively meant that two thirds of the area was enclosed, thus making the bay much more sheltered.

Then they dug a channel by the side of a village called Gross Islet (pronounced Gross Elay) and excavated the marshy ground beyond, thus creating an almost square lagoon about one mile long by a quarter of a mile wide. Sunshine Yachts had a small marina there, and several houses had been built near the shore. The restaurant, which had been built on the south-eastern corner, was called Captain's Table. Panorama Villas was on the south western corner, so the drive was a short one to the entrance of the 'Pub' as it was affectionately called.

We arrived just before nine-o-clock, and as there was no one else there, Liz took out a huge bunch of keys, and unlocked the office door and we went inside. She had arranged to meet her second chef who was to apprise her of the provisions that were needed for that evening and while she waited, she made herself familiar with the paperwork from the night before.

I decided to have a good look around. The road we had just travelled along ran at right angles to the road on which the St Lucian Hotel and Panorama Villas were situated. Had we carried straight on, we would have reached the main Castries road which runs between Castries, the capital city of St Lucia, and the furthermost northern part of the island. (Castries was named after a French admiral who was a governor on the island when the French administered it. In fact, the island changed hands fourteen times, before finally coming under permanent British administration in 1815 and then independence in 1978).

The whole of the north end of the island is called Cap Estate, which is a residential area, where we were eventually to end up living. This estate was only about four miles up the road. Castries and Vigie airport were about seven miles south of Rodney Bay, and the main international airport, Hewannora which is on the southernmost tip, is approximately thirty-eight miles to the south of that. Because of the appalling roads however, the time taken to get there was about two hours.

Captain's Table had a large car park area off the road, with two entrances. This area extended right across the property and could hold more than thirty or forty cars.

The entrance to the restaurant was through the main doors, left of centre when looking at it from the road. Next to these double doors on the left again was a single door leading to the office area. The office had a bay window, facing the car park and contained what most offices do throughout the world a metal desk, three or four chairs, two filing cabinets and a floor safe. The office took up the westernmost corner of the building, the door opposite the bay window that led into another large room, was to become the Yachtsman's Haven Bar. The French windows at the end, leading out to a veranda, were built over the lagoon itself. Walking through the main doors, there was an open entrance on the right about half way up the corridor, where there was a rather pretty little open area with plants, so that people could eat outside. Because this area was completely walled on all sides, it was rather like a walled garden. We eventually opened it up with wrought iron gates, so it could be approached from the car park.

If one continued up the corridor, passing the men's and ladies lavatories on the left, the area opened out into a sort of lobby, where guests would be greeted.

Immediately on the right was a large dining room, with about twenty tables, and this opened via French windows into the walled garden area on one side and the main bar area on the lagoon side. Heading straight through the lobby, one reached the veranda, which was roofed, with opening louvered glass windows all of which looked over the lagoon. Indeed, the whole area served as the main bar, which we called the Pub and was built over the lagoon itself. The other side of the windows was the dock area for yachts to tie up, and that ran the whole length of the building. Apart from the large bar, there were also seats and tables in this area running parallel with the dining room, where people could order a Pub meal. At the far end of the main restaurant area, all the wines were stored behind a wrought iron grill. Turning right would bring you through into the kitchen and storerooms. The kitchen was well equipped with gas cookers, run from butane tanks, fryers, microwaves, one very large walk-in freezer and a walk-in cooler.

Behind the fridges were the food store cupboards, and a back way out into the car park, which was also the staff entrance. Eventually we had to block this area off, because of the staff stealing food.

The opening times were from 5 p.m. until the last customer left, usually well after midnight. Subsequently, we were to open for lunch, but that was to be over two years later.

I had just finished walking around when Alphonse, the second chef arrived.

Alfie, as we were to call him, was a tall pale St Lucian (called a Redman by his peers), and we were to quickly learn that he was a Seventh Day Adventist. He went through the list of goods that the restaurant needed for that night, and at about ten-thirty we all piled into the van and drove down to Castries.

Liz was to receive her first shock. In normal circumstances, in say Europe or even Martinique, the list of provisions could be bought at one large warehouse. Not so, in St Lucia, we had to trawl the supermarkets...

The first one we went to had no sugar, potatoes, or greens, the second no sugar or greens, the third none of the above, and so it went on. Bear in mind that all this shopping was done at close to the hottest time of the day, and each time the van had to be moved. Parking in the centre of Castries was at a premium, so much so, that it often took more time looking for a spot near the shop concerned as it took to purchase the actual shopping. This day, it took almost four hours to obtain ninety percent of the items on the list, the other ten percent being unobtainable. We must have visited at least fifteen outlets to get as much as we did.

In the months to come Liz managed to cut down on the amount of shops she had to visit, as she got used to who would normally have a particular item and who would not. It was not unusual in those days however for there to be no potatoes or no butter or even no onions on the island. Usually, it was just bad ordering on behalf of the shop concerned, sometimes however the government was to blame.

I remember one instance when due to a factory opening on the island that had a licence to make orange juice, imports were banned. Then the quality of the local stuff deteriorated to such an extent that no one would drink it, so then the government eventually had to give way to public pressure and allow imports in once again. This caused havoc with the tourist trade who were looking for the highest standards of food and drink.

The first evening went off well and the takings were rather above what we had anticipated. Monday was a good day to start, as the restaurant tended to get busier later in the week. Soon bookings were piling up, and by the following Wednesday, the weekend was totally booked. We started to rub our hands in glee, thinking of all the money we were about to make. I was yet to find in life, that whenever I had this feeling of mercurial optimism, disaster was sure to follow.

By the time Friday had come around, I had made substantial inroads into sorting out an accounting system, and I was able to give Liz rudimentary reports daily. This was helpful to her, as the bar was not making the money it should, and we suspected that the barman was creaming off some of the profits.

By this time, I had also met most of the staff. The head chef was a Greek called Yannis, Yani for short. He was a short man, with a roundish face, black hair and two-day stubble that seemed to be a permanent fixture. Yani's body included a rounded belly, but he was not fat seemingly anywhere else. He was by far the best chef on the island, but he had two drawbacks. The first one was that he was supposedly a 'recovering' alcoholic, and a close second was his love of females, any females. Both these factors were to give us innumerable difficulties.

The junior chef was a young black St Lucian called Gregory, and he would stand in when Alphonse had his day off, which was Friday, our busiest day. (Seventh Day Adventist's cannot work between six-o'clock on a Friday until six-o'clock on a Saturday).

There were four waitresses and one head waitress. All were St Lucian and apart from Mary, the youngest, they were mature women. Mary was a sexy little thing, and she knew it. She had very Indian features, and although small, had a well-proportioned figure. She was not popular with the others, but was very popular with customers, particularly the male species. Sylvia was a woman of about thirty; slightly built and she always looked as though she had not quite had time to get dressed properly. Her hair looked rather like an Eagles nest. Minnie was over forty, and a large, framed woman. She had her special favourite customers, and they would swear by her. The trouble was she could be extraordinarily rude to others who did not meet her approval. Marylyn was about thirty-five, very thin and quite attractive except that she had her two front teeth missing. She was prone to getting fits of the giggles.

The last one, Barbara who was the head girl, was very different from the rest. She thought herself a cut above them and would act as hostess when Liz was called away. She was very attractive, dressed well and had a very good figure.

The barman was a man called Pedro. A heavyset type who knew his drinks backwards. He would sometimes double as a wine waiter if Charlie was not there.

Charlie was being trained as a wine waiter, but had such an arrogant attitude, that he did not stay with us long.

I remember once Charlie being called over to one of our rather more sophisticated customers, who told him the wine, was corked. Charlie immediately grabbed his corkscrew to take the cork out of the bottle.

"Aha de cork, it is not there..."

"No," said the customer patiently, "the wine is corked... bad," Charlie peered down the neck of the bottle. "De wine has no bad cork, der be no cork in de bottle, look," he thrust the wine bottle under the nose of the man.

The customer tried another tack. "Why don't you taste the wine I have already poured into the glass?" He suggested.

Charlie took the bottle and raised the neck to his mouth and gulped it down thirstily. "It's good," he grinned, smacking his lips.

Unfortunately, Charlie just would not listen, and so Liz 'let him go' and he got a job as a premier wine waiter with one of the larger hotels on the island.

Boris was the bus driver. There was no public transport in St Lucia, so people had to rely on mini buses. Because our staff needed to be in at a certain time, and were often late home, we laid on our own bus service, and Boris who owned his own vehicle used to carry out this function. There were a few minor functionary's such as Dodo and Dumbo who were washers up, and George who was our night guard and one or two others who were brought in to help at the weekend.

As Friday approached, we were to hear that there was a tropical wave heading towards the island. We had become used to these when sailing, so we were not too worried. Sometimes these weather systems were very large and had a considerable amount of wind in them, other times they were quite small, taking less than a day to go through, like the one we experienced sailing to the Virgins. In all cases, they were always very wet. We were to find that rain inevitably gave us problems, not only because we found that the roof leaked like a sieve, but it meant that the open areas such as the walled garden and the open veranda in front of the yachtsmen's bar, could not be used.

17 - THE STORM

The owners despair

As I have indicated before, weather forecasting in the Caribbean was notoriously unreliable, and so we just prayed that the tropical wave would not hit the island before midnight on Friday. By seven p.m. although the air was heavy and still, no rain had appeared, and we started to breathe a sigh of relief, by seven-thirty, the restaurant was full, as was the Pub area and the staff were really rushed off their feet, as customers demanded the usual immediate service.

The kitchen worked well, even though we were certain that Yani was drinking heavily again. All orders had been dealt with promptly and most of the diners were in the middle of their meal when there was a huge clap of thunder. Within seconds the rain came hurtling down. We quickly moved our guests from the Garden area to inside the restaurant, and those who were in the Pub area were moved further into the centre of the floor. The windows, although closed, were allowing water to spurt through.

For the first time we noticed a leak in the roof, and we moved some unfortunate Germans who were underneath it. Minutes after, another leak appeared, then another, then another. Pans and every available bucket were commandeered and placed in strategic places, but we simply had not enough to cope with the downpour.

The Germans commented with uncharacteristic humour that they had come to St Lucia to learn to dive but didn't realise that they were supposed to eat underwater too.

This comment was reported to Yani, and he suggested that he remind them that they would not have had it so good in a concentration camp... I couldn't see the connection, but I thankfully persuaded him that it would not be a tactful thing to say.

For some reason, Yani disliked anything that was German, and I was to find out the reason later. Apparently, he had once become over amorous with a rather large German female, and she had objected to his advances by attempting to remove a part of his anatomy which was fairly firmly fixed on. He had, so the story goes, suffered severe bruising that affected not only his walking ability for some days afterwards.

The weather worsened, and because there was quite a high wind, we became worried about a couple of yachts that were tied to our dock. They started to move around rather erratically, and I had visions of the whole dock area collapsing if the wind got much worse. I got hold of Dumbo, and with a yachting friend who had called in for a drink, we went outside in the downpour, and tightened the lines to the kedge (rear) anchors that had been dropped. (Both yachts were moored bow to the dock).

Some ten minutes later soaking wet, we ran back inside, our mission accomplished. It became quickly clear that our customers were not 'happy campers'. I could see their point of view, particularly those who had come out for a romantic supper. The meal was anything but romantic, as water trickled down their necks, and those that had come out for an ordinary meal or drink, shivered in the relatively cool air that was being blown through the bar and restaurant. To make matters worse, our little music trio had not turned up. No doubt their vehicle had been waylaid by the flooding which always appeared within minutes of heavy rains. But this meant we had no live music, which had been billed as a star attraction.

When customers in a mass start to get angry, it often proves to be contagious, and soon we had a very unhappy staff too, as they could see their tips getting smaller and smaller as disgruntled customers complained of the cold food. While the main cause of this was exacerbated by the water dripping onto it from the roof, and blasts of cold air emanating from the lagoon, which was now blowing through the gaps in the bar windows, it was still no consolation to the diners that the food had arrived at the table piping hot.

At this critical moment, the musical trio arrived, and during setting up the equipment, the guitarist was just inserting his electrical instrument into a plug when all the lights went out. For a moment, I thought that he had caused the problem, and cursed him, particularly as I realised with horror, that I did not know where the fuse box was, and even if I did, I did not have a torch to find the blown fuse. I mentally kicked myself, and then I suddenly noticed that all the nearby house lights had gone out too. It was a power station failure. In fact, we were to find in the future, that at the slightest hint of rain, the lights would invariably go out. We were told that the power station employees, who worried about reaching their homes, just switched off the diesel generators that were the source of our power and buggered off. I did not believe the story, but certainly, power would die at the slightest excuse of bad weather.

The atmosphere in the restaurant and Pub could have been cut with a knife.

There was total silence. At that precise moment Gregory, the young chef, panicked.

Whether he was concerned because there would be no tips for the kitchen that night, or simply that the food he had lovingly prepared, would not be eaten, was never divulged. He ran out from the kitchens and because he was as black as the night, only the whites of his eyes were visible.

As he stood in the centre of the dining room rather out of breath, he shouted at the top of his voice, "DON'T STOP DE EATIN', DON'T STOP DE EATIN'... De power is back soon... I tink..."

Except for the drip, drip of water and howling wind outside, there was not another sound in the blackness, then one customer laughed then another and then everyone was laughing. None of them could see a damn thing of course, some had their food swimming in cold water, and others had water dripping from their necks. The amusing side of the facetiously and yet panicky reaction from Gregory thankfully restored and extended the previous good mood, and soon there was much merriment from the whole restaurant.

From that time on, we did not look back. We managed to find some candles, and although they kept blowing out with the wind, they were better than nothing. The lights came on after about twenty minutes, and we offered to re heat the food and we served everyone free wine. It was dreadful stuff, and we were glad to be rid of it, but the alcohol percolated through, the trio struck up with reggae, and once people started dancing, the cold wind became a godsend. In the end, a good time was had by all.

By 10 p.m. the 'party' was still going strong, but the staff were worried about getting home because of the flooding, so we let them go early, and Liz and I with the help of one or two who lived locally managed far into the night.

We got home about 3 a.m. the next morning, the rain seemed to have eased somewhat, and we hoped that the next day would prove to be fine. When we reached our house in Panorama Villas we groaned as another desperate scene awaited us. The rain had come in through several holes in the roof, and there was water everywhere. We started to clean up, but gave up after two hours, eventually climbing into bed at just after 5 a.m. We knew we were in for a hard day on Saturday. Little did we know just how hard?

We were late up the next morning which worried Liz because she knew most of the shops closed by midday, and she had a heavy shopping list. We almost threw on our clothes, grabbed a bite of toast, and were at the Pub by just after nine-thirty.

Nothing had prepared us for what we were about to see.

As we walked into the front door, there was an extremely offensive smell. We walked further, and realised that the dining area, Pub section and kitchen had been completely flooded, the water having subsided, leaving a thick treacle smelly residue all over the floor. The place looked and smelled just like a sewage plant. In fact, we learned that the sewage pipe that ran out into the lagoon just near the bar, had backed up, and thus it was truly sewage that now covered the area.

"Oh Jesus, was all I could find to say," as both Liz and I

covered our noses with damp rags.

"Well, that settles it," said Liz, "there is just no way we can get rid of this by tonight, we'll have to close," she said mournfully.

I nodded, "absolutely, if it gets out that we've had sewage in our kitchens, I doubt if anyone will want to eat here again." Liz looked worried. "What about our bookings, we are almost full..."

There was only one thing for it. "Why don't we ring all the hotels in the area, and let them know we'll be closed for..." I looked at the mess, "for say, three days due to the flooding?" Liz agreed that was the best policy, as three days would give us time to clear the dirt, and thoroughly disinfect the place. Once that had been done, we would then have to think about repairing the roof, and to try and ensure that we were not flooded again by building some sort of protection in the area where the water and sewage had got in.

"What about the staff?" Asked Liz.

"I suspect quite a lot of them will not show anyway," I answered correctly as it turned out, "the roads around Castries will be bad. Those that do show up can be put to work." Liz rubbed tears from her eyes. "So much for a successful first week," she whispered.

"Well, these things happen," I assured her, and took her in my arms, giving her a hug. "At least you don't have to do your shopping..."

"Shopping," answered Liz, "yes I do, we need disinfectant, cloths, bristle brushes,"

"Shovels..." I added, as I looked at the floor. "If anyone had suggested I would be coming to the Caribbean to shovel shit, I wouldn't have believed them," I said as I steered Liz out of the front door, closing it firmly behind us. I thought of the common saying in the tourist industry, often used as a greeting, which we could now take literally: "Another shitty day in paradise?" Liz went down town to get the necessary items, and I put up a notice outside saying we were closed for three days for 'repairs', I then telephoned all the hotels asking them to put up a similar notice on their boards. I had just finished calling the few local people who had also booked, when I heard Liz coming back. We off loaded the van and by the time we had got everything inside, three of the kitchen staff had arrived, so we put them to work.

I had heard about the difficulty people in flooded areas had with cleaning up, but I never realised just what a major job it was. Our clean-up was of course compounded by the sewage, which stank to such a degree that it was not possible to spend more than fifteen minutes at a time within an enclosed room. We realised we had been lucky, in that neither the store rooms nor the walk-in refrigerators had been contaminated, but even then, it took us a full two days just to get the mud and sewage out. We then had to thoroughly disinfect the whole area, and by the time we opened the following Tuesday, the place smelled like a general hospital.

Strangely enough, the biggest problem was in the bar area, where the floor boards were slightly spaced. It was much easier to clean up of course, as the water and muck disappeared between the cracks and into the lagoon below, but some had obviously stuck to the underside of the floor, and on hot days, we had to use liberal amounts of disinfectant to disguise the pong. We never completely got rid of the problem.

We were just getting over the flood when the following Friday, we had another shock. We were told that a young yachtsman friend of ours, David Bell had died in mysterious circumstances. We had known him when he ran a small charter boat with his girlfriend Gloria, and we had often come across the couple when sailing in the Grenadines.

The story of his death was rather bizarre. David and Gloria had sailed down to Union Island where they had dropped their charter guests off. After he had seen them on to the aircraft at the small airport, he had gone to have a drink at the local hotel.

While there, he had got into a conversation with a couple of tourists and agreed to charter his boat to take them to Bequia, the island just south of St Vincent.

Unfortunately for him, one of the local charter boat skippers, buttonholed him for stealing his trade. A threat was made, and that was that.

The charter took place, and it was some months later that he was in the area again. In the middle of the night, there was a sound near the boat, and he got up to investigate. Gloria who had also woken, dozed off again, but when she awoke early the next morning, she was surprised to find David was not in his bed. She went up on deck and became even more concerned when he was nowhere to be found on the boat. She took some comfort from the fact that the dinghy was still tied on however, so she assumed he had gone for an early morning swim. After about an hour, when David had not returned, she raised the alarm. It was midday when David's body was found underneath his boat. There were no marks on his body, and it was assumed he had somehow drowned. I knew however, as did Gloria, that David was an extremely good swimmer.

Murder might seem to be a little extreme, just over a charter... But I relate another story here of what happened in St Lucia rather later, this illustrates the intense competition and rivalry for business in the area.

An acquaintance of mine, let's call him Carl, had developed a day charter business in St Lucia. Carl was English, and the day charter business was the right of the indigenous. He had received some veiled threats but had ignored them. One day he was sitting on his boat with friends who had brought him his mail from Castries. (All mail is sent to a post office box at the main post office on the island). He noticed one was a small parcel, and as he took the wrapping paper off the item, he saw it was a video. Thinking that some good friend had sent him a raunchy tape he went to put it on one side, and it blew up.

Fortunately, only his hand and arm were seriously damaged, the explosion had been far enough away from his body for it not to damage his face or vital organs.

Nevertheless, he was hospitalised for some days afterwards.

David's body was brought up to St Lucia by Freddy the Fart. I remember rather cruelly commenting that there was not much damage Freddy could do to poor David now.

David had indicated to Gloria, that if anything happened to him, he should be buried at sea. All the arrangements were made, and the coffin was brought out to the Pub the evening before the burial and placed overnight in the walk-in cooler. This caused us some problems afterwards, because most of our St Lucian staff would not enter that area, even long after the coffin had gone. A small buffet had been arranged for the mourners in the restaurant after the burial service, which was to be on Sunday, which was the next day.

A large motor launch, that had been chartered by Gloria, drew up to the Bar dock just before 1 p.m., on the Sunday afternoon. The few guests arrived, and the coffin was loaded on, we were about to move off, when we realised that the vicar had not arrived. We waited half an hour, and as the minister still had not turned up. We sent Yani to look for him. It was a great mistake, as it was one and a half hours later that Yani returned with the man of God, both looking decidedly worse for wear.

Liz was furious, because Yani was supposed to be preparing the dinner for that night, and clearly could not now be trusted to do so. As a result, she decided to stay behind while the burying party headed off for a spot about the three miles off shore, with two of us propping up the unfortunate minister who had already been sick over us as we tried to get him to the side of the boat before he threw up.

After that, we prudently decided to take the vicar down below, and we laid him down on a bunk in the main cabin in the hope that he might sufficiently recover to take the service by the time we reached our destination. We were to be disappointed. When we arrived, it was obvious that poor David would not have a ministerial send off, and so we asked Gloria if she would rather abort the whole thing, until we could find another minister. Thankfully, she suggested we get it over with. I was glad because I did not particularly relish storing the coffin for yet another night.

The skipper on the boat read a rudimentary service, and with some difficulty we carried the coffin to the side and launched it over the side. We watched sadly as it slipped below the surface, and just as I was about to turn away to console Gloria who was weeping silently, I saw the bloody thing shoot back up to the surface. Others had noticed it too, but I managed to get Gloria below, and left her with a girlfriend while I went back on deck to see what had happened. Joseph Thompson the skipper, spat over the side.

"Bloody idiots, they've not weighted the coffin," his hands

gripped the side rail as he stared at the bobbing box, now some twenty feet away from us.

At that moment, the minister staggered on deck and started to read the burial service. He seemed completely oblivious to the floating coffin. We got hold of him and firmly led him back to one of the cabins below and put him on another bunk and closed the door. He went straight to sleep.

Back on deck, I asked the skipper what we should do.

Joseph spat again. "I suppose we could bring it back in, and put an anchor in it," he answered helpfully.

"No chance," said another man standing nearby, "an anchor wouldn't fit," I nodded. "What about a length of anchor chain?" I said. Joseph looked doubtful, "I don't think we've got enough to make any difference," he grimaced.

"Well, we can't just leave it here," I said,

"Why don't we bring it in. and tip the bod. . ." Ventured another male friend.

"Then both would float, besides, I ain't particularly keen to open the bloody thing up," said Joseph, "are any of you?" The half dozen people standing around wore expressions that confirmed they were not eager to bring the coffin back on board.

One wag suggested we pour blood over the side, to attract sharks.

"Oh yeah," said Joseph, "and how many pints are you goin' to give?" The person with the bright idea remained silent.

"There's only one thing for it," said Joseph, "keep Gloria below I shan't be a minute," Joseph disappeared and a few minutes later he came back bearing an ugly looking Smith and Wesson Magnum revolver. "Now you guys haven't seen this."

We all nodded.

Manoeuvring the boat to where the coffin had drifted, Joseph fired six shots into the coffin, reloaded and fired another six. Slowly but surely, the coffin began to sink. It took about five minutes before we were certain it had gone, and we all sighed with relief. Gloria wanted to know what the shots were, and she was told that we gave David a twelve-gun salute...

As the last shot was fired, the minister appeared once

again on deck, bible clutched firmly in his hand, and promptly rushed for the side of the boat, where he no doubt emptied the rest of his stomach. We gently steered him below again, as he attempted to continue to read from one of the psalms.

We were glad to get back to the restaurant, and after a relatively short buffet, everyone went home, the minister being placed in a taxi we ordered for him. Gloria had decided to go back to America for a while, which was her home, and I took her to the airport the next day.

She had been gone two days, when I heard that the police were looking for her, apparently the minister was supposed to have got a certificate for burying David at sea but had neglected to do so. He had therefore been buried without a death certificate or proper paperwork.

Eventually a police officer who had heard that I had been involved with the funeral, came to see me, and he told me that the body would have to be exhumed.

"You're joking," I looked at him incredulously.

He shook his head gravely. "No man, it's the law, he'll have to be dug up,"

"But he was buried at sea," I explained.

"Makes no difference man, we have to have the body to get the paperwork in order."

"Well," I said, "If you guys can find the body, good luck to you..."

A very unhappy policeman went off to file his report. I never did find out what happened over the affair, but I was glad David's body did not show up, as I have no doubt that someone would have had great difficulty in explaining the bullet holes...

18 - THE ROBBERS

The cowboy law enforcers-

St Lucia had not the crime that was prevalent on the larger islands such as Jamaica and Trinidad but the increase in tourism inevitably brought out the criminal element. The biggest problem was drugs, as many Europeans and Americans used to come on holiday to the Caribbean because they knew they could obtain certain drugs more easily and more cheaply and use them without too much fear of detection.

A story I was told by a good friend of ours who was the manager of one of the charter companies on the island illustrates the laxity that was prevalent in those days.

I tell the story here as Michael told it to me.

"We used the services of the odd skipper to deliver yachts to Martinique, but there were two I stopped employing because I suspected they were running drugs. One morning these guys came to see me, and asked me if I had any delivery jobs to Martinique, and I told them no. They then asked if they could charter a yacht for a couple of days, as they wanted to get away to relax. Knowing that they did not usually have two cents to rub together, I asked them where they would find the £1,000 necessary for the insurance deposit and the cost of the charter.

"They said it was no problem, but they could only pay on their return. *It was well known that the Gendarmerie in Martinique were paranoid about drugs, with good reason, and they regularly searched yachts entering their territory." I knew this to be true, as we had been searched several times during our charter days and I remembered Laurie's story.*

Michael continued, "I told them no, even if they could pay the full amount in advance, they would not get a boat from me. They went off cursing and muttering and I thought that would be an end to the story. The next morning when I arrived at the marina, my dock master told me that Mary Lou, a forty-four-foot Benatau, was missing. There was no way it could have broken free on its own, so I immediately telephoned the police with my suspicions. Within an hour I had a visit from the customs people, and one of the men present was a Brit, who was Captain of St Lucia's only gun boat, the MV Minerva. I told them that I suspected that the men concerned would return the boat to its dock within a couple of days, and if they were asked, they would almost certainly claim I had given them permission. I assured them that I hadn't. A plan was agreed, whereby the MV Minerva would anchor just forward of the channel between Rodney Bay proper and Rodney Bay Lagoon, which effectively meant that any boat entering Rodney Bay would be seen immediately, and any yacht going into the channel would have to pass within a few feet of the gun boat. Two mornings later I was therefore astonished to learn that Mary Lou was back in the dock just as though it had never left. I called customs, and eventually they contacted the captain of the MV Minerva, who confirmed that they were still in place waiting for Mary Lou to show. I told 'em not to bother as it had docked. The Captain just did not believe me, until he came in via the gunboat's dinghy, and saw it for himself. Later I was to learn that the crew on watch had buggered off to Gross Islet for a jump up, and as luck would have it, our two smugglers chose that precise time to return. The men were disciplined of course, and the Captain told me that next time they would get the buggers."

They never did.

From our point of view, the biggest problem was not

drugs, but petty crime. At that stage there was no police post in Rodney Bay, the nearest one being Gross Islet. If one telephoned the police there, they asked you to drive up and fetch a policeman, as they had no transport. Not exactly a fast response team.

The first sign we had of serious problems was one night when a couple came into the Pub in great distress, they had been stopped and threatened by a man with a knife, and all their money taken.

They had only walked from the St Lucian Hotel to the restaurant, which in daylight was almost in sight of each other. After this incident, the problems started to escalate, and one person was stabbed, although thankfully, not badly hurt. We spoke to the Hotels and Restaurant Association who were our governing body on the island, and they invited a senior police officer to one of the meetings. When he had heard of the various complaints, he was heard to remark that as it was only honkeys (Whites) involved, he did not feel it was a serious matter, fortunately, most of his colleagues and the politicians did not share his view, and we were assured that a police patrol would be instigated.

Some weeks after this, we had another very distressed couple come into the Pub, who said they had been stopped by some evil looking men in a beat-up Suzuki and had been asked for their passports. Liz discovered that the passports had been returned, and that the people had not been robbed, so she assumed correctly that it was the new police patrol. This situation worsened as less and less people were prepared to walk the few hundred yards from the hotel, because of the possibility of being accosted by these men. Trade was staring to fall, so one night when I was not there, Liz set out to find the culprits. Sure enough, she was stopped by them.

They were in the beat-up Suzuki, and had no uniforms or other I.D.

"How do I know that you are policemen?" asked Liz.

"You don't have to know," answered one.

Liz got angry. "Don't be bloody silly, you are supposed to be here to protect the tourists, and all you are doing is frightening the hell out of them. It's the thieves you're supposed to be catching, not the tourists, if you carry on this way, St Lucia won't have any tourists left."

"What do you suggest?" Asked the sergeant chastened.

"Well, for a start you know it isn't a white man who is doing the mugging, as all the people I have talked to have indicated that it's obviously a St Lucian, so how about turning your attention to someone who is black and suspicious, that'll do for a start."

The upshot of this conversation was that Liz made firm friends with the sergeant, and he became even friendlier when he knew he could get a free beer after his patrol. I believe the culprit was eventually caught, but sadly our sergeant was suspended because of it.

Sergeant Jamieson always carried a particularly menacing sawn-off shotgun, and even used to bring it in to the Bar when he came for a drink. More than once, I had to persuade him to put the safety catch on as he waved it around in general conversation, and often he would use it rather like a finger, pointing at someone, to make a point. There is no doubt that by using this expressive method of body language, his argument was usually accepted.

One day a very dead black man, who met the description of the various people who had been robbed, was found at the bottom of a cliff not too far away. Sergeant Jamieson said the man had suicided himself while trying to escape, unfortunately the suspect had been blasted from behind by both barrels of a shotgun and had toppled over the cliff on which he was running towards. Naturally, the question posed was, if the suspect was running away then it was only over the cliff, and as the drop was over fifty foot, he would not have got too far, so why was he shot?

Sergeant Jamieson had however been very good to us, and while we had his protection, we had no problems. One night when we were very busy, a party of Germans got up and walked out without paying. Liz knew where they were staying, so she rang the hotel, and the assistant manager, who tracked them down in the hotel bar, came back with a message from them, saying the food was piss awful, and Liz could go and f ... herself. He said they were big fellows, and he wasn't going to argue with them. Liz was furious, because after checking with the waitress, and the barman, she learned that they had obviously enjoyed their meal, and had spent something over $100 on wine and other drinks apart from the food. When Sergeant Jamieson came in for his beer that night, she told him what had happened. He did not say much, he just finished his beer and bade us goodnight.

The story is taken up by someone we knew who was drinking in the bar at the hotel that night, the three Germans were standing by the bar, and had been drinking heavily. Most people had given them a wide berth because they were so loud and aggressive. He had seen the assistant manager go up to them, and their reaction to him, so he was surprised when they were approached by a small lone St Lucian with a long trench coat on. He said something to them, and they told him to fuck off, or else. With that the scene took on the spectre of a Wild West showdown.

Jamieson pulled out his sawn-off shotgun and said that he was a member of the St Lucian Police Force, and he was arresting them. The click of the safety catch being undone was totally audible in the silence that followed.

All three were then marched up the road to the Pub, where like naughty children, they apologised profusely to Liz, saying it was all a joke. With gun still pointed at their backs, they quickly and wisely paid up. The trio were then taken outside to the car park and given a thorough dressing down by Jamieson and eventually sent on their way. The word got around, and we never again had a non-paying guest.

We missed Sergeant Jamieson after he had been suspended, and although the mugging stopped, Liz had a nasty shock one day shortly afterwards. In the morning before setting off for the town for the purchase of provisions, she used to sort out the takings from the previous day.

We had had a particularly good weekend, and as it happened to be a Monday, she was counting the weekend's cash, ready for banking. With all the money still on the desk she heard a knock at the office door. It was quite normal for fishermen to call at that time of the morning but instead of putting the money in the safe, she opened the door. The next thing she knew she was on her back, and a large man was trying to tie her wrists. She struggled, but after she realised, he was looking around for something heavy to hit her with she stayed still. The thief then scooped up more than $10,000 (about £4,000) and ran out of the same door that he entered. I had just taken the van to the local petrol station to get it filled up, so I could not have been gone more than ten minutes. When I returned there was a tearful and trembling Liz undoing the string binding her hands. We called the police who eventually came, the officer in charge berating Liz for not struggling more. That was the total sympathy she got, and subsequently a rumour went around that Liz had faked the robbery so she could claim on the insurance. Small communities can be quite vicious sometimes and St Lucia was no exception.

Shortly after that incident, the Pub was broken into overnight, but because all the cash was kept in a floor safe, and wines and spirits were locked away, very little had gone missing. Whether it was the same man who had robbed Liz, I was never to find out, I was sure however, that our thief would return, so I decided to set up a sophisticated trap for him.

I had not bargained for the sort of problems such a trap would cause.

One evening just after the break in, I spent the whole night devising a method of retribution to deal with any future interloper and give him a lesson be would not forget. To this end, I carefully wired the metal desk in the office straight to a power point. I made sure that safeguards were instituted, wiring in a large red light above the internal door, which automatically went on when the desk was live. In case either of us entered through the main external office door, to which only Liz and I had the key. I rigged up a line made from string around the desk at waist level, with a notice that said DANGER 240 Volts. I finally wired the power point to the switch on the wall by the door, which showed a red light when turned on, so the power could be turned off long before reaching the desk. All this meant that whichever way we entered the office, there would be a red warning light indicating the 'live' desk. To make sure that there could be no accidents, I also instilled in Liz that both doors should always be kept locked. I also told her that even with the light switch off, the plug must be withdrawn from the socket in the wall before anything else was done, even if the telephone was ringing when entering the office.

By following these simple precautions, I reasoned that the only person, who could possibly get hurt, was a thief who would not wish to switch a light on.

Thus, it became a standard procedure for Liz and me when we were leaving the office for any length of time, to switch on the power to the desk.

Several weeks later, at 8 p.m. at night, the restaurant was quite busy, when I heard a piercing scream from the direction of the office. Liz and I were in the lobby at the time, and I looked at her in triumph. "Caught the bugger," I said. Liz's eyes widened and her hand went to her mouth.

"What's matter?" I asked, puzzled.

"Yani, I have just given Yani the key, he wanted to get some Brandy for cooking, and I was busy, so I forgot..."

"Oh my God," I groaned, and rushed through to the office, noticing the red light on above the door as I opened it. I went straight across to the switch and turned the power off. The office was in a shambles.

Mary the young pretty waitress was on the floor on her back unconscious. Yani was sitting upright in the corner with no trousers on, in fact with nothing on his lower half, except for his socks and shoes. He was looking very mournful.

I quickly leaned down to Mary, but as I did so, she sat up sharply, took one look at me and her rather wan complexion changed to deep red. She muttered something and got shakily to her feet.

"Are you okay Mary?" I asked worriedly.

She looked embarrassed and avoided looking at me. "Yes Mr. James, yes Mr. James, must've slipped Mr. James," she bolted for the door and shot out of the room towards the restaurant.

I frowned at the odd behaviour, and then as I turned to look at Yani, I noticed a screwed-up pair of red panties just near the desk. I picked them up and straightened them out in front of Yani.

"What have you been up to Yani?" I looked at him suspiciously.

He grinned sheepishly. "I could do with a drink," he said, as he started to pull himself up.

I went over to the plug and pulled it out from the power point and told him to meet me at the bar when he had got dressed.

As I went back into the lobby, I saw Liz looking worried, "is he all, right?"

"Yes, he's fine, but..." A customer walked in, so I told her I would tell her later.

Yani came through, and we found a section of the bar that wasn't busy. I bought him a coffee.

"Well?" I raised my eyebrows.

Yani, who was completely recovered now, grinned. "Well, I needed some Brandy for cooking, so I went and asked Liz for the office key."

"Yes, I know the story as far as that." I said.

"Yeah, well... I had just gone through into the office and switched the light on, when I saw your sign, so I kept well away from the desk. What I didn't know was that Mary had followed me in. She's been on my case for the last few days, suggesting things..."

"Things?"

"Yeah, things, like shouldn't we get together, you know..."

I nodded. "So?"

"Yeah, well, I could see she was fired up like, so I thought, well why not, she's an attractive bit of crumpet and she was very turned on, and to cut a long story short, we went into a clinch and when things began to get hot, she slid down her panties, and lifted her leg for an easy entry. I guess I must've thrust a little too hard," Yani wiped his brow at the memory, "'cause unfortunately, she unbalanced. By this time, she had her back to the desk. I suppose she thought the desk would be a good base to..."

"Never mind what she thought the desk would be," I stopped him, "then what?"

"I heard a sizzling sound and at the same time felt as though a fuckin' elephant had trodden on my balls. Mary was screaming as we both catapulted backwards with her on top of me. I can tell you for nothing that 240 volts through a hard on is a hell of a lot more effective than a cold bucket of water. I had just rolled out from under her when you came along. Bloody shame, 'cause I was having..."

"Well, it bloody well serves you right," I snarled, "perhaps next time you'll think twice before letting your sexual desires get the better of you in working time, and with a member of your own staff." I was quite annoyed as I realised either of them could have been badly hurt.

Still grinning, Yani downed his coffee and when I refused him another, he went off to the kitchen. I could have sworn he walked with a swagger.

The thing that really irked me was the story I was to hear the next day.

Apparently, Mary had told the other girls that she had experienced such a massive orgasm, that it had completely knocked her out. Yani's sex appeal was thus doubled or trebled due to this incident. I don't think Mary ever realised that she had been electrocuted.

The next time I was to catch Yani 'at it' was not with a member of staff and the situation was to be far more embarrassing.

Sadly, at Liz's request, I disassembled my thief catcher the very next day, but strangely, we were never burgled again. Perhaps the 'word' had got around. If so, then it had served its purpose.

19 - THE U BOAT AFFAIR

The sailors Revenge

Despite the start-up difficulties, the restaurant was now doing well, and we began to get a good reputation for excellent food. Providing we could keep Yani sober, and well away from the female staff, we reckoned we could not go wrong a rather naive conclusion.

At this time, two famous actors were filming a comedy in the south end of the island, and we got a call one day to ask us if they could come to lunch with their wives. We didn't usually make lunches at that time, but given their celebrity status, we agreed to put on a special meal. Once one opens a restaurant, you cannot close it to others, and as there was a Royal Naval Destroyer on a goodwill visit to Castries at that time, we had some sailors who dropped in for a drink.

They spotted the celebrities, and we were concerned that Royal Naval autograph hunters would ruin their meal, but they took it all in good part.

The sailors were delighted and promised that they would return with their mates the same evening. They explained that it was to be their last evening on St Lucia, as their ship was moving off south the next day.

From time to time, yachtsmen who were travelling back home, would leave their yachts in the lagoon near to the Yachtsman's Bar, and ask us to keep an eye on them while they were gone. I was always careful to warn them that we could not be responsible for these boats. If someone paid a fee for their boat tied to our dock, then that was different.

Someone who I had met while sailing owned a small Catamaran. One evening about two weeks before the celebrities' lunch, he had come and told me he and his girlfriend were going to the States for a couple of weeks and would I keep an eye on the boat which he had moored about fifty yards off our dock. I had nodded my assent with the usual warning. It was quite easy to see from the bar, and it was the only Catamaran in the lagoon at the time.

The night after the lunch, the sailors duly arrived with about ten others and were soon in good spirits. The bar area started to fill up when I noticed a man called Kruger chug up to our dock in a dinghy. Kruger was an infrequent visitor because he used to charter quite a lot down in the Grenadines. I assumed when I saw him that he must have dropped off some charter guests in St Lucia. He always had his dog with him that looked as old, ragged, and dirty as Kruger did.

I did not particularly like him, as not only was he a scruffy individual, but after a few drinks he would use foul language, which of course did not go down well with female guests within earshot. Kruger owned quite a large Catamaran called Rosie, which took about six guests, but I never came across anyone who sailed with him, so did not know whether he ran a good boat or not. If his personal cleanliness was anything to go by, I doubted it.

Kruger was normally a surly individual and drank on his own, but as soon as he saw the sailors, he made a beeline for their party. At first, they ignored him, but I noticed as the evening wore on, they had included him in the general chat and merriment that was going on. It was near 1 a.m. when I sensed the conversation was turning a little unfriendly, and I moved nearer so that I could overhear what was said.

Kruger sneered and waved his hand away from his body. 'Ze British navy is useless, I know, I fought zem in ze war.'

'Oh yes matey,' said one sailor 'and what did you do?' Kruger put his right hand on his chest 'I vas ze man who sank ze Royal Oak battleship,'

'You sank a battleship?' said another incredulously.

'Me, I sank the Royal Oak, wiz all the crew on board,' he banged down his beer glass on the bar counter.

It was clear, they didn't believe Kruger. 'Oh yeah, what did you use mate, a shotgun?' There were general guffaws.

Kruger shook his head, staggered slightly poking a rating in the stomach.

'Pow, pow' he said, 'I vas ze torpedo officer on U-boat U47 und ve got into Scapa Flow, und ve sank the bastards, it vas on 14th October 1939.' He grinned.

Suddenly one of the sailors realised that what Kruger was saying was correct.

'My uncle was on that ship mate, you killed him, you fuckin'...

I quickly intervened, by buying the sailors a free round, and with a friend, we got hold of the drunken Kruger and steered him back to his dinghy. He apparently did not wish to go, but I told him that he was not welcome to stay while the sailors were there, and I strongly advised him to get back to his boat while still in one piece. As we helped him into the dinghy, his dog bit me for my pains. I got hold of it and threw it in after him. When he had gone, I really thought that was the last of it. I remember one of the sailors asking me what Kruger sailed, and I told them he sailed in a catamaran.

'Ah, thought the bugger couldn't sail a proper boat,' was all he said.

The next morning, I was checking something in the bar, when I looked out into the lagoon. Something was wrong, I thought, but could not quite place what it was. I suddenly realised with a start that something was different. The catamaran belonging to my American friend had gone. I frowned as I walked over nearer to the window.

'Oh Jesus,' I said.

'What's the problem?' Liz asked as she walked through to the bar.

'Isn't that a mast sticking out of the water?' I asked as I pointed my finger at where the catamaran had been.

'Good Lord, it's sunk,' answered Liz.

'Or it has been sunk,'

'What do you mean?' Liz looked at me in surprise.

I told her about the near-fracas the night before and what Kruger had said. 'I'll bet you anything that they sank the catamaran after they left the Restaurant last night...'

'But that's not Kruger's boat,' said Liz, 'that's...'

'I know, the stupid buggers have sunk the wrong one.' Our American friend returned to the island within a couple of days, and I pointed out that I had simply found the vessel had sunk one morning, I decided not to tell him of my suspicions.

Once refloated, he said he found the water had come in through two faulty seacocks, which he was sure he had checked before he left for the States. He never did learn what might have happened, and what I believe did happen. Members of Her Majesty's Navy had almost certainly sunk the catamaran. I hoped it was good practice for them because they were shortly to go to the Falklands.

20 - THE YACHT RACE

Fair is fair in love, war, and yacht racing.

Shortly after the catamaran incident, I was talking to an old yachting friend of mine, Jasper Cartwright, who was an engineer for a new yacht chartering company in Rodney Bay Lagoon. We were lamenting that there was no yacht racing on the island.

We had organised one or two small affairs when chartering, but the races were between the two charter companies concerned and included only three or four boats.

"Why don't we organise a major yacht race ourselves for all comers?" I asked, we talked some more about the idea and Jasper became quite enthusiastic. We felt we should run races under the auspices of the local yacht club of which we were both members, so we decided to seek out the opinion of the then secretary.

Tracking him down, we carefully outlined the idea of a three-day yacht race to Martinique. St Lucia had a public holiday coming up, which always fell on a Thursday, so we reasoned it would not be too difficult for most interested people to get the Friday off, making a long weekend of it.

The secretary listened to us in silence. Then he frowned as he spoke.

"But, if you have yacht racing man, it will interfere with the social side of the yacht club."

I looked at him in surprise. "But you're a yacht club, which means that you should be promoting the sailing of yachts."

"Noo man, we don't want any smelly yachtsmen around here, this club is a nice club, we can bring our wives and children for lunch at the weekend and lie on the beach, what do we want to organise yacht racing for?"

Well, he had a point. It was obvious the St Lucia Yacht Club, whatever its beginnings had become a social club and it seemed as though the members did not want to change it.

On the way back to the Pub with Jasper, I started to formulate an idea.

"Why don't we start our own club?" I suggested.

"What, you mean a yacht club in competition with the yacht club?" He grinned at the thought.

"Not really," I answered, "our club would be solely for yachtsmen and should encourage offshore yacht racing."

"But we couldn't possibly afford a club house..." Jasper looked thoughtful as he said it.

"No need, we could use the yachtsmen's Haven bar at the Pub, I'm sure Liz would agree to it, the room is quite large, it is not being used, and the drinks licence is already set up..."

We went to the Pub and had a look at the room I had suggested, and as Liz seemed quite keen, we agreed to go ahead with the project. The St Lucia Yachting Association was born. Jasper became the first secretary, me the treasurer, and we invited a prominent St Lucian to become Commodore. Within a few weeks we had over sixty members. We both realised however, that it was important to get the first race off the ground and so I suggested to Liz that the Pub sponsor the three-day race to Martinique, which I had originally suggested to the St Lucia Yacht Club.

There seemed to be a substantial amount of enthusiasm for this proposed race, as there was something in it for everyone. Yacht racing for the keenest, Club Med and the Martinican girls for those keen in another directions, and shopping in Martinique for the rest, the latter was probably the biggest draw of all.

It was agreed that the starting area would be between two temporary buoys which we would lay in Rodney Bay, and that a motor launch would precede us to St Anne's on the south-eastern part of Martinique and drop the two same starting buoys to act as a finishing line. St Anne's would be the anchorage for the first night, and I telephoned Club Med and asked them if they would allow the participants in the race to utilise the hotel facilities. Their answer was in the affirmative, so the first leg of the race was set.

We decided that the second leg on the Friday would be a downwind leg from St Anne's to Diamond Rock on the south western end of Martinique, then north into Fort de France Bay, finishing between the same buoys planted by the motor launch which would set off from St Anne's early on the Friday morning. To make the start in St Anne's more fun. I invented what I think was the first 'Le Mans' start for Yachts.

The idea being that all racing yachts would be moored just off St Anne's beach, and on a gun being fired, the skipper and one other would jump into the water, swim for the shore, retrieve a coloured ribbon tied to a palm tree, and swim back to the boat. No one on the yachts would be allowed to make any preparations for sailing until the two swimmers were firmly back on board. Then the anchor had to be pulled up and sail raised, no engines were allowed of course. This method of starting was to cause much hilarity and confusion as we shall see.

Once the second leg had been completed, the yachts were to be free to moor either in Anse Mitan (on the south side of

Fort de France Bay) or Fort de France itself, Fort de France being the capital city of Martinique situated on the north side of the Bay.

The Saturday was to be completely free for shopping, and Sunday would be the third and last leg of the race, with a start in Fort de France Bay and the finish in Rodney Bay.

We decided that each leg would have a winner, and then there would be an overall winner for the three races. The Pub would give the major prize, and we trawled around various companies in Castries until we had all the other sponsors. I was keen to get the Martinique Yacht Club involved, so waiting for a day when I knew Freddy the Fart was not flying; I hitched a lift on one of the St Lucia Airways charter flights and had a meeting with the Commodore and secretary of the Yacht club there. The Martinicans were delighted that St Lucia was going to organise races again, and soon there was to be a good liaison between the two organisations. The upshot of my visit was that the French insisted on hosting a party for us on the Saturday night, with food and music laid on.

As preparations continued, we realised we had another problem. The boats that were being entered for the race were a polyglot of charter boats and private entries, ranging from a sixty-footer to thirty-four-footer. For those of you who are uninitiated in the ways of sailing boats the physics of speed of boats under sail are in direct proportion to the waterline length. This meant that to give the smaller boats at least half a chance of winning, we needed to invent some sort of handicap system. I worked out a small programme on my computer, and we fed all sorts of magical figures into it. If the result did not seem fair, we added a fudge factor to adjust. It was all very unscientific, but in practice worked quite well.

By the time the day came we were delighted to have fifteen entries. Some charter companies had entered their own boats, but had also been generous enough to charter out their yachts at a reasonable price to locals wanting to join in. I had been offered a Sparkman and Stevens forty-four from Sunshine which was quite a fast cruiser. I had picked a team which consisted of a young American boy I knew called Brodie, two St Lucian's from the Sunshine dock crew, Archibald, Liz's business partner, Brodie's St Lucian girlfriend, Philippa and another girl called Angie who was half British and half Arab.

Jasper, who was the favourite to win had a forty-three-foot yacht, built in Argentina called Eleanor, it was sleek and fast, and he was my main target.

There was one small yacht sailing which caused much mirth because all the men on board were considered 'light on their feet' They were all Europeans, and as I knew them all quite well, I didn't believe a word of the malicious rumour.

Nevertheless, their yacht was christened Aphrodite by the rest. Certainly, they were the least experienced bunch of sailors in the race.

Rodney Bay seems quite large until there are fifteen large yachts in it jockeying for position. The start line was about ten yachts wide, and the idea was to have a running start down wind. This meant that we had to position the yacht in the water so that we would cross the line about two or three seconds after the gun. If a yacht went through early, then it had to return and go through again. If it was left too late of course, then all that would be seen would be the sterns of all the other yachts sailing off into the distance, the gun went off as I was some hundred yards from the line. It had been interesting watching, as to how different skippers approached the problem of starting. One of the yachts Keep me Young, kept going through the line beforehand and swiftly gybing thus going around in a perpetual circle. To turn a yacht in a complete circle means that the jib lines must be transferred from one side of the boat to the other, twice for each circle, and each time the newly positioned foresail must be winched in. The main is easier because the boom, on which the main sits, is simply allowed to move across with the wind. Nevertheless, it is prudent to reel in the slack on the main sheet (main sail) otherwise the boom travels with too much force and is there is a danger of it ripping off the mast.

Unfortunately, for the crew of Keep Me Young, the skipper decided to try these gyrations about ten minutes before the start. Perhaps his watch was fast. The first circle was carried out in an exemplary manner, but we noticed a fast deterioration in the crews handling by the third circle. The yacht went through the line for the fourth time just ahead of the gun, and in their effort to turn quickly, when the yacht came about, the person allocated the job of looking after the main, had clearly run out of steam, or had lost concentration (or both). As he realised the boat was gybing, and the line running through his hands because of the wind force on the sail, he must have attempted to hold on to the line, with painful results. We heard a yelp from the yacht, and as the boom came swinging round at some considerable speed, it completely wrenched off the mast. Unfortunately, by this time, the culprit yacht was blocking part of the start line, so others had to swerve to avoid the stricken vessel. One yacht called Lady Penelope, ploughed into the stern of it, the force knocking the skipper of Keep Me Young, who was by then beside himself with anguish, straight into the water.

We had kept well clear, but I was disappointed that Jasper crossed the line just in front of us. We were so close that one could almost touch the stern of Jasper's yacht from the bow of our own. Jasper was so pleased to have beaten us, that he turned and gave me a 'V' sign. As did he so he took his attention away from his direction for a split second. The wind changed slightly, and I saw his boom lazily arching across in a gybe. On the deck was a young man, a relative of Jasper's who had gone along for the ride. He was standing on the starboard side of the deck looking towards the tangle of yachts behind. He never saw the boom, and no doubt did not know what force propelled him into the water, where he landed quite unhurt. Of course, it was a rule that a man overboard had to be picked up, which not only meant Jasper had to turn his boat around to do that, but because of the considerable gaggle of yachts now coming up to the starting line, he would have to wait for them all to go through before he could get the unfortunate youth back on board. Jasper was not a happy man as we sailed past him waving frantically and cheering at the top of our voices.

Despite the difficulties caused by Keep Me Young the yacht with the separated boom, it was surprising how quickly the field got sorted out. We led the race past Pigeon Island on the westernmost part of Rodney Bay and turned to starboard. The wind in the Eastern Caribbean is predominantly from the east, and as we were to turn north east when clearing the northern end of St Lucia, it was going to be a hard beat up to St Anne's, and we knew we may have to tack several times to get to the finishing line. The wind speed was about twenty-five knots, and the seas running around seven feet, which was about normal.

The sail took just over five hours, we were passed by two faster boats, but on handicap we came second, which pleased us no end, as none of our crew had raced together before.

The last boat in was the one dubbed 'Aphrodite' which arrived some two hours later. Because of the size of their yacht, they had taken quite a drubbing in the channel, and I was told that the sea had washed down below more than once, making their bunks sopping wet. There was much hilarity over this of course, with comments like, 'that will curb the buggers.'

Club Med gave us a great welcome, and for those that have not read my book A Shitty Day in Paradise, I should explain that Club Med do not normally allow anyone but hotel guests to participate in their activities. This is because the residents are given beads with which to purchase drinks, money not being acceptable in the bars. Also, meals are paid for in the price of the deal. In our case we arranged beforehand for dinners to be laid on for everyone, and we paid in advance. Yachtsmen could buy beads at the reception desk, and so a good time was had by all. Club Med have a show in the evening which is put on by the staff and sometimes guests are inveigled to join in. It is usually excellent, and we thoroughly enjoyed it. On the way back to the boat, we noticed several 'notables' from St Lucia taking a dinghy back to their boat, packed with unfamiliar young females. Their wives had been left at home.

l also saw a couple of people off the yacht called Lady Penelope snorkelling, which I thought rather odd in the dark, but did not think any more about it until after the start the next morning.

Yacht racing is extremely hard work. The adrenaline that one feels coupled with the fresh air, the sea and the physical exertion ensures a good night's sleep. This together with the wine and good food, guaranteed that I slept like a log that night, and thus was not aware of all sorts of sexual shenanigans going on in the cabins next to mine.

I woke early and went on deck. The sun had just risen, and it was obviously going to be a beautiful day, there being not a cloud in the sky. I looked either side of me and was surprised to see that the yacht which had the separated boom, Keep Me Young, was moored about three boats up from ours. They must have had the offending part repaired and sailed up after dark.

All the boats were moored bow to the beach, and I noticed two were very close to the land no doubt in the hope that the shorter the swim for the two crew, the faster the take off. As I went below, I saw Brodie's girlfriend coming out of a cabin that was certainly not Brodie's, and shortly afterwards I was to see Angie appearing out of another cabin which was inhabited by the two St Lucian's. She looked quite pleased with herself. Quite what had gone on, I was never to find out, but the St Lucian males were quite useless that day, they seemed to be completely drained... In future races, I was to make myself unpopular by segregating the males from the females.

The gun was fired, and there were splashes as we all dived for the water. I have always been a strong swimmer, but I realised that the two yachts that moored closer to the beach would be first away. The other swimmer from my boat was Angie, who beat me to the shore, got her ribbon and raced past me heading for the water. Clearly whatever had gone on the night before had not sapped her energy...

I had a bit of difficult untying my ribbon, and I could hear the crescendo of my crew urging me on. At last, I loosened it and sprinted back down the beach. Within a couple of minutes, I was hauled on board, breathless, with the ribbon firmly clenched in my teeth. Such was the excitement that it was over ten minutes later, before I realised that it was still there.

The Aphrodite boat was the nearest to the shore, and as they drew in their anchor, while at the same time putting up their sails, I could see them headed for disaster. Sure enough, they had not left themselves enough space to turn and they went hurtling straight for the beach and were lodged solidly into the sand when I last saw them. They were followed soon after by the other yacht that had moored close in, and there was much merriment on the other boats as these rather comical scenes unfolded in front of our eyes. There is nothing quite so funny as a beached yacht with part of the crew in the water frantically trying to push the hull back into deeper water while the rest of the crew on deck attempted to give unhelpful advice.

We had stayed a reasonable distance from the shore, and while this meant a longer swim, we were easily able to turn to starboard as soon as our anchor was up.

We were slightly behind the boat next to us on the port side, but as they had pulled their anchor rode too quickly, and the forward motion had taken them too far into the beach it allowed us to get away before them, although they managed to free themselves quickly afterwards.

There were two more boats further to port, one of them turned to port and the other to starboard, with all the attendant crunches, sounds of metal upon metal and human voices cursing that is normal in collisions at sea. When the confusion sorted itself out, we found we were third away Keep Me Young was just in front of us.

The crew, of Keep Me Young had done well to get away so quickly but even though they were under full sail, they suddenly came to a shuddering stop. It was quite funny and so unexpected the people on board fell over with the force of the halt. I narrowly missed ploughing into their stern and was as puzzled as they obviously were that they had stopped. I knew there was no reef in that spot so certainly they could not have hit anything.

That evening when we all got together, I learned what the snorkellers the previous night had been up to. They had obviously tied a line around the propeller of Keep Me Young and fastened it to some underwater mooring which had been originally placed there by Club Med for a heavy vessel to be secured to. The crew of Lady Penelope who had got tangled up with Keep Me Young at the start in St Lucia no doubt thought some retribution was due.

Lady Penelope sailed past Keep Me Young, the whole crew cheered and laughed, throwing balloons filled with water and flour. Before the end of the race, they were to wish they had not been so obvious in their exuberance.

We were now second to Jasper, who had turned to starboard out of the bay and was down winding parallel with the south end of Martinique. He had a large blooper (A very large foresail, that does a similar job to a spinnaker, but is much larger and heavier) and was really moving away from us quite quickly. We turned the corner to follow him, but because we had no blooper or spinnakers, we put up another main, and poled it out on the other side in a method called wing on wing. We still had a large jib, and I was satisfied that once we had set our sails, we would keep up with the boat in front of us, blooper, or no blooper.

The other yachts were strung out behind us, and I was feeling pleased with our progress, when disaster struck. The pole which held out the second mainsail buckled when there was a slight change of wind, and the port main came crashing on to the deck and ripped down the middle. We quickly took the whole gear down and straightened the pole out, putting it between two dinghy oars and lashing them to act like a splint on a broken arm. I shouted for the torn main sail to be shoved below, and for our other spare to be brought up. Fortunately, we had anticipated problems and we had a third main sail on board, stowed below in the forward sail locker.

I yelled to Angie who was the only one not gainfully employed at the time.

"Get the sheet, get the sheet, quickly," I could see that we were being overhauled by yachts that had started after us.

Angie rushed down below and came back up carrying what we discovered were bed sheets.

"Not the bloody bed sheets," I yelled unkindly, "we can't sail with them, can we?"

By this time, Angie had unfolded one of the sheets, and the wind had caught it taking it overboard. "That's bloody down to you," I shouted unkindly.

I should say here that yacht racing either brings the best out in one... or the worst, with me it was quite definitely the latter.

"We'll have to go back for it," shouted Angie, no doubt worried about the cost of replacing the article now floating

341

gracefully on the sea like some huge Manta Ray.

"Not likely," I growled, as I noticed another yacht coming abeam of us, their crew annoyingly amused at our antics.

Brodie had taken the ripped main below and was just coming back with the new one, when Angie simply jumped off the stern.

I was furious and wished I had not suggested she would have to pay for the bed sheet now floating some five-hundred-yard s away.

We had no choice of course, we had to gybe, and go and pick her up with the bed sheet she'd retrieved. While this was going on, we had the humiliation of Aphrodite sailing past us, who had at last got free of the beach. Their crew waved and jeered. "Don't worry about losing your bedding, you can sleep with us tonight," one shouted, "running out of sails?" Shouted another.

I scowled and gave them a rude sign as we passed going in the wrong direction.

It took us a further two hours to reach Diamond Rock on the south-West corner of Martinique, and because of the delay, we were now trailing seventh. I gained a bit of time going between Diamond Rock and the mainland, some of the others, not knowing the area, left the Rock to starboard. Once we had passed the Rock, we turned north for the short sail up to Fort de France Bay, and on reaching it; we headed for the finishing line some four miles east into the bay. Because we were now into wind, we had a substantial amount of tacking to do, and we eventually crossed the line sixth, having made up one place.

The night was a 'free' one, when everyone went their own way, to do their own thing. We had anchored in Fort de France so that we could transfer our substantial shopping more easily the next morning, and we were just about to leave the boat to head out to a local restaurant, when we were hailed by two men in a large tender.

"Hey, you," shouted one of the men with a thick European accent, obviously German.

I paused as I was halfway down the ladder about to climb into our dinghy.

"Vud, you move your boat please," shouted the other one as the tender came nearer.

Fort de France harbour was not the easiest of places to anchor, partly because the holding was not good in some areas, and partly because the place was so busy, there being at least a hundred other yachts anchored in the same area. Once anchored, you would not normally consider moving until ready to sail and certainly moving at night would have created a further hazard, which I was not going to indulge in without a very good reason.

"Why do you want us to move?" I asked, puzzled.

The two men now drew alongside, and the one driving the rather swish tender stood up. "I have been instructed by the Captain of Lady Bertha," he turned and pointed to a large motor yacht slowly approaching the harbour area, "to request all these boats to move." He swept his hand over the whole area where we and a dozen other yachts were anchored.

"You're joking," I said, in amazement.

"No, no joke, ve have to dock at the port over there," he pointed to the dock where boats could pick up petrol and diesel, "und ve need to get through."

I smiled, "Even if we moved, and I have no intention of doing so, all these boats you see around us, are almost certainly empty, so us moving alone, is not going to help you, besides," I added, "there is a channel large enough for you to get through," I pointed to an area to our stern.

The man ignored what I said. "I have to insist you move, the Captain wishes to come through here," he pointed his finger straight at our boat. "If you do not move, your boat may be damaged."

"Bloody cheek," said Brodie, "if you damage our boat,

you'll have a writ first thing in the morning, and if your Captain can't get his gin palace through, then he'll have to anchor out until the morning, when there'll be more space."

I nodded in agreement, starting the engine of our dinghy, and left them shouting after us. To be prudent, we decided to eat at a restaurant overlooking the harbour, just in case, but as I had indicated, the motor yacht had plenty of room to berth, and the Captain managed to get through the melee of yachts without hitting one.

Although it was dark, the night was clear, and Fort de France harbour is very well lit, so we were able to watch the whole operation. What I was not to know then, was that Lady Bertha, which was owned by an African Prince, was going to cause us some considerable grief in the future.

We had a great evening eating French food, and plenty of French wine. The two St Lucian's had not joined us, as they had relatives on the island, and had gone off into the interior. They indicated that they would not return until the next day. I half wondered what Angie was going to do that night. I did not have long to wait.

We got back to the boat about midnight, and as I was tired, I decided to turn in straight away, leaving the others up on deck talking and drinking. I could hear much hilarity, as I undressed, and as the night was hot and sticky, I decided to have a quick shower. Just as had I finished drying myself in the cabin, hanging the towel on a rail provided, the cabin door opened. It was Angie, completely naked and with a mischievous smile on her face. I thought for a moment that she had entered the wrong cabin by mistake, and I was embarrassed as I too was naked. I was soon to learn differently. Angie was not only an extremely fit female, but extremely good looking with a figure to match. She had jet black hair, which she normally kept up, but now it fell to her waist. She advanced quickly and silently towards me, putting her arms around my neck. She then whispered that she had come to apologise for jumping off the boat that morning, which almost certainly lost us three places. Her breasts pressed against my chest and her hips closed on mine as she reached up and kissed me full on the lips.

I am not quite sure what was going through my mind at that moment, and if I could remember, I would not put it in print here. My body however, reacted as would any male in similar circumstances, and I accepted the clinch, realising that she was fully aroused. Her kiss was very sensuous, and it was as she was drawing away, that the cabin door swung open and there was a flash, as Brodie took a picture. Angie broke away laughing, and Archibald and Philippa were standing behind Brodie. I shoved Angie roughly outside the cabin, and closed the door, locking it, while shouting abuse at the perpetrators of the joke.

I heard much merriment going on above for a while, but I got into my bunk and drifted off to sleep. I knew I would have to get hold of the film before reaching St Lucia to prevent it being shown around island until eventually, Liz would find out what had happened, the joke could easily be passed off, but the problem was the photograph would show me fully aroused with Angie clinging to my neck.

The next morning, as the official race organiser, I had a visit from three of the crew of Keep Me Young, who registered an official complaint against the crew of Lady Penelope. They charged that the crew of that boat had deliberately fouled their propeller with a line, preventing them from sailing out of St Anne's Bay. After much to-ing and fro-ing in the dinghy, I called the three man 'rules' committee to hear their complaint, and we naturally questioned the skipper of Lady Penelope. As expected, he strongly denied any wrongdoing by either himself or his crew, and although I had seen him in the water in St Anne's with snorkelling gear on, I could not of course prove that he or his crew had tampered with Keep Me Young. In the end we had to deny the complaint, but the skipper of Keep Me Young, told me that "those bastards haven't heard the last of this," a prophecy that was to come true all too quickly.

The committee hearing took most of the morning, so I was late going out shopping. One of the things I bought while at the supermarket was a thirty-five-millimetre film, even though I had no camera with me. I was returning to the dinghy dock by taxi, when I saw one of the race boats drawn up to the dock next to the motor Yacht Lady Bertha. It was all St Lucian crew, and they were loading their boat from a large truck parked nearby. If there had been a plimsoll line, theirs would have been several inches below the water line.

In the late afternoon we moved over to the south bay of Anse Mitan, which was a nicer anchorage than Fort de France, and moored next to Lady Penelope. The Saturday evening was a great success, the Martinique Yacht Club did us proud, the food was excellent; there was more than an ample amount of wine, and dancing until the early hours. Some of our crews were very much the worse for wear, and I guessed rightly, that there would be a rather mixed start in the morning.

We had no incidents that night, and I firmly locked my cabin door just to make sure. The next morning the race was due to start at 10 a.m., and the Martinicans had kindly agreed to set up the start line, which was to be a windward start to make things a little more difficult. The motor launch had returned to St Lucia to prepare the finish line.

Our two St Lucian crew had joined us on board just after 7 a.m., about half a day late, and because they were both noisy, it ensured we rose in good time. We noticed that some of the crew, of Lady Penelope had been diving under their boat, just to check that the threat levelled by the skipper of Keep Me Young of the previous day had not been carried out. One of the swimmers gave me the thumbs up sign, so I assumed they had found nothing amiss. By 9.30 a.m. we were ready to move off and prepare for the start. We knew we had to be in the first three to get a place in the overall position, so the start was critical. Lady Penelope obviously had similar ideas as they were taking in their anchor rode at the same time as us.

We picked up our anchor without any problems and turned under engine to port, intending to get free of the numerous other anchored boats before hoisting sail. It was as I was negotiating my way through them that Brodie drew my attention to Lady Penelope.

"Hey James, I think Lady Penelope has a problem with their anchor," I turned and saw their anchor rode was pointing straight down from the bow, which suggested they were over the anchor itself. There were three of the crew straining to pull the thing up. I turned our boat and motored slowly alongside.

"Problems," I shouted.

The skipper came to the rail. "Yeah, we've just stripped our windlass trying to hoist the anchor, its fast, so we are going to have to dive on it." I nodded, sometimes one could be hooked onto rubbish below, which made it difficult to pull it up. I remembered that while chartering I had pulled up a bicycle on my anchor in Fort de France. There was nothing we could do to help, so we turned back, and headed for the start line, it was then I started to wonder whether someone had been monkeying about with their anchor. As we went through the start and turned to head out of the bay the crew of Lady Penelope were still struggling to get their anchor on deck.

I was to learn afterwards that their anchor had mysteriously 'fallen' into a ten-foot hole on the seabed, and the hole had also mysteriously filled itself during the night. Of course, when the crew checked the next morning, there was nothing wrong with the underneath of Lady Penelope, and when the skipper had checked the actual anchor some hundred feet away, the chain simply disappeared into the sand which was not unusual when one had been dropped in fairly a soft seabed. Just as it must have been a quite a feat to dig the hole under water it was an equal feat to dig the anchor out, particularly, as the crew of Lady Penelope did not have breathing apparatus, which again, I was to learn later, the crew of Keep Me Young had.

After the start we made good time to the end of the Bay and turned south to head straight for St Lucia. Apart from Lady Penelope, two other boats had not made the start, one was Aphrodite, and the other a private yacht with a Swedish crew on board. Both were suffering too much from the previous night's activities, to wake up in time. In mid channel, I handed the wheel over to Brodie, saying I had to go below, and I quickly dived into my cabin, got the new film, found Brodie's camera, took out the film inserting the new one. In the darkened cabins I took the necessary shots to reach the same number indicated on the film used indicator and went up on deck.

When no one was looking, I threw the offending film over the side. I felt a bit of a heel doing that, as Brodie had taken almost thirty-six shots of the race, but I felt a lot safer in doing so.

We arrived back in St Lucia, completing an up-wind leg into Rodney Bay, and finishing fourth. In fact, we were to finish fourth overall, which I reckoned was quite reasonable considering I had done most of the organising.

Lady Penelope arrived some five hours later, with their crew not at all in a happy frame of mind, but by then the crew of Keep Me Young had dispersed, so apart from another official complaint, which inevitably went the same way as the previous one, the matter was left at that. I did wonder if the feud would be perpetuated in future races. It was and became so bitter that we had to threaten both crews with expulsion before it was terminated.

A good time was had in the Pub that night, and, considering the hotch potch of yachts taking part, most being amateur sailors, the race had been a great success, and was to remain on the racing calendar for some years to come. It was only after Liz and I left the island years later, that I understood the offshore yacht races started to run down, and nowadays the small amount being organised are under the auspices of the St Lucia Yacht Club, the Association having been disbanded, a shame, because we had some great fun.

21 - A NORMAL DAY

In an abnormal place

In case any reader is foolish enough to consider buying or running a restaurant in the Caribbean (or anywhere else for that matter) I relate in this chapter just what was involved daily. I have picked a normal day at random, which happened to be a Thursday, which was a moderately busy day for us.

7 a.m. got out of bed and exercised for one hour. We found that if we did not exercise, the combined effects of food and drink tended to cling around our bodies like proverbial fatty leeches.

8 a.m. showered and had a light breakfast, leaving home at about 8.40 a.m.

8.45 a.m. arrived at the restaurant. I did the bills, accounts and prepared the money for banking from the previous day's takings. During this time Liz collected various notes from the chefs and waitresses to be able to compile the day's list for purchasing provisions.

9.45 a.m. we had a quick coffee and by 10 am, were in the van headed for town. Our first stop was the bank where we paid in the money. This was usually accomplished by 10-30 am, and we then drove to the first supermarket. After finding a parking space within a quarter mile of the place, we spent the next half hour searching the shelves for necessary ingredients. There was no apparent order of categories, and the jam for instance, could easily be found amongst washing powder one day, and vegetables the next. We repeated this in three or four supermarkets, and on this day, we could find no potatoes on the island, so we eventually bought yams at the local covered market. By the time we had finished normal shopping, it was just after 12.30 pm.

We still needed to buy imported beef steak, which we could only buy from one company. Fresh fish because we had no fishermen call at the Pub the previous morning. Local Pork, which we had to buy from the local Co-op and prepared land crabs which we used as a starter. The latter is called Crab Farci and is a stuffed local land crab which is quite delicious.

We also needed some christophene which we could not find in the local market, so we had to try and find them at one of the smaller shops on the way back.

Christophene is a small squash peculiar to the Caribbean, and we served it stuffed, often with melted cheese. This was a dish that was sought after by tourists and locals alike and was served with the main meal as a vegetable. (*Recipes at the end of this chapter, you see what good value this book is*).

We collected the steak, imported directly from the United States; the local stuff was too chewy for the palette of the normal tourist. Then we arrived at the fish dock and were told that "de Great Chef has bought all de fish for de day," this was a local restaurateur who was one of Liz's main competitors.

Liz was now beside herself with worry, as the restaurant sold more fish dishes than anything else, and we were almost completely out. We were told that there may be more coming in later that day, so I suggested to Liz, that we get the rest of our provisions, and go back to the Pub before it all went off, and that I would return later in the day, to see if there was any fish to be bought. If not, I would go to a small fishing village some twelve miles south of the capital, where it may be possible to find some.

We got back to the Pub at 2.30 p.m. and off loaded the van and packed the purchases away in the refrigerators and storerooms and then rushed home for a light lunch of fruit and yoghurt. We ate quite sparingly during our time running the restaurant. Perhaps we became disenchanted with food...

At 3.45 p.m. I dropped Liz off at the restaurant and went back to the fish market, but there was still no fish available, so I carried on to the fishing village.

Because of the poor roads, I did not arrive there until about an hour later. There was no fish, so I turned around and headed back to the capital, where I again called at the fish market, but again there was no fish so at about 6.30 p.m. I got back to the Pub, where Liz told me that a fisherman had called in about 5-o-clock, and she had purchased both fish and lobster from him. I was not particularly happy, as I had spent almost three hours in the heat and dust of the day, for absolutely no purpose.

The restaurant opened at 5 p.m. but as the first hour was 'happy hour', which was two drinks for the price of one, most of our customers were yachtsmen (*yachtsmen were by far the meanest of all customers spending the least and taking the best deal on offer. I knew why of course, they were also the poorest*) with a smattering of tourists, both types just drinking not eating.

Just after 6.30 p.m. As I drove Liz home to shower and change for the evening, she told me that Yani had not turned up, nor had two of the waitresses. We knew, we were going to be a busy that night, and we also knew just how much harder the work was when we were shorthanded. I cursed Yani under my breath for his lack of responsibility.

We strongly suspected that he was turning back to the bad old days of heavy drinking, and sadly this proved to be the case, but we were to suffer many more trials and tribulations before we finally came to the decision to disengage with his services. As it happened, in the end, Yani beat us to it.

The reason for the non-show of waitresses was not unusual as most of them lived in poor conditions, and the slightest cold would be enough for them to become genuinely laid up. The other problem that was to plague us, was transport. If any of them missed the transport bus we had laid on, it was often impossible for them to find their own way in.

By 7.30 p.m. we were back at the restaurant, where we found one waitress had managed to get a lift to work, but because all the others had to do her work before, she arrived, she was ostracised by them for the evening, which did not help the harmony of the place.

At 7.45 p.m. the water went off, and we found we had a burst pipe, fortunately outside. As I could not get anyone to repair it that night (*or for three days afterwards*), we had to use soda water for washing up. This meant gathering all the bottles together and topping them, which proved to be a full-time job for Dumbo. The other major job was the flushing of the lavatories, so we had to have the head waitress watching as each person entered the lavatory', and then there was a mad scramble to pour a bucket of soda water down the closet before the next customer came to relieve themselves.

We did manage to glean some water from the burst pipe itself but even then, this incident cost us a small fortune.

As it happened this specific day was busier than most, so I was roped in to serve at tables. I was particularly stressed that night, and I remember one British couple asking me if I was any relation to Basil Fawlty, of the BBC programme 'Fawlty Towers'. I was not amused.

By nine p.m., we were out of some of our prepared dishes, thanks to Yani not turning up, so Liz had to go into the kitchen, and help with the cooking. At 9.30 p.m. just as we were starting to breathe a sigh of relief, a party of fifteen Canadians came in wanting dinner. We had to get several tables which had just been vacated, put together, no sooner had we sat them down, then a party of ten Americans came in. None of these people had previously booked.

Liz, having created some starters in the kitchen came back out to help the taking of orders. One of the Americans took a liking to her, and kept making indecent proposals, grabbing her whenever she went near the table. In the end she loaded his food with garlic and then told him she was allergic to it. What with avoiding him and dealing with the Canadian's all who wanted different items on the menu and all on separate bills. (*We called the Canadians the fish and water brigade, because they were even tighter than the British, and inevitably, they always seemed to want separate bills, which gave us problems when we were busy*). We were kept on a constant move.

Our musicians did not turn up that night either, so we were

constantly being asked if the meal was to be discounted because there was not the billed music. At 1 a.m. as the restaurant was starting to empty, a bunch of German yachtsmen came in from a yacht charter, and we all ended up singing German beer songs until the early hours.

When everyone had gone home after about 2.30 a.m., we had some cleaning up to do, the money had to be put in the safe, and we fell into bed just before 3 a.m.

We knew that Friday was one of our busiest days, and that we would have to be up within four hours to start the cycle all over again.

Quite how we did this for four years, six days a week, I cannot think. But if you are considering starting a restaurant in the Caribbean, you have been warned. The best fun is writing about it thirty years or so afterwards!

RECIPES
Stuffed Christophene
Ingredients:

2 Christophene
110 grams Mature Cheddar Cheese-grated
2 medium sized onions-finely chopped
55 grams Butter
Salt, freshly milled black Pepper and grated Nutmeg

Method:
Boil Christophene for 30 minutes, cut in half and remove centre seed.

(The seed tastes like a chestnut and is the cook's perk, delicious to eat).

Scoop out flesh of Christophene Sauté chopped Onion in oil or butter until golden.

Mix with flesh of Christophene, season well and add grated Nutmeg.

Spoon Christophene mixture back into shells and dot with butter.

Sprinkle with grated cheese and bake in oven at 180 degrees Centigrade for 30 minutes.

Mashed Pumpkin

Ingredients:
1 Kg Pumpkin (about 2 lb).
225 grams of Onions
Salt, freshly milled black Pepper, nutmeg grated
Cream and Butter

Method:
Slice both Pumpkin and Onions
Layer in a large saucepan. (Pumpkin, Onion, with seasoning) Place on top of stove with 1 tablespoon of water. Bring to simmer point shaking constantly.

Simmer for 20 minutes, shaking occasionally.

Remove from heat and mash, adding Butter, a little cream and seasoning.

Stir in fresh grated Nutmeg, use liberally.

Rum Punch

Ingredients:

1 Bottle of Dark Rum
One and a half cups of sugar
1 cup of Lime juice
2 Tea bags in 4 cups of water
1 tablespoon of ginger (or 2 teaspoons of ground ginger)
2 teaspoons ground cinnamon
2 teaspoons of fresh grated Nutmeg 1 dash of bitters.

Umm! Yo Ho and a bottle of the above will keep the cockles of your heart warm. It's also a very good aphrodisiac, taken in reasonable amounts of course. But you must be sitting on a beach in the Caribbean at sundown for the magic to work...

SAILING ON SILVER

AND BEYOND

22 - THE WEDDING

For better or for worse

Many Caribbean islands offer Europeans and Americans an all-in holiday that includes a marriage service as well as the honeymoon. Interestingly, although most of these marriages are second or third attempts, we came across several couples who were getting married for the first time. Because their families were not usually present, I was occasionally asked if I would be the best man. The last time I agreed to do this proved to be rather more memorable than I had thought possible.

Bob and Susie Hall had been one of our first customers at the Pub when they were in St Lucia on holiday. We had liked them both. Susie was a vivacious blonde and lots of fun, while Bob had a dry sense of humour. He reminded me of the 'Bob' in the Likely Lads, a comedy program on BBC.

Six months later they returned, coming to see us on the first day after their arrival. They told us that they had decided after several years of living together, to get married. Susie had seen an advertisement in their local newspaper about special marriage deals in certain St Lucian hotels, and as they had enjoyed their previous stay on the island, they settled for St Lucia again. They both asked us if we would help, and Bob asked if I would be his best man, as his best friend could not make the trip from England. It was agreed that the wedding buffet be held at the Pub, and as none of their relatives were coming for the wedding, they said they would invite fellow guests from the hotel to make up the numbers. They reckoned the party would not be more than about twenty, people. (It turned out to be nearer fifty).

Usually, the minister was brought to the hotel to officiate the wedding, but Susie was keen to get married in church, so on Monday morning I took her up to meet the vicar at Gross Islet who was delighted to agree to perform the ceremony, which was set for the following Saturday.

Susie had not brought a dress out with her, so Liz flew up with her to Martinique where they found exactly what she required. Liz found a lot of other clothes that she assured me she required too, so all in all, it was an expensive trip for both. When they returned, slight alterations had to be carried out to Susie's wedding dress, and there was a general feeling of excitement building up with the Pub's staff, as the day drew near.

Susie was particularly keen to be driven away from the church in something other than a motor car. She had made some enquiries at the hotel, and they advised her that the riding school nearby might be able to help her, as they had some traps (two wheeled buggies) which they may consider hiring out. When I heard of the idea, I was a little dubious, as I knew that the horses from this school were somewhat wild. Susie was insistent however, so I suggested that they hire an experienced driver, but she would have none of it, so we arranged for a horse and trap to be delivered to the church after the service.

I spent a good deal of time with Bob, so that I could glean enough information to provide a reasonable best man's speech, and it was during this time that he indicated he wanted to have a stag night on the Friday, the day before the wedding. He had invited several new-found friends he had met at the hotel, and it was decided that we would eat at a

357

restaurant the other side of town and then gravitate to the (then) only night club in Rodney Bay called Lucifer's which was part of the St Lucian hotel.

Liz arranged a hen night for Susie at the Pub, which was inevitably going to be somewhat less boisterous, at least that was the general idea.

Friday evening came, and I picked Bob and two of his new-found friends up from the hotel, the others followed in a taxi. We had a reasonable meal and plenty to drink, so by the time we got to Lucifer's, we were all in good spirits.

Lucifer's was situated in a large basement of the hotel, and the whole of the inside had been transformed to look like an underground cavern with seats and tables inside smaller caves, which was supposed to give a degree of privacy. Other than that, it was like any other disco worldwide, in that it had flashing coloured lights and was otherwise darkened. There was a small stage where impromptu acts were carried out, and the billing for that evening was Queen Aphrodite. We knew Aphrodite (Aphro for short) quite well; she was a mature woman of indeterminate years, but still with an excellent figure. She would occasionally pick up men in the Pub, but although we quite liked her, she was not encouraged to use the restaurant as her stamping ground for obvious reasons. I had heard that she was a very good belly dancer but had never seen her perform until that night.

As she walked into the club, despite the darkness and the supposed privacy of the 'caverns' Aphro spotted me immediately and came over, she had her usual wig on which was black and set in a huge bouffant of dark curly hair, but underneath her short jacket I could see she had little else on. I introduced her to the party and told her that Bob was on his stag night. I wished I had not done so, as I saw the gleam in her eyes as she looked at him.

The show was quite good. Aphro managed to get up to all sorts of gyrations, and while being saucy was not over the top.

It was obvious however, that the thirty-minute display was meant to impress only one person, Bob. To say that he was affected by Aphro's interest would be an understatement, and by the time she came back to the table, this time without coat, and wearing the flimsiest of garments, Bob was in a high state of expectancy.

As Aphro sat down at our table on Bob's knees, there followed some smooching and canoodling, which started to get more than a little embarrassing, as both Aphro and Bob appeared to be letting their passions run away with them. I decided to spoil their fun by reminding Bob where he was, and that he was getting married to Susie the next day.

All that managed to do however, was to heighten Bob's desire, and he asked one of his new-found friends if he could borrow his hotel room. At first the man refused, but after Aphro suggested that it need not just be a one-on-one affair, the man changed his mind and they all staggered off together. I just hoped that Susie didn't happen to be in the hotel lobby when they arrived there.

I stayed about another ten minutes or so, but as various 'ladies of the night' kept approaching our table, I decided it was time for me to go. It was a short walk from Lucifer's to the house, and I was surprised to see that there were already lights on when I arrived. When I got in, Liz and Susie were having coffee.

As Liz made me some coffee, we swapped stories about the evening with me leaving out the more obviously embarrassing bits and trying to keep Susie engaged in staying where she was. It didn't work for too long, and she stood up saying she must get back, as poor Bob would be waiting for her. Some hope I thought, as I stood up with her and offered to escort her across the road.

After giving me a quick perfunctorily goodnight kiss, Susie disappeared into the hotel, and I returned home. I didn't know the room number of Bob's friend, and as I did not know the other man's last name either, I could not warn Bob that Susie was back. Besides, I told myself, he was big enough to look after himself, and while being best man, it was hardly my job to interfere with his private life.

Liz was furious when I told her and said that I must go back to the hotel and try to find him. I was in two minds, when our phone rang, as it was after 2.30 in the morning, I knew it could only be from one person.

I picked up the handset. "Yes?"

"James, it's Susie, do you know where Bob is? He's not here, and the bed has not been slept in. I'm worried," she added.

"Oh, I shouldn't worry, Susie..." I yelped as Liz kicked my shin. "He's probably in one of the bars..."

"No, he isn't," replied Susie, "I've looked everywhere, James you don't think..."

I wasn't sure quite what she was going to say, but I stopped her. "No, I am sure he's fine, he was with one of the other guys..."

"Which one?" She asked.

"Er, the chap called William, he has blond hair and..." I could have kicked myself as I said it.

"Oh, you mean William Bullock, thanks James, I'll find out his room number and see if Bob is..."

I swallowed my second cup of coffee the wrong way and had a coughing fit.

Liz raised her eyebrows and gave me a hefty swipe on the back.

"No, no don't do that" I spluttered out, with a strangled gasp, "William could be in bed without any clothes on" I added weakly. "I'll come around and knock him up myself."

"Oh, James, would you? I'm so sorry, I'll meet you in the lobby." With that she put the phone down.

Liz had sat close, listening to the telephone conversation. "Problems?" She asked, sweetly.

I scowled at her and told her what I was going to do.

"What if he's still with Aphro?" asked.

"Well, I'll just have to separate them, and somehow get Bob back to his room without Susie finding out," I smiled as I started to imagine what I might find.

As I was walking out, Liz called after me. "Oh, and tell Aphro from me, if you're not back in ten minutes flat, I shall be over there with a bloody machete."

"She's not my type, I answered truthfully."

I got to the lobby of the hotel to find Susie waiting for me. She had already woken up the scowling night receptionist and had got William's room number. I realised that there was no way that Susie was going to let me go alone, and perhaps her woman's intuition had already alerted her. I hoped to God that Aphro had left by the time we got there.

The room number was 113 at the end of a long passageway, which led out into the rear garden of the hotel. I knocked hard, and shouted that it was me and Susie, I emphasised the Susie, and said we were looking for Bob. I heard some grumbling going on inside, and then William swung the door open. He was naked from the waist up, but had some trousers on, which judging by the undone belt had been hastily pulled up.

"Bloody glad you've come, I can't get a bloody wink of sleep with these two shaggers," he saw Susie for the first time, as she pushed past me into the room. "Oh, bloody hell," said William.

There were two double beds in the room, one had obviously been used by William, the other contained Bob who was lying on his stomach, and Aphro, who I was amazed to see, was completely bald without her wig, slipping quickly out of the bed. She smiled at Susie, as she retrieved her wig. I thought it rather amusing she should pick the wig to put on first, because she had nothing else on. She smiled again at Susie, who had stopped in full flight, and was staring at the

361

seemingly unconscious form of Bob. "Don't worry dearie," said Aphro, as she slipped on her sparse clothing, "he's not half bad... for a honkey," with that she glided past me and was gone.

"You bastard's," screamed Susie, "you rotten bastard's," she raised her handbag and brought it down on the back of Bob's unfortunate head. Bob who had no doubt buried his head in the pillow in a desperate attempt not to be noticed, let out a yelp of pain.

Susie then picked the large lamp off the bedside table and threw it at Bob just as he turned to fend off another handbag attack. The heavy brass object hit him on the upper cheek, and he let out another howl of pain.

Susie stamped out, and as she passed me to go through the door, she snarled, "it's your fault you bloody well led him to this." I watched for the swinging handbag, but she carried on through into the corridor. A split second later, she poked her head back into the room and shouted, "and the bloody wedding's off." With that she ran off in floods of tears.

"Oh shit," I said.

I looked at Bob, who already had the makings of an extremely bad black eye, and I suggested he get some ice which should alleviate the worse symptoms. William, still grumbling went off to find some from a machine down the corridor.

Bob, completely naked, sat on the edge of the bed holding his face. "Jesus, James, what am I going to do?" I sat on the bed with him, and as William came back with the ice, we put some into a napkin and applied it to Bob's cheek. William was not at all happy, mainly because he had obviously been excluded from the festivities but had been kept awake because of them. "I knew I shouldn't have let you use my room," he kept saying.

"It's a little late for that," I replied gently. "In any case, there is nothing else we can do tonight, I'll ask Liz to look in at Susie first thing in the morning, and in the meantime, I suggest we conjure up a story that will help the situation." I smiled confidently.

On my way back home, a little ruse was emerging in my mind. I could not let the wedding fail now we had all worked too hard to prepare it. I climbed into bed at just after 3.30 in the morning, and Liz woke up as I did so, looking at the clock. I hastily told her what had happened and what I was going to do in the morning to try to get things back on track. Liz sniffed and turned over. I reluctantly turned the alarm on for 6 a.m. It was going to be a busy day.

I felt I had just about dozed off when the alarm went off. I had a shower and dressed quickly. Liz, always an early riser, got up too. I suggested that she go over to Susie in her room and that I would join her shortly. I then telephoned a doctor friend of mine, Jonathan Sethia, and told him what I needed. He was reluctant at first, but after offering him and his girlfriend a slap-up meal in the restaurant, he agreed.

Jonathan promised to be at my house by just after 8 a.m. I then rang William's room and after some considerable delay, Bob answered. I told him that both he and William should be at my house by eight. They both turned up just before, Bob looking decidedly the worse for wear. He had the largest black eye. I have ever seen.

When Jonathan arrived, I told them what I wanted each one to do. William was a little reluctant at first but eventually after some bribery, he also agreed to the plan.

The way things were, we were not going to make too much money out of this wedding I thought to myself afterwards.

Sending Bob and William off to the local hospital, with a note from Jonathan, we walked over to the hotel, found Susie's room, and knocked. Liz opened the door, and whispered that Susie was in a bit of a state, as we walked in.

Susie was sitting crossed legged on the bed looking very red eyed. She glowered at me. "Susie," I said before she could speak, 'I want you to meet Doctor Sethia, Doctor Jonathan Sethia...'"

"Doctor..." Susie looked queryingly at Jonathan.

He smiled, his even white teeth contrasting his good Indian looks. "It's good to meet you Susie, and don't worry, I am sure that Bob is not badly hurt..."

Susie looked alarmed. "Badly hurt..."

"Yes," said Jonathan, sitting on the bed near her. "I have sent him off to hospital to have his cheek X-rayed, but I don't think he'll have any permanent damage..."

Susie frowned.

I took up the story, "You see Susie, last night it was William who took Bob back to his room because he was so drunk. He put Bob to bed, who by then was quite unconscious, and as he was still wide awake, he went out again, meeting up with..."

"But if what you say is true," said Susie, now looking decidedly unsure of herself, "why did I find that woman in bed with Bob?" I nodded. "You see after William had paid the girl off, he suggested she go, but apparently in the hope of getting two bites of the cherry, so to speak," I said smoothly, "she climbed into bed with Bob, not knowing he was completely out for the count. She had obviously just realised this when we got to the room," Jonathan nodded, and laughed "In my best medical opinion, Bob would have been in no fit state to do anything during the small hours of this morning, as his alcohol level was such, that he must have been totally incapable." I thought he lied beautifully.

"So, I don't blame you for reacting the way you did," I said, "and of course Bob did get very drunk on the night before his wedding and..."

Susie let out a yelp of anguish, "oh poor Bob, what have I done..."

I held my hand up. "Don't worry, I don't think the hospital will keep him in, and I suggested to William, who took him

up there early this morning, that I should take you up there."
By 10 a.m., we had collected Bob from the hospital where at
Jonathan's behest they had painted some purple disinfectant
onto his face, so that he looked even worse than he had done
before. Susie was most repentant, particularly after William
had made his 'confession,' which was to cost the Pub a lobster
meal for two.

For my part, I felt I was justified in my little ruse, as after
all Bob had been rather drunk at the time. In any case, almost
anything was worth the saving of the wedding which was
about to take place. By the end of the day, I was to wish that I
had not interfered.

The wedding was scheduled for 3 p.m. that afternoon, so
despite the morning shenanigans, we still had time to arrange
everything.

Liz had brought in some staff early, and after duly
delivering Bob, Susie, and William back to the hotel, I went
back to the Pub to help. Liz had been busy making some
cocktail snacks for the buffet afterwards, leaving Yani and
Gregory free to concentrate on the major items of food. As I
took a tray of the cocktail bits into the cooler for her, I noticed
Liz's full-length mink coat hung up in a polythene wrapping
amidst the various bits of food. I was surprised, as I had
forgotten that she had brought it out from England, when we
first came out to the Caribbean. On returning to the kitchen,
I asked why it was there.

"'Because the West Indian climate is not good for fur
coats," she answered. "And besides, the moths would get it if
I put it in a cupboard, and so the cooler is the best place for
it, it was too expensive to be spoiled," She added.

"What about thieves," I ventured rather stupidly.

Liz looked at me. "And who, in the West Indies is going to
run off with a fur coat?"

I smiled and nodded at her logic. Susie had persuaded the
hotel manager to give her away, and they set off in a car well

ahead of us. Liz joined Bob and me, and we gave him a good strong Bloody Mary, before driving over to the church. I had to smile, Bob really did look as though he had been in an argument with a ten-ton truck, and he received the appropriate sympathy from all concerned, sympathy which he certainly did not deserve.

Unfortunately, Bob was not the best of actors and instead of accepting Susie's obvious distress at what she had done, he had belaboured the point to the extent where Susie was becoming a bit suspicious. I told him to knock it off, and act normally.

The wedding service went off without a hitch and apart from Bob's face looking a little out of place on the wedding photograph the picture was duly taken.

Susie looked most attractive in a white lace dress, and one could not have believed the transformation since the early hours of the same morning.

After the service, the horse and trap were brought to the front of the church, with the photographs completed, and with a beaming vicar and all of us looking on, the bride and groom climbed in. Bob took the reins from the handlers, and he confidently whipped them down on the horse's flank. Now in normal circumstances, a trained horse would have cantered off at a reasonable pace. The problem as I suspected later was that the horse used for the day, was one that had not even been in a trap before, and the confines of the two shafts plus Bob's over enthusiastic thrashing of the reins was more than the poor animal was prepared to accept without a show of rebellion.

There was a sudden jerk, throwing Bob and Susie backwards against their seat and the horse simply bolted out of the churchyard, turning left on one wheel at the main road in the manner of a formula one-race car, and then disappearing from our sight. A taxi which had been driving along the road had to swerve violently to miss the sudden appearance of the couple, and the driver who had just bought himself a large ice cream from the local post office ended up with the lot up his nose. When I first saw him, I thought he had been shaving while driving.

I realised that at the speed the trap was going, it would not take long for some disaster to happen, and as the handler ran after the disappearing trio, I grabbed Liz, and we rushed to get in the van.

Quickly starting it, we drove carefully through the throng of people who were headed for the entrance, no doubt expecting to see an upside-down trap in the middle of the road. Surprisingly, as we turned left, we could see nothing but the empty road, apart from the enraged taxi driver, and various people walking towards us on the roadsides all with their heads pointed the other way at a cloud of dust.

We continued cautiously to the cross roads, where we would normally have turned right to get back to the Pub, but we could clearly see the dust cloud had gone straight on across the major road. I silently thanked God that nothing had been coming the other way. The road opposite the one we were on, was not really a road at all, more a mud trail and it was quite wet after the recent rains. We knew the riding school had their headquarters about half a mile down the track, so we crossed over and negotiated the stones and pot holes on the lane we now found ourselves in. It was a quarter of a mile further on when we came to the sorry looking couple.

The wheel had come off the left-hand side of the trap, and occupants and trap had tipped over into the sewer drain. Bob had hurt his arm and could not move it properly, but Susie seemed fine, except that her wedding dress was torn and soiled and they both smelled like sewer rats. The horse had completely disappeared.

We helped them both into the van and managed to turn it around in the small space just as the handler caught us up.

He appeared intent on claiming damages from poor Bob, but I ignored him and put my foot down hard on the accelerator, and when I looked in my rear-view mirror, I was pleased to see that our rear wheels had sprayed wet mud all over the unreasonable handler.

When we got back to the Pub, Liz took Susie back to the hotel to change, and I had Bob taken to the hospital, this time for a genuine problem to have his arm checked.

Liz arrived back at the Pub with Susie before Bob returned, and I told them both that I had just telephoned the hospital, and they confirmed that they had found a cracked bone in his arm. Whether they had or not, it was the general practice to put any suspect limb into plaster, as this gave all the student nurses much needed training in the art of treating broken limbs. The fact that they had someone who would also pay for this was a bonus.

Although a bit shaken at first. Susie suggested we not wait for Bob, and start the buffet and as the musicians arrived, we all soon started to dance. As time went on, I noticed from time to time that Susie was getting rather inebriated, but I passed it off as being natural in the circumstances. After all, I told myself, she has had rather an unusual day. The last time I noticed her before Bob returned, was that she was dancing a rather slow piece with Yani. She seemed to be clinging to him a bit more than I would have expected.

It must have been about twenty minutes later that Bob arrived back, now with his right arm in plaster and in a sling. It was dark outside, and the party was going full stretch in the Yachtsman's bar. I looked around for Susie but could not see her. I spied Liz and extracted her from some hopeful St Lucian male who thought he had captured his partner for the night.

"Have you seen Susie?" She shook her head. "No, perhaps she's in the lavatory?"

I shook my head, "No, I have checked, both ladies and

368

gents are currently empty. I hope she's alright," I added, Susie had been drinking rather a lot and we were always a little worried when guests drank heavily, because it would be very easy to go outside on the veranda for a breath of fresh air and drop into the lagoon, without anyone noticing. I went outside, and looked down towards the water which was lit by the lights from the Pub. We couldn't see anything, which was somewhat of a relief.

"Oh, wait a minute," I said suddenly, "I remember seeing Susie and Yani heading for the kitchen..." I sighed with relief. "Yani is probably showing her the kitchens," I said.

Liz frowned. I told I would go and check, which I did, but as I walked into the kitchen there was the usual bustle of waitresses coming in and out, and Gregory busy on preparing some fish dish. "Have you seen chef?" I asked him.

He did not look at me. "No sir,"

"Gregory," I growled...

Just then Sylvia came in. "Have you seen chef, Sylvia?" She looked at me in amusement, "I tink he be in de cooler," she grinned, as she grabbed the fish dish from Gregory, and disappeared in a fit of giggles into the restaurant.

"In the cooler?" I repeated aloud. Puzzled I walked over opening the heavy door and walked in closing it behind me. I heard a muffled sound ahead and switched the light on. I could not believe my eyes.

Susie was laid backwards over several boxes, her skirt around her waist, with her feet on the floor and her arms tightly around Yani. Yani was wearing Liz's fur coat and was on top of Susie. It did not take more than a second for me to realise precisely what was going on.

"You can't do that in here," I yelped at Yani.

He turned his head and grinned, the movement in the lower part of his body continuing to be in motion without a break in rhythm. "I can and I am." He said turning his attention back to a giggling Susie who had taken not the slightest interest in me.

I was furious, stepping forward and tearing Liz's fur coat off his back. Yani was naked apart from socks and shoes. "Well, if you can, then you can bloody well continue without 's fur," I snapped as I turned to leave, I saw Yani's clothes in a heap on the floor, and I scooped them up and went out followed by a yell from Yani.

I placed his clothes on a kitchen counter and went to find Liz.

"What on earth are you doing with my coat?" She asked when she saw me.

I told her.

"God that bloody man, I'll..." Liz clenched her fists.

"Well, I shouldn't worry, I think I might have cooled his ardour somewhat."

I was told by a giggling Sylvia that Yani had not stayed very long in the cooler and had appeared with a cardboard box round his nether quarters, and the rest of him displaying rather large goose pimples. Susie had come out and gone straight over to Bob. The last thing we saw of them that night was both in an embrace as they wandered aimlessly around the dance floor.

The next day, Susie acted as though nothing had happened, and they continued their honeymoon, leaving for England a week later.

"I think we'll give weddings a miss for a while," I said, after they had left the island. We were to be involved with two more, but they went relatively smoothly, thank goodness.

It was some years later that we were to call on Susie and Bob who by then lived in Tunbridge Wells in Kent. They were very proper and responsible. They had two children and Bob was a respected member of Rotary. We had the feeling that they were uncomfortable with our visit, as our presence, no doubt brought back memories that did not quite suit their present environment.

23 - THE GUN BOAT

I go to war against the USA - and win

We had been running the restaurant for just over a year when I was approached by a man I knew slightly. He was an English businessman living in Antigua and his name was Michael Partridge. Both he and his wife owned a nice little forty-foot ketch called Grecian Lady. He told me that he had gone into partnership with some friends of his to use it as a charter boat, but that the skipper had been taken ill and had to return to the United Kingdom. He was now desperate, as a couple who had booked a holiday on the boat, were due to arrive in St Lucia within the week, the charter guest, being the daughter of a well-known family of a large departmental store chain in the UK. Michael asked me if I would take over the charter for him, the problem was, the guests were due in only three days' time.

I must confess that I had missed the sea, and because of the short notice, the offer was quite attractive financially, so I decided to do it, little realising it would bring complications in the future.

Liz could not leave the restaurant of course, and I was therefore worried about cooking on the boat. I had never been a very domesticated animal at the best of times. When I mentioned this to Michael, he told me that I should not concern myself, as the guests would almost certainly want to eat out.

I flew up to Antigua, to pick up the yacht, and stayed with Michael and his wife overnight. He was a large framed, fit looking man, with a thatch of blond hair and a ready smile. He was the sort of man one imagined would be attractive to women.

Christos, his wife was quite tall about 5' 8 with dark smooth hair and green eyes that positively sparkled. She had a roundish impish face with a small nose and perfectly shaped mouth. When she smiled, as she did often, she showed off perfectly white teeth. Her figure was in keeping with the rest of her, being well proportioned in all the right places. I had to admit that she was one of the most attractive women, that I had met, apart from Liz

She was also extremely intelligent, and had travelled widely, so the evening I spent with both was delightful.

The next morning Michael took me down to St John's, the capital of Antigua, where Grecian Lady was moored, and after showing me around the boat, he wished me good luck, giving me a nice cheque for the charter. I had asked him whether he wanted the boat returning to Antigua, but he suggested to me that we keep it down on the dock at the restaurant, as it was likely that future charters would start from St Lucia. As a quid pro quo for us looking after the yacht, Michael kindly said that Liz and I could use it any time we wished.

Although I was against night sailing for reasons already stated, I had little choice but to do so in this case, even though it would mean me staying up all night. I needed to be back in St Lucia to provision the boat in time for the guests and had not enough time for a normal day sail. Fortunately, Grecian Lady had a self-steering gear, so the trip would not be so arduous.

There were no incidents on my sail back, and I arrived in St Lucia tired but exhilarated. I provisioned the boat the next day, and after saying my good-byes to Liz, I picked up my charter guests from Vigie airport early the following morning.

By the late evening we had reached Bequia in the

Grenadines.

The charter was uneventful. My guests were extremely easy to get on with, and although I did some cooking because we spent quite a lot of time at Tobago Cays where there are no restaurants, they seemed very appreciative of my efforts. The charter was only for a week, and they had already arranged to return home via a chartered aircraft from Union Island to Barbados.

During the charter, I had heard of the American invasion of Grenada on the radio, but I didn't realise that the world press would be congregating in the Grenadines. The reason for this was that there was a ban on journalists allowed on the invasion island.

The night before my guest's departure, we sailed across to the little island of PSV, which was owned by the sole hotel on the island. My charter guests had kindly offered to take me out to dinner for the last night, and I had accepted.

When we got to the restaurant the place was alive with American reporters and I was glad that we had booked our dining room table earlier by radio. We had an excellent meal as usual, and after dinner I was introduced to one of the network people by a friend of my daughter, Paddy, who lived on the island of Petit Martinique, just across the bay from PSV.

During the conversation, Paddy mentioned that he had tried covertly to get some of the network team into Grenada via his large motor launch. They had been spotted by the US Navy and turned back, I answered that I thought any fast boat approaching the island would inevitably be seen and what was needed was perhaps a bit of stealth. . . I could see that what I was saying had created some interest among the network people who were listening in, but soon afterwards, I took the charter guests back to the boat, and thought no more about it.

I was surprised the next morning to be awoken by a banging on the hull of Grecian Lady. I was fast asleep, and thought perhaps I had slept in. Looking at my watch, I saw it was just after 6 a.m. I quickly pulled on some shorts and went up on deck, where I found one of the network team hanging on to the side from a dinghy.

373

"Hey James, sorry to wake you."

I said it was time I was up anyway, and I could hear my guests were also moving down below.

"What's up?" I asked.

The man, whose name he confirmed was Mike Wilson, grinned.

"When we were talking last night, I got the impression that you might have an idea regarding a trip to Grenada. The thing is James; there are six of us who would be interested in paying $250 per head to be put on the island." He pointed his hand in the general direction of the island.

I looked at him and smiled, shaking my head. "I very much doubt that anyone can guarantee that..." "Naw, we realise that, but if you have a good idea, we would sure be happy to pay for it."

I invited him on board and told him the way I would deal with the dilemma.

He was thoughtful for a minute, and then asked, "would you be prepared to sail us in this boat?" I had to admit to myself that $1,500 would come in very useful, but I had to consider whether there would be any danger to the boat by me getting involved. I said I would think it over and as I had to get my charter guests over to Union Island by noon for their Barbados charter flight, I suggested we meet that evening back in PSV where I had intended to stay the night anyway.

Mike looked thoughtful. "The tackle you suggested we would need, where would we get that?

"Probably Barbados, there is no one near here that would stock the sort of gear I have indicated."

Mike nodded, "Yeah that would be my thought too. Do you mind if I have a word with your guests?"

I raised my eyebrows.

"Well, it seems to me that if they've chartered a plane to go from here to Barbados, maybe we can do a deal with them and with the aircraft Charter Company to hitch a ride, and then return on the same aircraft. We could make it worth their while financially," he added.

I did not tell Mike that the woman was heir to a huge fortune in the UK and could probably purchase the little airline out of petty cash. I said that I had no objection to them talking to them, and when they came up on deck, I introduced them, and I went below to cook breakfast.

The upshot of their discussion was that Mike and one of his colleagues sailed across to Union with us, and I saw them off on the charter flight. Mike told me not to await their return as they may well hold the plane over until the next day, which is what they did.

When I got back to PSV, I sat down in the cockpit with a piece of paper and a Grenada chart and worked out a plan. I realised that these people where obviously prepared to pay much more than they had offered, and so I decided that I would ask double their current offer. I also worked out a plan if we were boarded, as there was no way I would want to risk Michael's yacht.

By the time they appeared the next day on Paddy's launch, it was around lunch time. In their absence I had decided that I needed to talk to all the people involved and I invited them to come to the yacht as soon as they had their lunch.

By 2 p.m. the six were seated down below in the cabin of Grecian Lady. I decided not to advertise the fact to the world that we were having discussions.

"Right gentlemen, I assume you got all the kit I suggested you could buy from Barbados?"

Mike nodded.

"Okay, I realise that it is going to be a huge coup for you guys if you can get on the island, how you get the news out is not my affair."

"Satellite phone," answered Mike.

I nodded. "The price I will do this for is $500 per person, as although the risk is small, it is still a risk, and this not my boat. There are conditions to this, however. Firstly, I have got the typist from the PSV hotel to type out a charter document in duplicate, which you should all sign, so that I can truthfully say that you chartered the yacht to take you down to Trinidad. You need to produce a story that is satisfactory to me why you would want to go there.

"Secondly, I'm the skipper, and you follow my orders precisely. Under no circumstances should there be more than two of you on the deck at any one time, it would look suspicious for me to be seen sailing alone, and it would odd if more than three of us was seen on deck.

"Thirdly, I cannot guarantee that this will come off, and if there is in my opinion a situation arising where we or the boat is in danger, I will immediately abort the charter.

"Now, this is how I suggest we do it." I explained to them in some detail about how I intended the plan to work. I told them that for the ruse to work we would have to sail by 4 p.m. that afternoon.

By 3.30 p.m. I had the six people on board, with all the tackle they had purchased in Barbados, plus their camera equipment, which was considerable. I was glad that no one was going to have to sleep on board, as I doubted there would be room.

We sailed out of PSV right on schedule, but instead of heading for Grenada, I took an easterly course, towards Barbados. This was quite hard going, because we were headed close to the wind, so I had to carry out a series of quite long tacks. Just before sundown, I reached a position in the Atlantic which would cross an imaginary line between Barbados and Trinidad, and I turned south on a course that would take us about five miles off the south west coast of Grenada.

If we were boarded the excuse would be that the newsmen were travelling to Trinidad so that it would be easier for them to get a plane from there to Grenada when restrictions were lifted, as they realised that their attempt to reach the island via the motor launch had been aborted.

The weather was perfect, for which I was grateful, as it became obvious that some of my passengers were not very good sailors.

We were in sight of Grenada lights at the northern end by just after 11 p.m. in the evening, and I checked my bearings, we were dead on course. I suggested to four of the passengers that they should go below, as I had previously indicated to them.

It was about midnight, when my heart gave a jump, and I felt my stomach muscles tensing. I could hear a high-speed boat, and it was coming towards us. I turned to Mike who had stayed on deck. "I think we are about to be overtaken; you did leave the message I asked you to at the High Commission in Barbados?" Mike nodded. "Yeah, I spoke to a Dorothy Perkins there, and said in my best British accent that I was sailing on Grecian Lady with one James Dalby, and we were leaving Barbados within the hour for Trinidad. I also said that I would be grateful, bearing in mind the Grenada invasion, that if we had not arrived in Trinidad by the next morning, at say noon she should alert the authorities. She gave me the number to call her, so if we don't arrive in Trinidad..." He grinned. "I guess the shit will hit the fan." I very much doubted it, but the fact that we had registered the trip from Barbados to Trinidad could be useful if anyone checked our story.

We could both hear heavy diesels quite near us now, and I told Mike to ensure that the lights were kept out below, and the others kept out of sight.

Minutes later a very strong searchlight switched on and they called us on channel 16. "The yacht sailing south west of the east coast of Grenada, this is Coast Guard vessel USS Nimbus, State your destination and course please."

I handed the wheel over to Mike, as I went below to take the microphone.

"This is yacht Grecian Lady, would you switch to channel 44 please," they knew of course that channel 16 should only be used for contact and emergencies.

"Affirmative 44."

I spoke into the microphone, "US Nimbus, this is sailing yacht Grecian Lady sailing from Barbados to Trinidad on 205 degrees."

"State the purpose of your visit,"

"For your information Nimbus, it is on charter and the purpose is pleasure."

"Are you aware that this is a war zone?" Said the voice at the other end.

"I was informed by the British High Commission in Barbados of the exclusion zone, which I have been careful to avoid," I answered truthfully.

"What are you carrying Grecian Lady."

"I have 6 guests on board." I answered.

There was silence at the other end for a moment.

I then called them again. "Nimbus, please turn off your searchlight, as it is destroying our night vision."

"Grecian Lady, please hove to, we are sending a boarding party across."

I then played what I hoped was my trump card. "USS Nimbus, this yacht is in International waters, flying a British flag, my registration number is Uk13654. I reject your request to hove to, and I am continuing my course as planned. I repeat that I am in International waters and as you can see, I repeat I am flying a British flag."

I switched to channel 16. "May Day, May Day," (the international distress signal) which I knew they would be listening to.' 'To anyone listening to my transmission, this is Lord Dalby I repeated the name, Lord Dalby. I am sailing outside the exclusion war zone as given to me by the High Commission in Barbados, and my route as indicated to the British High Commission is Barbados to Trinidad. I have been called by a United States warship that I am to be boarded. I have refused their request as it is a flagrant contravention of International Maritime Law. Would anyone listening contact the High Commissioner in Barbados immediately and inform them that we spoke to Dorothy Perkins this morning of our intended trip and registered the fact with her. As soon as I return to England, I intend to take this matter up in the House of Lords and with the State Department of the USA. It is quite disgraceful that American ships should threaten to board..." I carried on in this vein, trying to sound as pompous as I possibly could. It wasn't difficult.

As I stopped speaking, a West Indian voice whom I recognized as Paddy, and who had been listening out for any such call from me. "This is PSV, I heard your distress signal, and I want you to know that I am trying to contact the British High Commission at this time, over."

I thanked him and asked him to stand by for further messages.

We had now sailed past the halfway mark to Grenada, and I knew that if the USS Nimbus did board us, they would not be able to take any action against us, although they may have been suspicious in which case, they would simply escort us to the end of Grenada, and we may have to abort the plan. When I got back on deck, there seemed to be no movement towards them dropping a boat, and I kept my fingers crossed.

The Nimbus switched out their light, but stayed with us for over an hour, only turning back when we were approaching the south west corner of the island, but still some way off.

Whether it was the fact that I had mentioned the name Lord Dalby (There is one). Alternatively, the US gunboat captain had considered the problems of boarding the boat belonging to a person in a position equivalent to one of their Senators and perhaps causing an International incident, or whether the intended call to the British High Commission was a factor, I will never know. Whatever the case, it worked, as it should have done as I had no intention of breaking the exclusion zone, even though it was clearly illegal anyway.

There was now a feverish movement down below as a large package was brought up and with a compressed air cylinder, the package was blown up into the shape of a large inflatable with a hard fibreglass chine. Shortly afterwards we slid it over the side and tied it close in. Then the two fifty hp engines were manipulated up the galley steps, and so large were they that it took four people to get the motors fixed to the rear of the inflatable. A fuel tank was brought up, and connected, and then a large forward cover, under which was stored all the camera equipment. All this was done while we were under sail, which made things very difficult, but I knew that if we stopped, the Nimbus would certainly see us hove to on their radars and turn around with probable unpleasant circumstances for me.

I told Mike the bearing he should follow with the compass he had purchased in Barbados, and when near to shore what he should look for. "I reckon it should take you no more than 30 minutes to reach there, and they will not be able to stop you, even if the USS Nimbus can see you on radar, which I doubt. In any case you will soon be in shallow water, and I strongly suspect that this part of the coast is not guarded because it is not highly populated." The last time I saw them was in the inflatable disappearing at speed, with a makeshift US flag being held up on a pole by one of the technicians, and another holding up a placard showing the network they belonged to just in case there were any US Marines lying in wait. I assume they got to the island without problems, as I was to hear reports from their team some days later. In fact, once the Americans knew that some press had got onto the island, I suspect they opened it up to the rest but perhaps my guys they stole a march for a couple of days at least. I hope it was worth $3,000 to them.

My main problem now, was to get back. I could not turn around of course, so I kept on my present bearing until I was well south of Grenada, and then turned north up the western side, but extending the distance from the island.

I did see some ships in the distance, but thankfully I did not receive a call from them.

Had I done so I had a reasonable explanation ready, I was by now very tired having been up all night, but I found my way back to Bequia by sundown the same day. Only then did I breathe a sigh of relief and really feel safe.

I had radioed Paddy with a code word as soon as I was well clear of the north of Grenada, and he telephoned the British High Commission in Barbados, saying Grecian Lady had arrived safely. He just did not say where.

The next day I sailed for St Lucia, arriving there just after 5 p.m. All in all, it had been a very profitable charter.

24 - THE GREEKS BEARING GIFTS

Sex and jewels don't necessarily go together

The following Monday I received a telephone call from Christos who thanked me for doing the charter for them she told me she had heard from the couple, and they had been absolutely delighted.

"I hardly dare ask you to do something else for us," she said.

"Oh, what's that?" I enquired.

She explained that her husband had gone back to the United Kingdom on some training course for two weeks, and she thought it would be a good opportunity to get the bottom of Grecian Lady scraped and re painted.

"What I thought was, if you could sail her up to Martinique, say next Monday," she hesitated. I thought she sounded a little breathless. "Then I will arrange for the boat yard up there to take her in on Tuesday."

"How long will it take?" I asked, looking at my date watch.

"Well, as you know James, they have the high-speed water jets up there, so they reckon two days."

"That sounds about right," I said, "but I couldn't stay on the boat..."

"No of course not," she laughed "I will book you into an hotel while the boat is in dock, of course all your expenses will be paid, as well as a week's charter fee..."

It seemed straight forward and another trip to Martinique by boat, where I could buy good cheeses and wine, had the desired effect. I said I would do it.

381

Liz was becoming even more concerned over Yani's drinking, he had started again in a small way, but now he was becoming thoroughly unreliable. She told me that while I was away, she had been rushed one day, when the kitchen had run out of potatoes.

Yani had volunteered to go and buy some and had not returned. Eventually with the help of a friend, Liz found the van at one of Yani's known haunts and had found him fast asleep in the back. He was in no fit state to work, and so she took him back to his apartment, where in front of his girlfriend, he had propositioned Liz to sleep with him. "I wasn't very flattered," said Liz, grinning, "because he could hardly stand up, never mind anything else." Liz and the pissed off girl friend had managed to get him into bed.

The next morning Liz had been phoned by a friend and told he was in hospital. She was surprised, so she telephoned the medical centre, but the sister on duty declined to give her any details.

"What's wrong with him, apart from too much liquor," asked Liz.

"It's a very personal problem,"

"What sort of personal problem?" Asked Liz, trying to ascertain whether her chef had something that would preclude him from touching food, and she asked how long he might be incapacitated.

"I cannot say," was the unhelpful answer.

"Well, can you tell me if its infectious or contagious?" Asked the impatient ...Liz.

The sister laughed, "I sincerely hope not," and then added, "no it's not that sort of problem..."

"In that case when will he be discharged?" The sister made some enquiries of someone else in the room, "probably this afternoon, but he is finding it a little difficult to walk. At this stage there was some giggling in the background.

Liz rang off, and phoned our doctor friend, asking him if he could establish what the illness was.

A few minutes later Jonathan returned Liz's call.

"Did you manage...?" Asked Liz.

"Yes, Yani is suffering from severe burns to the penis and testicles,"

"WHAT...?"

Jonathan laughed, "yes, apparently his girlfriend took exception to something that was said when you delivered Yani home yesterday. They had a fearsome row, and he got himself out of his bed where you had left him and he drank even more booze, collapsing unconscious on the floor. His girlfriend, who has now vacated the apartment, incidentally, was rather handy with a lighted cigarette... I think you can safely say that Yani will not be sexually inclined for some weeks to come..."

Liz sighed. "I suppose one should be grateful for small mercies, thank you Jonathan," she said as she put the phone down.

"Yani will have to go," said Liz after relating this story, "I just can't cope with his excessive drinking any longer."

I sympathised with her. The problem was that when he was sober, he really was an excellent chef. He had the ability to throw ingredients into a pan and produce something mouth-watering, seemingly without even noticing what he was doing. Even the way he put food on a plate made it look appetising. He was also an excellent trainer of staff and quite a good organiser when not inebriated.

In other words, he was just a natural, and even when drinking heavily he was still good.

I had previously suggested to Liz that we try taking a tougher line with him and we agreed that she would order the barman and waitresses that under no circumstances was Yani to have anything alcoholic. She subsequently found that more brandy than usual was being used in the cooking, so she instructed the waitresses to put salt in any brandy delivered to the kitchen.

Yani was furious, charging Liz that she did not trust him...

"Well, you must have tasted it, or you wouldn't have known," said Liz.

When Yani returned from the hospital that evening, he was walking rather strangely and was in obvious pain. He immediately asked if he could have a brandy for medicinal purposes, and Liz was furious, and she really laid into him with some considerable verbal admonishment. He was so taken aback that afterwards he said to Robert, our son who was out from his English school, that he thought Liz was a bit vexed with him. Robert told him he had better believe it, and that his job was now very much in the balance.

The next day, Yani came in to the Pub, seemingly sober, and presented Liz with a beautiful gold brooch. He was most contrite, and apologised for his past misdemeanour's, promising that they would not re-occur. Liz was quite touched, because she knew Yani had made the brooch himself, and there is no doubt that the gift softened her resolve somewhat.

Yani was not only a gifted chef, but he also designed and created brooches and necklaces that were quite outstanding. They were usually intricate designs in filigree, and superbly crafted. Had he not been a chef, he could have easily made a good living from his other talents.

Liz proudly wore it, and several nights afterwards, when Yani was again absent, Liz was taking an order from an American lady who had been holidaying on the island. She noticed Liz's brooch.

"What a lovely brooch you have," she commented.

Liz smiled, "yes, a local man made it..."

"Not by a man called Yani, by any chance?" Asked the American.

"Why yes, as a matter of a fact, it was," Liz smiled.

"Wait until I get my hands on him," said the American woman grimly.

"Oh, why?" Asked Liz.

The American woman sniffed. "I met this man last week in a bar, and we got talking. He told me that he was in the business of making brooches and necklaces, and I was so impressed with some samples he had with him, that I gave him an advance of $500 to make me one, in fact, exactly to the design you have there... Since then, I have not been able to contact him...and I'm going home tomorrow."

Liz had a sinking feeling as the story unfolded.

She knew exactly who the brooch had been destined for, and she immediately took it off and handed it to the American.

"Here, you take this one," said Liz, amidst the American lady's protestations, "Yani works for me as a chef," explained

Liz, "and I can easily get him to make me another one." At first the American Lady refused point blank, but Liz was insistent, and eventually the woman left extremely happy. Of course, Liz never did get a replacement.

"What's that saying about Greek's bearing gifts?" She asked me later.

I laughed, and for some inexplicable reason, I thought of Christos who was also half-Greek.

I sailed Grecian Lady out of Rodney Bay on a beautiful Monday morning. The sail up to Martinique was quite slow, as the wind was light, but I had all day to get there. The peace and quiet of sailing alone, in a deep blue sea with the sun shining down was extremely relaxing after the previous few hectic days, and I felt quite refreshed by the time I reached Fort de France.

By the time I arrived it was late afternoon, and as I did not feel like shopping, I put it off until in the week.

The next morning, I took Grecian Lady round to the small dry dock and spent most of the day helping the operatives to get her out of the water. When we inspected the bottom of the boat, we found a considerable amount of osmosis. The latter is not unusual among fibre glass yachts, and although the reason for it is not fully understood it must be treated. The theory is, that osmosis occurs when a fibre glass hull is immersed in water before being properly cured. Such is the commercial demand to get yachts in the water as soon as possible after building, that invariably, some boats are launched before they should be. What then happens is that nasty underwater blisters appear, which when scrubbed, fall out of the hull like powder leaving a concave blip. I suppose if not treated, these blisters would eventually work themselves right through the hull with disastrous results.

Grecian Lady had some quite large blisters, and I decided to call Christos to tell her, as the price of the refurbishment repairs were about to rise substantially. I was surprised that there was no reply to her telephone. I tried several times that day without success.

In the end, I told the boatyard to go ahead with the repairs, because I knew it could not be put back in the water as it was.

Although it was not my job to do so, I worked hard on the

boat most of the day, and it was late evening before I checked into the hotel that Christos had booked me into in Anse Mitan.

The next morning, I went to the supermarket and bought a taxi full of goodies, which I then took back to the boatyard. It must have been just after lunch when I arrived there, and I noticed they had just put Grecian Lady into the water, it being finished an hour or so earlier. I asked for the key, and they told me there was already someone on the boat, so feeling rather apprehensive, I unloaded my shopping by the quay side and paid off the taxi driver. As I turned around, there was Christos standing on the deck. She was wearing white shorts, and a loose blouse, which had a tie around her neck. I could not help but noticing that she had little else on, certainly not under the blouse. I must have looked surprised. She smiled at me showing those perfect white teeth and jumped on shore. I could smell her light but attractive perfume, and thoughts rushed through my mind, which seconds later, I mentally poured water on.

"Hi Christos, I didn't know..."

She gathered up some of the shopping and went back on deck, turning as she did so. "Well, I got through my work more quickly than I thought, so I decided to fly down and sail back with you to St Lucia... You don't mind, do you?" She suddenly went serious, but her eyes were laughing.

"Of course not, it's your boat," and then I had a sudden thought. "In fact, I didn't realise that it would be finished so early, and I planned to sail down tomorrow... but now we can go today and still be in St Lucia before nightfall," I grabbed another few carrier bags and followed her on board.

She had gone down below while I was talking and she poked her head up from the galley steps, holding out her hands for the bags I had taken from the shore. As I bent down to give them to her, she leaned her breasts on the top step of the galley ladder, substantially accentuating all she possessed.

Christos shook her head. "The reason the boat is ready in such good time, is because you worked so hard on it yesterday, you see I have already spoken to the boatyard people." She took the goods and disappeared below again,

386

shouting so that I would hear her. "In any case, I want to do some shopping this afternoon, and I would like to take you out to dinner tonight." Her head appeared again, "to thank you," she smiled. For some reason I had an uneasy feeling about Christos's plans. Although I was not desperate to get back, I said there was no need to buy me dinner, but she insisted.

She almost read my mind when she added, "Oh I noticed that your things were in the aft cabin, so I've put my stuff in one of the forward ones..."

That answered the question as to where she was going to sleep. I knew the aft cabin was the best on the boat, as there was a full-sized double bed in there, whereas the forward cabins only had bunk singles.

"Oh, it's okay," I said, "I'll get my gear out, so that you can move in..."

Christos would not hear of it. "Certainly not," she said, "I'm the interloper, I'll...stay forward." She gave me a rather odd sideways glance and smiled.

Christos took me to the finest restaurant in Martinique, it also happened to be the most expensive. I had fresh water crayfish as a main course, which was truly delicious. The wine I recall was a vintage Chambertin, which we both chose because we liked it, even though one is supposed to drink white wine with fish.

The wine reminded me of a lovely little story, which I told Christos during the meal.

A young man of eighteen had just finished his education, and his father had congratulated him on his successful grades, which would mean an almost certain entry to Cambridge University.

"Now, my son, as a special treat, I am going to send you to Paris for the week end. It is time another part of your education was dealt with. I happen to know a certain Madame Marseilles who has an entree to some beautiful women consorts, and it is my intention to arrange for you to meet one of these women, and for you to be royally entertained for the whole weekend." The son thanked his father for his generosity and said he would be delighted to go to Paris for the weekend.

387

*He duly went and met the most beautiful woman he had
ever seen, they went to the finest restaurants, they danced
until the early hours, and the experienced and beautiful
companion hugely enhanced his sex education.*

*When he returned and his father asked him how he had
got on, the son enthused about the wonderful time he had in
Paris.*

*"Well, tell me," said the father impatiently, "where did
you go?"*

*"Er... oh, er, I do not remember exactly where we went
father, but the food was out of this world and..."*

*The father frowned and leaned forward eagerly, "Well
the girl, what about the girl. what was her name?" The son
let a wistful smile spread across his face. "Oh, she was out of
this world too father she was beautiful, passionate, tender,
intelligent, and... But do you know her name just escapes
me..." He had a pained look on his face, and then he smiled
again, "but there is one thing I do remember."'*

*"Yes, yes, prompted the father straining further forward
so he would not miss what was coming next.*

*"The wine, ah the wine, it was a Chambertin..." Said the
son.*

We had an excellent meal and Christos was good company.
As we had both travelled quite a bit, we discussed the various
parts of the world we had been to, she was highly intelligent,
and our conversation spanned a wide range of subjects.

Because it was such a nice evening, we decided to get the
taxi to drop us at the top of the city of Fort de France, and we
walked back among the dazzlingly lit shops on the road that
led down to the waterfront. All too soon, we were back on
Grecian Lady, and Christos asked me if I would like a drink.
We both had a liqueur, and when she had finished hers, she
thanked me for being such an interesting companion and said
she was going to turn in.

I waited for about quarter of an hour for her to settle while
I relaxed in the cockpit. Occasionally a small dinghy would
put, put, by, but apart from that there was only the sound of
the occasional slap of mast halyards from the various yachts
in the bay drifting on their anchors in the slight breeze.

I got up and went below, turning the cockpit light out as I

went. As I opened the aft cabin door, I went to switch on the cabin light, and was annoyed because it didn't work. I stumbled against the wardrobe as my night vision was still adversely affected by the cockpit light. Despite these irritations, I felt very relaxed, and took off my clothes, feeling for the bed and slipping between the sheets. As I moved my leg to spread out, it was then I came upon a feeling of exquisite velvet. It was naked skin.

I thought for a moment that Christos had misunderstood who would sleep where, and I felt panic run through me. It lasted less than a second as I felt warm arms embrace me, and then those lips...

The next morning, I got up early, and was on deck preparing to sail when Christos came up. She looked cool, collected and very happy with life. I was wondering how on earth I would explain to Liz what Christos was doing on board, when she said she had decided not to go to St Lucia with me after all. I probably looked surprised.

"I think my presence there may be misunderstood," she smiled sweetly. After a hearty breakfast, she took her leave. "Until next time?" she said.

When I went down into the aft cabin later to replace the bulb, I found none there. It had been removed.

Two weeks later I received an envelope postmarked Antigua. There was a large cheque in it, much more than I had expected. There was also a one-page letter accompanying it which read'.

Dear James,

I enclose my cheque, but you will see that I have increased the amount we agreed, because the service you gave was way above what I expected... I am well advised by friends, who have seen Grecian Lady since your return that she was beautifully handled by your expert touch, and that her parts below the 'waterline' are positively glowing; we hope to see you and Liz again soon.

Christos.

I felt hot breath reading over my shoulder, "How nice of her," Liz said.

25 - THE CHEF AND THE SCHOOLGIRL

Those that complain should consider the possible
repercussions

Yani was getting worse again. Since the brooch incident, Liz had hardened her heart somewhat, particularly when she now found Yani constantly drunk. One very busy evening she had put through a load of orders for cooking, and when the waitresses complained that the food was not being prepared, Liz went into the kitchen to find that Yani had all the kitchen staff cleaning the extractor fans.

When she asked Gregory what on earth they were doing, he said that de chef had ordered them that no more cooking would be done until the fans were cleaned. The fact that the fans needed cleaning was not in doubt, but the timing of the instruction was not conducive to keeping customers happy. Liz told them to get on with the cooking, and then asked where Yani was.

"He's in de cooler, Miz Liz," thinking that she was going to find another sexual escapade, she burst in with a broom handle in her hand. As she said later, she had every intention of shoving it up a very painful place...

As it happened, Yani was sitting on a side of ham, smoking.

Liz stopped short, still with the broom handle at a threatening angle. "What the bloody hell do you think you are up to," she asked.

Yani looked up and grinned. "Me I'm smoking the ham..." Despite his excess booze, he saw the swinging handle move rapidly in the direction of his head and dived out of the cooler before Liz could aim a second blow. Later that evening he complained to Liz that she had countermanded his instructions in the kitchen, and a result he could no longer continue as chef.

"Good bye then Yani," answered Liz, "you can collect your pay tomorrow."

Yani drew himself up, swaying gently forwards and backwards. "I'll do that, I'll be here for my wages at eleven. Now, I need to go and buy some... Er provisions, can I have the van keys please," He held out his hand.

As it was past 11 p.m., Liz turned to him. "Piss off Yani," she said through clenched teeth, "before I do some more harm to your reproductive organs, to ensure that nothing like you ever gets the chance of life on this planet." She moved towards him threateningly, and he wisely shot out of the front door.

The next day he did not appear at all, and Liz contacted an agency in Britain who dealt with catering staff overseas. They said that they had a couple of highly qualified chefs who were particularly interested in going out to the West Indies and they would fax over their details that day.

The following day, Yani called in to see Liz during the early afternoon. He was dressed extremely smartly and had shaved.

In fact, he looked so clean that Liz did not at first recognise him. He pleaded for his job back, saying that he had joined alcoholics anonymous, and was now on the road to recovery. Liz did not believe a word of what Yani told her and was therefore surprised when she telephoned someone who she knew was connected to the AA people and it was confirmed confidentially that Yani was indeed a new member. The woman concerned also asked Liz to take Yani back, saying that if he lost his job, he would go to pieces, and perhaps undo all the good work AA had achieved for him.

Liz told me afterwards, that she was made to feel that the total responsibility for Yani's future situation rested entirely upon her.

Much against her better judgement, she said she would give him one more chance.

Cockroaches are endemic in the West Indies, it being impossible to keep them down particularly where food was concerned. The West Indian roach is large, usually much larger than any known beetle found in Europe. They can fly, but generally they just sit and glare at you. No doubt with the thought that I was here eighty million years or so before you lot, so why should I be the one to go?" I am not sure why people are repelled by the sight of roaches, but they are, and I confess I do not exclude myself. Perhaps it is because they are a deep blood red in colour, they have large antennae which they wave around with gay abandon, they breed faster than flies, and they invariably carry disease and dirt, although they always appear bright and shiny. They also appear to have the ability to disappear into almost any microscopic crack the moment they feel they are threatened.

Yani and cockroaches seemed to have some sort of affinity. He is the only person I have ever met who appeared to like the revolting creatures. Whenever one was seen in the kitchens, Yani would catch it and put it into a box which used to rest on one of the counters. From time to time, Liz would see the box, without opening it, stick it in the walk-in freezer, and send it down with the rubbish the next morning.

She never did find out whether this served to kill the pests, or whether they simply unfroze on the rubbish tip and continued their unmitigated plunder. But at least she reasoned they were not plundering our food.

Yani was always extremely upset when he found his box had gone missing, and a game of hide and seek developed. Because she never opened the box, it was some time before Liz realised that the box she was gaily putting into the freezer, had potato skins in it, and the box containing the roaches had been placed elsewhere.

Usually, some member of staff would alert her to the new hiding place, and the whole charade would start again.

Yani however, was getting more careful, and Liz had not been able to find the new box. She knew that three or four roaches were caught daily, but was worried that someone would stumble across it, inadvertently tip the bloody thing up, thus creating an army of roaches marching through the dining area.

One of the problems with the restaurant trade is that invariably one comes across some very nasty people indeed. We had one family who we dreaded coming in to the restaurant. The man was an English accountant for an old established business in St Lucia. His name was Tom Bradshaw. He was a skinny little man with rimless glasses and thin lips. We called him Himmler. His wife Molly was of similar build and had a permanently downward pointing mouth. She always looked thoroughly miserable, and rarely missed a chance to complain. They had a twelve-year-old daughter who was strangely podgy, but obviously she belonged to them because she had the same hang dog expression. She had a pimply face and wore glasses. Somehow, both suited her. Her name was Marigold, and she was totally uncontrollable, rude, and offensive to our staff, to us and anyone she took a dislike to, which was almost everyone. The Bradshaw's doted on this little monster, and she could do no wrong. She broke wine glasses, plates and because of her habit of swinging backwards on her chair, she broke at least three to my knowledge.

We could never quite understand why they chose our restaurant to eat in, until we realised that other restaurateurs had banned the family. Liz suggested that they be offered a table in the garden, as that area was a little more private, and the yells of Marigold were somewhat muffled by the plants surrounding the tables. This was done, by us persuading the Bradshaw's that we only offered the garden seats to our good customers, and the ploy worked.

One evening when the restaurant was full, we heard the most awful screams coming from the garden area, and Liz rushed through to find that a cockroach had landed on the floor near Marigold. The child made a scene quite out of proportion to the appearance of the unfortunate insect, and her screams so frightened the pest that it took to the air, an

393

unusual occurrence for a cockroach, as they far preferred scuttling into a quiet corner somewhere.

Marigold's screams were such that guests at other tables became extremely concerned, as of course, tourists were not to know that the large frightened flying insect was not some sort of venomous tropical beast. The result of the flying roach created near panic at some of the tables, and eventually it made its escape through into the bar area, where it again caused some fuss, until it found a gap in the windows and fled for the lagoon.

All this time, little Marigold was screaming at the top of her voice, and despite her mother trying to mollify her, they eventually had to leave. We were grateful that they were going, but Liz was livid when Tom Bradshaw refused to pay the bill.

When asked why, he said the crab Farci had been bad even though he had eaten it all of course.

The chaos they left behind them, took some time to quieten down, and when Yani learned that his crab Farci had been criticised his eyes narrowed, and he scowled. "The next time they come in here," he said, "I will personally ensure that they get the very best that I can produce." And then he smiled, which made Liz feel most uneasy.

The cockroach had not been within three feet of Marigold, but by her divulging a fear, was to have serious repercussions for her when she next visited the restaurant, which was just over a week later.

Liz was first aware that the Bradshaw's had come in when she heard the raucous voice of Marigold yelling from the garden area. She immediately called Yani who was on one of his almost sober days, and he immediately dried his hands and went out to the Bradshaw table.

He stood before Tom Bradshaw looking most contrite, apologising profusely for the crab Farci being off last time but assured him that he had prepared the dish especially for the family this time. Tom Bradshaw was mollified, and all three of them decided to have Yani's Farci as a starter. Liz knew that Yani's attitude was extremely unusual, and she decided that he must be trying harder to impress. She could not quite get rid of the feeling of uneasiness but soon the restaurant was busy, and she was involved with other things.

Crab Farci is made from a land crab that lives in burrows near to the shore. It is quite small, which is why it is generally eaten as a starter. The crabs are caught in traps and purged before killing. The shell is then cleaned out and the white meat mixed with onions, bread crumbs and herbs and then grilled. They are quite delicious, and in my view far tastier than their sea-based cousin.

Soon the crab Farci was delivered to the table by Sylvia and the Bradshaw's tucked in. It was obvious from their expressions that they were enjoying the meal and Liz who passed by the table asked, with some apprehension, if everything was okay.

Tom Bradshaw said it was the best crab Farci he had ever tasted. Molly and Marigold were too busy eating to even recognise Liz's presence.

As Liz walked on through the restaurant, she noticed Sylvia watching the Bradshaw's eating their food, from where she could not be seen. Her hand was over her mouth, and she appeared to be gagging. Liz went over to her.

"Are you all right Sylvia?" Sylvia looked at Liz and grimaced. "Oh yes Miz Liz, I'm fine, don't know 'bout them though," her head inclined towards the Bradshaw table. Tom Bradshaw was just scraping the remains of the meat from inside the shell.

Liz frowned, "why, is there anything wrong?" Sylvia looked at Liz and giggled. "It's the chef Miz Liz, he prepared a special Farci for the Bradshaw's."

Liz, knowing that there was only one way to make crab farci, frowned as the feeling of uneasiness came back to her. "What do you mean 'special'?" Sylvia hesitated, "well you know chef keeps live roaches in a box, well, dey not alive anymore."

"WHAT," said Liz, looking at her incredulously, "you don't mean..." Sylvia nodded. "Yes, Miz Liz, chef took de box from its hiding place on top of de cooler, and mashed 'em all in with de crabs," she turned and looked at the Bradshaw's, and Tom who had a thin smile on his face, which almost said, 'you see, it pays to complain.'

"Oh no," Liz was horrified, but there was nothing she

could do about it; the contents of the shells had been well and truly cleaned out.

At the end of the meal, Yani appeared again in the dining room. Liz saw him and went up to him. "I want to see you after we close," she wagged a finger at him.

Then almost as an afterthought, she asked him where he was going.

"I thought I would just spread a bit of good will, and see if the Bradshaw's enjoyed their meal," said the smiling Yani innocently.

Liz scowled at something he had in his hand. He held up a small box, which was gift wrapped. As the box was about the size one would expect to contain a small piece of jewellery, Liz assumed it contained some of his hand made gold designs and thought no more of it.

Tom Bradshaw had just paid his bill, when Yani approached the table, and ascertained that the meal had been enjoyed by all. He was holding the gift-wrapped box in his hand.

"What's that? " Asked Marigold pointing at the box.

"This?" said Yani turning it over and looking intently at it. "I don't know, I just found it on the floor..." He ensured the box was within her reach.

"Give it to me," she said snatching the box out of his hand.

Yani made a grab to retrieve it, saying he would have to hand it in, as it obviously belonged to someone.

Marigold laughingly avoided his hand and started tearing off the paper. As she opened the box, there in all its glory was the largest cockroach that anyone had ever seen.

"I've been feeding the bugger on a special diet for weeks," explained Yani afterwards.

We never saw the Bradshaw's again.

26 - THE CHEF GOES WITH A BANG

There are worst ways to go...

Things with Yani went from bad to worse after that, and if he did come in, he was usually so drunk as to be incapable of work. His demise came on the night of Carnival, possibly the busiest night of the whole year, when he was supposed to organise a large buffet. First, he did not arrive at the restaurant until most of the preparation had been completed, and then when he did arrive, he simply got in everyone's way, ordering his kitchen staff and the waitresses to do various cleaning jobs, in the middle of the cooking and serving.

Liz told him to go home, stating that he was an absolute pain. The next time she saw him, he was standing behind the roasted suckling pig, with his tall chef's hat askew, and one of the Pub lavatory seats around his neck. The head of the suckling pig had Yani's sunglasses on. He was waving a knife as he attempted to carve, and cut quite deeply into his finger, which of course spilled over the surrounding food which meant that some of it had to be re prepared.

The next day, Liz told the usual contrite Yani that she had enough, and unless he was prepared to go into an institution and dry out properly, he would lose his job.

She made it quite clear that he could not return even for

that night. Despite this, Yani did come in at the normal time, and he was totally smashed. When I tried to steer him out, he challenged me to a fight. Eventually I managed to call an AA friend of his, and we eventually got him into a car to take him home.

Some days later he came to see Liz in the Captains Table, and he was in quite a state.

His hands were shaking as though he had Parkinson's disease, and he told her he had experienced DT's and had some horrific hallucinations.

Liz got hold of Archibald, and we decided to take him over to Barbados to an institution there that dealt with people with mental problems, including alcoholics.

Archibald chartered a St Lucia Airways aircraft, which was easy to do, as he was the chairman of the company, and together we managed to get Yani on the aircraft

Not realising that he was terrified of flying. we had a most memorable flight as we could not keep Yani in his seat, and I only just stopped him opening the door at ten thousand feet, as he insisted, he was going to get out.

We handed him over to the doctor in charge, and he told us what the treatment would cost, and we agreed to pay it, knowing that Yani had no money to do so. The plan was to get him to repay us at so much a week, when he returned in six weeks or so, which the doctor indicated it would take to perform a cure.

During Yani's absence, Liz agreed to take on a chef from the English agency, for a trial period of three months. The man, whose name was Alec Green was told of the situation, and that the job could turn into a more permanent one. It was a wise precaution.

I collected Alec Green from the airport when he flew in, and he seemed a reasonable sort of person. He was much younger than Yani, and did not have the same cooking skills, but was quite a good organiser which was what Liz wanted.

By this time Alphonse had reached a high standard of skill under Yani's direction and even Gregory had made substantial progress.

During this period, I started to get involved in other things. I bought a part share in another restaurant, became quite heavily involved in an accounting services company, and in a car distributorship.

It was in relation to the latter that I had to travel to Martinique one day, deciding to fly up there in a chartered Saint Lucia Airways plane. A good friend of ours, John Golds, owned a medium sized yacht and was sailing from Martinique back to St Lucia the next day, so I arranged to sail back with him. This suited Liz quite well too, as she wanted me to buy a few provisions that could not be found in St Lucia, and as there was rather a lot she needed, it would be easier to return the goods on a boat.

I completed my business early and joined John's yacht at Anse Mitan. I knew he had guests on board, but I had not asked who they were. Imagine my surprise therefore, when I found it was Christos and her husband and another couple who I had not met before, but who I was to learn were part of the Royal Household.

Once I was aboard, John sailed the yacht to a small bay on the west side of Martinique, where we were to spend the night. The captain of Mark's boat was a St Lucian who also did the cooking and waiting, and so as soon as we arrived at our destination, Leopold went down below and brought up the rum punch. There was a large cockpit table on this yacht, and as we all sat around drinking, I felt a very definite pressure on my leg. It was Christos shapely leg squeezing against mine.

She looked at me over the table with mischievous eyes.

I looked across at her husband, who, while being quite a genial type, was substantially bigger than I was, and I resolved to lock my cabin door that night, as I did not feel inclined to incur his wrath and be chucked overboard.

I was allocated a cabin next to Christos and her husband, and as the evening wore on, and more and more rum punch was drunk, I decided it would be prudent for me to get below first. When I said I was turning in, Christos who was sitting opposite me, entwined her legs with mine, just as I was standing up, and my consequent stumble suggested that I had rather too much to drink. I decided to accentuate this somewhat, and I staggered down the galley steps, once out of sight, I rushed to my cabin and locked the door. I resolved that my usual evening shower could wait until the morning.

I had just got into my bunk when I heard the others coming down. Good nights were said to Mark, and I heard his cabin door close. I could clearly hear the whispered voices of the other four in the main cabin, and then the door of the cabin next to me opened and closed. I heard Christos giggle, and then with a considerable shock, I heard the man's voice. It was not her husband.

The cabin wall was thin and the bunk where I lay was next to it, so I had no choice but to listen to what was going on. He was speaking in French, presumably because he thought that a more romantic language. There were the usual sounds of grunting and sighing and then everything went quiet for a few seconds. Then I heard the man gasp "Je suis arrive," which in French translates to *I have arrived* or in cruder terms I have come." This was confirmed when I heard Christos say, "Jesus, couldn't you hold it longer than that?" From that comment I got the firm impression that the 'Royal household' was not quite up to it. I smiled to myself, as I turned over. I must have dozed off because about half an hour later, I heard a noise outside my cabin door, and as I turned towards it, I could hear the handle of the door being turned.

There was quite definitely the sound of a male snoring in the cabin next door, so I knew exactly who was trying to gain entry. I tried to make the best impression of the sort of snuffling sound that one might make while asleep, and after a very slight tap on my door, which I ignored I was left alone.

The next morning, I waited until I could hear sounds of others moving before I got up. I was leaving my cabin as Christo's husband came out of the one opposite.

I realised that I had witnessed my first 'wife swap'. I have often smiled to myself, when watching a Royal occasion on television, and have seen the pompous little man who was on board that boat, who 'arrived' too early.

On the way back to St Lucia, I put a trawl line out behind the yacht, and for the first time ever, I was to catch a large fish. When we eventually heaved it on board, which we could only do by loading it onto the dinghy first, we found that it was a Kingfish, and it weighed about 60 lbs. I duly delivered it to Liz that night, and she said that she would keep it in the freezer until she had a large party who wanted a predominantly fish meal.

Two days after I got back Yani telephoned Liz from Barbados and told her he was cured. He then asked her to send him one thousand dollars, as he wanted to buy some knives for the kitchen. She did not send a thousand dollars, and was rightfully apprehensive at Yani's request, as it suggested that the cure was not going to last very long.

When he returned to work, he certainly looked much better, and appeared to be off the booze. We noticed however, that he was acting quite strangely, and it took us some time to realise that while the institution had temporarily (as it turned out) got him off liquor, he was now completely addicted to drugs, Valium in particular.

Shortly this combination was to prove fatal, but Yani had one last surprise for us.

We were approached regarding an offshore fishing competition and had been asked if we could open the yachtsman's Haven bar after the event. The Prime Minister was to give away the prizes on the same evening of the competition, so all was set.

Most of the boats taking part were quite large motor launches which were involved in day fishing charters, and I was invited to go along on one of them. I was rather surprised to hear that Yani had entered with Gregory and even more surprised when he turned up at the start with a small dinghy, which carried a tiny outboard motor. There was great hilarity as it was obvious that Yani was well away with booze once again, and the size of his dinghy meant that he could not possibly get far enough out to catch a large fish. I also noticed that he had only a small trawl line, whereas the larger launches had all the proper gear.

We set off from the start line, and I thought Yani's dinghy would be upset by the wash of the other boats as we gunned away from him. From time to time during the afternoon, I would swing my binoculars at Yani and Gregory who were only a few hundred yards from shore, and both appeared to be sound asleep. Fifteen minutes before the closing time I had another look and their little dinghy was a hive of activity, Yani was straining on the line and Gregory was bent forward over the side of their boat. I assumed that they had caught their line on an anchor or had fouled it somehow.

Our boat had caught a few Jacks and a couple of Barracuda, but nothing over 10 pounds. The competition was not for the total weight of fish, but the largest single fish caught, so I knew we would not have a chance of winning.

As we headed back for the finishing line, I saw Yani crossing it ahead of us, and I could not fail to notice that they had a very large Kingfish which straddled the dinghy sideways. For a split second, I thought about the fish I had caught earlier in the week, and wondered if... I discounted this suspicion as soon as it entered my mind, as I knew Yani's dinghy had been empty at the start, and as all boats were under surveillance by the organisers, he would not have been able to put a fish on board before the competition.

The fish were weighed as the various boats moored up to the Pub dock, and there was no doubt that Yani had won by a large margin. People were amazed that he had managed to catch such a large fish so close inshore with such rudimentary tackle.

Yani basked in the congratulations and said he had been taught how to catch fish by his father, and to prove his point he showed them how to do it by making little whistling and hissing noises, which soon everyone was attempting to copy.

"No, that's not quite right," Yani said, "you must hold your head just under the water, and with your lips pursed, and your tongue forward in your mouth..."

"It never fails," he said.

For weeks afterwards, various people could be seen going out in dinghies with a fishing line bending over into the water doing the 'Yani' call in order to catch a fish, they never did of course.

The Prime Minister came, and preparations made for the final ceremony when I took a close look at the King fish he had caught. I frowned as I racked my brain for an answer. There was something about the creature that looked familiar and then I realised that it had an abrasion on the side in the same place as mine had as I had caught it on the oar locks while trying to pull the thrashing thing on board. I rushed out of the yachtsman's Haven bar and into the kitchen and entered the freezer. It took me only seconds to realise the fish had gone. I rushed out again and approached Liz.

"That fish I caught the other day have you used it?" I asked. Liz looked at me, "no, I'm sure we haven't, I told Yani to keep it until we had a large booking from a group"

I left the perplexed Liz before she had finished, and raced back to the yachtsman's bar, just as Yani was being handed the cup by the Prime Minister, plus a cheque for $500. The room exploded with clapping, and Yani turned and looked at me with a half grin.

I was about to stop the proceedings, when I realised that if Yani swore he had not used the fish in the freezer, I could not easily prove otherwise. Everyone, seemed happy, and so I decided to let things stand as they were.

Yani then had the effrontery to offer the fish to the restaurant at the full value, I told him to stuff it.

It was many months later, after Yani's spectacular demise, that I eventually got the true story out of Gregory who was not originally aware of the ruse. Early on the morning of the competition, Yani had apparently taken the fish out of the freezer and tied it under the dinghy. During the day, the warm water had obviously defrosted it, and when he thought the time was right, he pretended they had caught it. Gregory knew immediately, as Yani not being a sailor, had tied a very un-sailor like knot, and Gregory had to jump into the water to cut the thing free.

The last we heard of Yani was some three weeks after that event, when he did not turn up for work. Liz assumed that he had drunk too much, and as she was planning to fire him anyway, she did not think too much more of his absence. Later that evening his new girlfriend came in to the Captains Table very tearful, saying that Yani had died that morning. Liz told me the story afterwards.

The girlfriend had caught him having sex with another girl while sitting on the lavatory in his house. She had been understandably peeved, and remonstrated with him, where upon he had said, "have I ever been unfaithful to you?" She had sworn at him affirming that he had, and then she attempted to throw the other woman out of the house. There had been a fight, and Yani had a heart attack when attempting to part the two females.

He probably died the way he wanted to go.

Liz and I went to pay our last respects and attended his funeral, arranged for the next day. He was undoubtedly one of this world's characters, and we both had a soft spot for him. I couldn't help the feeling that as the dirt was thrown on top of the coffin, Yani would open the lid, and climb out. He didn't of course.

27 - THE AFRICAN PRINCE

Money cannot buy everything

Liz being the extremely attractive woman she is, the attention she received from various amorous West Indian males was sometimes extreme. None was quite so extreme however, as the story of the West African Prince. We were aware that there was a large motor yacht plying the Caribbean that belonged to an African Prince, and we had come across it most recently in Martinique when we had been asked to move our yacht from its mooring, so that it could pass.

One morning I was on the dock at the Pub, when I noticed a rather smart motor boat approaching with two men in it. I identified it as being one of the tenders belonging to 'Lady Bertha', the yacht owned by the Prince. Soon they were alongside, and I recognised one of them as the man I had met in Martinique, perhaps fortunately, he did not recognise me.

"Gut Morgan, I would like to arrange for our boat to tie up on your dock please," I looked at the small motor boat. "Sure, you can tie up here, will you be long?" I asked.

The man laughed, "no, no, you have misunderstood, zis is only der small boat, and it is the Prince's boat we wish to tie up. Ze Prince has heard of your gut food und wishes to dine here tonight with a party of twelve."

I confirmed that we would be delighted for the Prince to dine but I expressed some concern over the depth of the water at the dock, as I thought it would be too shallow.

The man shook his head. "Once, ve have taken a sounding, and if the large boat comes in stern first, it vil be okay."

I assumed that the man knew what draft his boat drew underneath the waterline and I realised that if he could get the boat into the lagoon, the channel being quite shallow, then he would probably be okay, besides there was only mud underneath, so even if the bottom was scraped, little damage would be done. The man wanted me to move both the yachts that were currently on the dock, but I agreed only to move them further to the side to give him more room. It was not to be too long before I wished I had moved them altogether.

Later that morning the large boat came in and swung round so that the stern was pointed towards the dock. I thought the captain was more than a little clumsy in his manoeuvring, so I placed plenty of fenders and old tyres along the dock area, so that it could absorb some quite hard shocks, which as it turned out, it had to. It took the captain over an hour to get in position, and it was somewhat of a relief when he dropped his anchor and finally reversed in a straight line.

Almost immediately, I found that we had a problem in that the dock was not designed for such a large vessel. We had no large cleats, on which to attach their lines. The whole dock area was connected to the bar, and the poles or stilts from the dock were embedded in concrete under the water. I felt these would be strong enough to hold the craft, so we organised their lines in such a way that they were simply put around the poles, both ends of their line being taken back to the moored vessel.

Judging by the mud that was stirred up during the captain's manoeuvring, I reckoned his propellers had dug a good two feet out of the bottom of the lagoon.

Oh well, a bit of free dredging I thought to myself.

While this was all going on, I had time to take a good look at the large motor yacht. It was about one hundred and forty-foot-long and twenty-six-foot-wide, I guessed that the draft was about eight feet.

I was invited on board to look around. She was certainly a beautiful boat; the exterior was finished completely in white on classical lines. It had five decks, and while the structure, engineering and navigational equipment was all state of the art. The main salon was finished in rich mahogany, with thick piled light beige carpets on all the enclosed decks, until one reached the crew's quarters. Some of the paintings on board were indeed priceless, and I noticed at least one Van Gogh, and a Renoir. A beautiful Sheraton table that seated twelve graced the dining room. The boat deck contained a very comprehensive library and a lounge area with dark blue leather couches and chairs.

The main navigation area was next to the lounge and contained every conceivable electronic gadget that a ship even twice its size would not necessarily carry. On the wall was a large picture of a Nigerian oil well, which was the source of the prince's money. The huge captain's quarters were also on the boat decks aft of the lounge. The crew's quarters and three twin berth cabins were on the lower deck. The guest cabins were nicely furnished again in a classical style, with antique furniture and four-poster queen sized beds. All the cabins had en suite facilities; the crew quarters had only showers as opposed to a bathtub. The master stateroom and the aft stateroom had king sized beds, bathrooms with large bathtubs as well as television, and stereo CD systems. In the master stateroom, the only indication that the owner was African were several leopard skin rugs adorning the floor, and a rather nice African carving of a nude black woman carrying a load on her head.

The aft deck was quite large as was the boat deck, and the top sun deck could be transformed into a sea of cushions for private lounging.

The Prince himself was not nearly as attractive as his boat, and when he came into the Captains Table that night with his entourage, I took a good look at him. He was in Nigerian dress, complete with the little pork pie hat, that I knew well from the days I had spent in Nigeria.

During his stay with us, I never saw him, but that he was sweating profusely, and no doubt his three hundred odd pounds contributed to his discomfort in the heat.

When he smiled, he showed several gold teeth, and his voice was loud. He stayed on the dock for over a week and during this time; he found out that both Liz and I were once in Nigeria. After several days he invited us on board for dinner with some other notables, but I was getting rather concerned, as it had become obvious that he had fallen for Liz. I was even more concerned when his Danish captain told me that the Prince always got what he wanted.

Not this bloody time, he doesn't, I snapped under my breath.

Liz told me he was harmless, I considered he was anything but harmless, and I warned her to watch out.

I was right.

The 'incident' came a day before the boat was due to leave. I was away from the island until the evening, and the Prince, no doubt knowing this, had asked Liz to come and have a look around the ship and have a drink. She said she would be free at about 5 p.m. and she went on board at that time. She thought it was odd that most of the staff were nowhere to be seen, and she assumed that they had been given shore leave for the day.

She refused an alcoholic drink and so the sole remaining member of staff had made tea. When he had gone, and the tea finished, the Prince took her around the ship ending at his stateroom. Once in there, he shut the door and made a proposal to Liz, which she could not mistake as the Prince had undone his fly's, producing an elephantine member. She politely told him that she was married and had no interest in the fornication he had suggested, deftly stepping past him, and leaving the stateroom. He followed her as she tried to find her way out, and he chased her down a corridor leading to the dining area, and then round the dining table three or four times, before she could make her exit.

She told me afterwards that he was extremely fast for his size, and she nearly didn't get away. Had she not, she was quite sure she would have been raped. The Prince came into the restaurant for dinner that night as though nothing had happened.

After his meal, he asked if Liz and I would join him for a liqueur. I did, but Liz declined, saying she was too busy. The conversation went like this. "Your wife is very beautiful," he smiled. "Yes, she is." I agreed.

"I would like to make a proposal to you," he leaned over

confidentially.

"Oh," I raised my eyebrows, wondering what was coming next.

"I am a very rich man; I will exchange one of my oil wells for your wife." I laughed uneasily.

I never did find out if he was serious or whether he really thought I had the power to enforce her to comply. He then tried to persuade both Liz and me to accompany him to the Grenadines as his guest, promising to pay our return airfares.

We both refused of course.

The next morning there appeared to be a very bad-tempered African Prince on board. And it appeared that his captain had suffered some tongue-lashing. For the motor yacht to cast off, all that was needed was for the lines on the deck at either side to be pulled around the poles holding the dock, for them to then pick up their anchor and they would be away.

As leaving the dock was such a simple operation, I decided that they did not need anyone to help, so I had stayed out of the way. I was just inputting some accounting information into my computer when I heard the most awful crash from the bar area.

I ran out into the yachtsman's bar, and I saw that the whole of our dock area had been pulled away and was now floating behind Lady Bertha, the lines still in place around the poles.

I saw the Danish captain come out of the wheelhouse area, and look aft in disbelief as the dock and, the other two yachts tied to it were following the large motor yacht like two obedient puppies.

I realised that we now had a major problem, as I knew the removal of the dock area would have undermined the Pub bar, and we were to find this was the case.

Fortunately, I was able to secure the services of a carpenter to shore up the underneath section of the Pub until the dock could be re-built, which was some six weeks later.

What had happened, I was to learn later, was that the Danish captain, harassed by his master's castigating manner, had completely forgotten to instruct the crew to cast off. With the boat not moving, he assumed that it was stuck in the mud, so he applied full power...

The damage was extensive, as not only was the dock destroyed, the Pub bar undermined, but the two boats that were attached to the dock were also damaged, although fortunately, not very seriously. We never did receive any compensation for the damage. We eventually obtained a court order to enable us to seize the motor yacht. The trouble was, we never saw it again.

If you ever come across our African Prince, please let me know...

28 - THE DEMISE OF FREDDY THE FART

Those that fly should remember Icarus - there are things you should not fly too near to.

Everyone knew it must come eventually. It was just a matter of time before Freddie bought it. One just hoped that one was not on the aircraft at the time. The pains people went to ensure they did not fly with Freddie were the talk of the town. His last trip was a charter down to St Vincent, with some rather Latin looking men with very heavy cases.

In those days, St Vincent had allowed about three hundred banks to register there without all the attendant restrictions that most countries place on companies calling themselves a bank. I suspect there were also some tax concessions too.

The story was that he was flying down the windward side of St Vincent, and one of the passengers expressed an interest in looking at the volcano. St Vincent is famous for their volcanic eruption in 1979, when the spectacle could be seen from several nearby islands, including St Lucia.

Freddie was always glad to oblige, and as there was usually a mist hanging over this part of St Vincent, I have no doubt that Freddie decided to get under the mist in order to give his passengers a close look. They got a close look as the aircraft smashed straight into the side of the volcano.

411

It took some time for a search party to find the bodies, but when they did, they also found the luggage belonging to the Latin looking charterers. Their cases, along with the dead bodies were eventually transported to Kingstown, the capital.

The bodies were put in the morgue, and the cases were taken to the police station, awaiting the next of kin to claim them.

During the time, the luggage was in the care of the police, one of the cases just happened to fall from a table where they were being kept. It split open divulging the contents, which turned out to be stacks of used Canadian dollars. The officer in charge diligently counted the money from that case and the other suitcases that were then opened, and the grand total came to just over $2,250,000. A report was duly filed, and the policeman in charge went home.

The next morning on his arrival at the offices the money and suitcases had mysteriously disappeared. There was an enquiry of course, but no blame could be attached to anyone concerned. It is rumoured, but probably quite untrue, that a certain police inspector shortly afterwards left the force, and went to live in California, where he apparently came into a huge fortune from some unknown Aunt...

Freddie's body was flown back to St Lucia, and some wag suggested he should not be buried at sea but thrown from an aircraft. I did not go to the funeral, but I understand this is what transpired and because the 'burial' party were high on booze before the plane took off, his coffin nearly took two of the mourners with him.

That would have been a really fitting end to Freddy's career.

29 - THE NAKED LADY

Forbidden sex in the sun created a problem for us

Liz and I had just moved to a new dwelling on the way towards Cap Estate and for the first time we were living in a detached house within its own grounds. The end of the garden backed onto the lagoon itself, and we had our private boat dock.

We had no boat of course, so we used to loan our dock out to specific people who did not want their yacht moored to the Pub dock because of the noise. One day we were approached by Godfrey Worthington. Godfrey was a funny little man, with tight blond curly hair, a small moustache, wearing large tortoiseshell framed glasses with lenses that appeared to be about quarter of an inch thick. I don't think I ever saw him in any dress other than a creased old green shirt, and soiled white shorts. The problem with Godfrey was that most of the time, he did not wear anything, particularly if he was on his boat. Liz had once approached the dock with some mail for him and had retreated at the sight of the naked Godfrey, with what appeared to be an elephant's trunk hanging between his legs.

With his sort of equipment, one would have thought that the women would have been crawling over his boat, but poor Godfrey, while trying desperately to get women to sail with him, was singularly unsuccessful, until he produced a ploy that was to have some repercussions for us.

Godfrey was an associate university professor of some unknown educational establishment in the depths of Ohio.

413

When I spoke to Americans about this university in the States, they had never heard of it, so I guess it was not quite in the Harvard or Yale class.

Godfrey left his boat on our dock, and returned to the university for a term, telling us that he would be back in the holidays. He duly turned up with a rather nice young thing who he explained was a student. We learned that he had somehow or other persuaded the educational institution he worked for to grant credits to anyone sailing with him during the holidays. He argued that their experience of the Caribbean would help in their studies.

I am sure that the young women who frequented his boat, (they were always young attractive women, and only one at a time was allowed on his boat for the scholastic experience) had no knowledge whatsoever of Godfrey's real intentions and that the experience he had in mind was not conducive to their schoolwork.

The result was a continuous file of young girls who would leave his boat in a state of high dudgeon, and Liz would inevitably be the first to hear the extraordinary stories of happenings (or in most cases, suggested happenings) on Godfrey's boat.

One poor girl that fled his boat was in complete shock when she reached our house. Liz took her in and gave her a brandy. The girl, who it transpired had never seen a naked male before, said that Godfrey had entered her cabin naked that morning with what appeared to be a huge python between his legs. She thought he was playing a joke on her, and that she was about to be bitten. She had reached for her hairbrush and bashed the 'snake' over the 'head' as hard as she could. Godfrey was in excruciating pain and was only then she realised that that the thing was attached.

Liz said to me later, that she had heard of people having gnomes at the bottom of their gardens, we just had Godfrey.

I have no doubt that stories filtered back to the university, which meant there was a very definite dearth of young ladies coming down for 'credits'. On his third trip to the Caribbean, we were surprised to see yet another girl on his boat, we learned she was called Maureen, and she appeared towards the end of his stay.

414

At first, we thought she was another student, but we were quickly to learn that she was his only daughter, undoubtedly the apple of Godfrey's eye. I have rarely met a father who was so protective over a daughter as Godfrey, I suppose he thought the world was filled with lecherous males like him.

Maureen was surprisingly attractive, not at all like Godfrey, either in looks (*which was fortunate for her, as Godfrey was certainly no oil painting*) or in the way she conducted herself. She normally lived with her mother in Florida and had come down to spend a couple of weeks with her divorced father. She was an outgoing girl and would happily chat to anyone who was in her vicinity. If it happened to be a male, it would only be seconds before Godfrey would sidle up and ensure the conversation did not contain any reference to her spending time with the person, either alone or with others.

When he spotted, what he considered was an 'approach' he would swiftly wheel her away in the other direction, saying, "my daughter and I are going sailing, or my daughter and I are going..." I think she rather played along with this protectiveness, because West Indians could be very suggestive and quite persistent. Thus, despite her twenty-two years, she was able to be a bit of a flirt, knowing that Godfrey was never far away, and would immediately come racing to her rescue.

Our son Robert, who was then sixteen, was out for his holidays, and when Maureen and he met, they got on like a house on fire. Godfrey, considering Robert's age posed no sexual threats, encouraged the friendship.

Just before her return to the states, we had an incident which caused us some grief with Godfrey. It happened at about 5 a.m. in the morning. Liz and I were fast asleep in the bedroom of our house which was on the first floor, when the telephone jangled. It took some time for us to answer it, as we had only got to bed about two in the morning. It was Jasper, who lived nearby. He told us his daughter who had been sleeping in a bedroom on the ground floor, had been attacked by an intruder. Fortunately, she had not been hurt, but he cautioned us to check to ensure our doors and windows were locked as he felt the person could be still in the area.

Liz and I went rather groggily downstairs, and as I checked the French windows, Liz went through to check Roberts's bedroom, as she knew he often slept with the doors to his room open, and they opened straight on to the garden. As she walked into the room, she saw the doors were indeed open, and went to close them. Unfortunately, there was something in the way of one of them, so she stumbled across the room to turn on one of the bedside lights, hoping that she would not wake Robert. After closing the doors and checking they were locked, she headed back towards the bed to turn off the light, it was then she saw two pairs of feet sticking out from under the covers.

I heard her yelp, and thinking that the intruder might have got in, I rushed towards Roberts's room, to be met halfway there by a furious Liz.

"What's wrong?" I asked worriedly.

"What's wrong, what's bloody wrong is your son is in bed with Maureen..."

At that moment there was a knock at the back door, and picking up a heavy hammer, I went to answer it, only to find Godfrey's worried face peering out of the gloom.

"Sorry James," he said, "but I saw your lights on and... Well, I can't find Maureen, she's not in her bed, and I have just found one of her shoes in your garden." He held up a soft canvas shoe that belonged to Maureen, I think something terrible has happened to her," Godfrey was now almost in tears.

I shook my head, as my brain was racing. Wondering whether 'terrible' in Godfrey's parlance, would be covered under the heading of going to bed with Robert. I suspected it would be. I decided to say nothing about the liaison, but I raised my voice as I was sure by now that our little nest of 'lovers' were fully awake.

"No," I said soothingly, "I am sure she probably just went to the lavatory..."

Godfrey shook his head, "no, I checked the whole of the boat... You don't think she slipped overboard, do you?" His face took on a frightened look.

"No. of course not," I said, as Liz brought him a cup of tea. "In any case, she's a good swimmer, if she had accidentally

416

fallen in, it wouldn't be a problem."

Godfrey took a sip of his tea and then yelped, as it was still very hot.

"Look," I said staring at Liz, and nodding my head urgently towards Roberts bedroom, "drink your tea, and then GO BACK TO YOUR BOAT AND CHECK AGAIN."

Liz had taken the hint and gone back into Robert's room, and found him sitting up in bed, quite alone and grinning like a bloody Cheshire cat, Liz said afterwards. She came back to me and whispered that Maureen had gone.

"I hope she is not caught by the guy who has just been at Jasper's..." I said in a low voice.

I wished that I had not said anything, as now Liz became thoroughly alarmed.

Godfrey finished his tea, and I went back with him to the boat. I was first down below, and after Godfrey told me what cabin she was normally in, I tapped softly, but there was no sound. I walked in, and there was Maureen supposedly fast asleep on the bed. I called Godfrey, and he came in.

"I just don't understand it," he said, "she was not here and, in any case, why should her shoe be in your garden?" He held up the one shoe as I gently shoved him out of the cabin and quietly closed the door.

"I expect she and Robert were playing around last night (*I wished I had used a better description*) and she shed a shoe, but why don't you ask her in the morning?" I thought of telling him about the intruder but decided he had had enough shocks for one night, and as he had not queried why we were up at 5 a.m. in the morning, I left it at that.

Liz had been most annoyed at Robert, and he was looking somewhat subdued when I got back to the house. I felt that if he had been twenty-two and had seduced a sixteen-year-old girl that would have been one thing, but the other way around, "well what the hell," I said to Liz. However, she was not happy and made her thoughts well known to the unfortunate adolescent.

The second shoe was never found, apparently, they had been in the garden and passion had overtaken them. Had Godfrey looked more closely, he would have found other more intimate pieces of underwear, and I dread to think what

417

he would have thought then. Fortunately, I found them early the next morning before Godfrey was up.

We got back to bed about 6 a.m... We did not have to be up too early the next morning, so I resolved we would sleep in until nine, and I set the alarm accordingly. Little was I to know that the Gods had not finished with us for that morning.

It must have been about 7.30 when I was woken up by a female singing downstairs. Liz was asleep in bed beside me so I knew it could not be her. I was angry now, as I assumed Robert had smuggled Maureen back into the house. I didn't feel like facing an angry Godfrey again, so I got up and put on a dressing gown.

Liz woke up, and immediately heard the singing too. I left her putting her shoes on as I went down the stairs.

As I entered the main rooms, I could not believe my eyes, and as they were tired. I rubbed them to ensure the apparition in front of me was really there.

Looking through the French windows from the inside of the house, was a slim white girl of about twenty-five, with cascading brown hair down to her shoulders. As she heard me, she turned and came towards me with her hands held outstretched with a smile on her face. She was totally naked. She had a magnificent figure, and as I was about to be engulfed by this superb specimen, I heard Liz's feet at the bottom of the stairs. I ducked under the girl's arms, as Liz entered the room.

Liz was livid, "Robert," she yelled.

Robert came through with an old pair of shorts on and looked in amazement at the girl.

"If this is another of your..." Liz did not finish.

"Hang on Liz," I said "there's something wrong here," It was the vacant look in the girl's eyes, she was either stoned on something, or had another problem.

Liz quickly realised that there was something desperately wrong with the girl too, and she got another dressing gown to cover her up. When we had done that, we sat her down and tried to question her, but it was useless, she was in a complete dream world.

Eventually I called the Gross Islet Police Station, and to our surprise, they said they knew the girl, and they would send a policewoman down for her.

It took some time for her to arrive, as of course as they had no transport, the police woman had to walk. Subsequently we found that the young girl was a Swiss citizen on holiday. Apparently, she had come across her fiancée with a St Lucian girl in their hotel room. This shock coupled with the fact that her father had died recently, had sent her out of her mind.

The boyfriend had callously left her on the island, and she was not to be found. She was eventually discovered after the police had been alerted to her wandering aimlessly down a road in Rodney Bay. They had taken her to the police station at Gros-Islet but as they hadn't a cell there that was secure, they had taken her clothes away, so she could not escape. Apparently, they were handing her over to the Swiss Charges de Affair's that morning to be put on an aeroplane for Switzerland.

We guessed that the girl had probably been the intruder that had walked into Jasper's daughter's bedroom. We never did hear what finally happened to her. Nor did we find out how she got into the house and had to assume that she had been there all night. "I think we've had enough young females for one day," growled Liz, scowling at Robert.

30 - THE MEDICAL SCHOOL

When discussing the holocaust, be aware who you're talking
to

Marcel de Croix was a British subject born in Switzerland,
and he was married to a particularly attractive and pleasant
Chilean woman. We became very friendly with them as they
used to eat regularly at the restaurant.

Marcel was an interesting man, he had been involved in
large projects, and had caught a financial cold. When I first
knew him in St Lucia, he was between marriages and was
brash, rude, ate like a pig and drank like a fish, which for a
diabetic was not the way to a long and happy life. I remember
he once joined us on a Martinique yacht race, and on one of
the evenings, we went out to eat at a fish restaurant. We
decided to have their speciality, comprising a large dish of
seafood, including crabs' claws, mussels, Cray fish, lobster,
and a host of other sea creatures laid on a bed of rice.

The dish was quite enormous, and far too much food for
the six of us who were there. The idea was that one would take
a small amount from the central dish, and eat it, going back
for more. I was suddenly aware of missiles whizzing past my

head and when I looked up from my plate, I was amazed to see Marcel cracking the large crab pincers with his teeth and spitting out the shell. Then he stuffed five crab legs into his mouth and the sight of this large man with five legs protruding from his face as he crunched them, was quite funny. He came from a good family, so it was even more surprising that his table manners were so appalling. Fortunately, after he married his Chilean wife some three months later, he did attempt to conform somewhat but his practice of loudly breaking wind whenever he felt the need continued right up to his early death.

Because he was so rude and brash, he was almost certainly universally disliked. It was however his extreme prejudice that was to give us the most trouble.

Marcel did not consider the black race to be much more than animals, and he treated them as such. The most serious transgression though was to be towards members of the white race.

Just after the naked lady affair, we heard that a local off shore medical school had closed due to financial failure. Those of you who keep track of the news will recall that the main excuse for the US forces invading Grenada, was because there were about two hundred American students at a medical school there.

It is very difficult for school leavers in the States to obtain entry into a university to train for a medical career. The competition is intense, mainly because a medical qualification is virtually a licence to print money. To overcome this difficulty, medical schools sprang up outside the USA, and for a large fee, a student could gain credits, which would eventually get him or her onto a USA medical course. It was a sort of back door arrangement.

The school in St Lucia was owned by several New York Jewish people and thus the students tended to be predominantly Jewish. The first sign of the closure came when a large group of students filed into the Captains Table side of the restaurant one evening, a few them in great distress, as in some cases the work they had achieved over the last twelve months would be completely negated. Liz was sympathetic to their plight, opening the yachtsmen's bar so that they could grieve in peace. Enter Marcel de Croix who knew of the closure because the school had been nearby to where he lived on the island.

After a few drinks at the bar, he decided to go in to console the students. It was only a few minutes afterwards that a student urgently called Liz to intervene.

Liz came to me and asked me to get Marcel out quickly as there was going to be a fight. I was to discover afterwards that he had advocated that gas ovens be set up locally, and the bloody Jews be thrown in. He was of course, referring to the current owners, not the students. He had either forgotten that most of them were Jewish, or ignored the fact, but this comment coming on top of their already considerable grief, had created a highly volatile situation, to say the least. I managed with difficulty to extract Marcel without him being pulverised, which was no mean feat.

It always amazed me that one was caught up in so many incidents, which were not of one's own making.

31 - THE MAD MONTH OF MAY

Oh, happy days

After four years running the restaurant, we were never quite sure why May of each year proved to be so disastrous. Perhaps it was the fact that it was the end of our season, and everyone was tired, but this month really took the biscuit for disasters. It was also the last May we were involved with the business.

The month started out with Mary, our most attractive waitress falling in love with a local man, who was to ditch her, when he had achieved what he wanted. She died a rather horrible death soon afterwards and we were subsequently to learn much later that he had given her a rum punch laced with gramoxone (rat poison). Shortly afterwards our elder daughter ran over our bus driver (quite by mistake). She had been driving the van between the Captain's Table and Castries and had gone to overtake when a bus stopped on the roadside. This man stepped out into the road from behind the vehicle; she didn't have a chance to stop in time, and next thing she knew a body was being thrown over the top of the van and landing in the road behind. Fortunately, he was not killed, but she could not have chosen a worse person to hit, as we then had no staff transport while he was hospitalised.

Because of this, we went through several days of staff not turning up, or turning up late, and in one case, not turning up at all, as the temporary bus driver we had managed to hire, overslept.

Alec Green the new chef had started to get a grip on the staff and found that most of them were concealing food under their clothes when leaving at night. One evening when the staff were searched upon leaving, bits of cheese, carrots, onions, and steaks all appeared, and one waitress who had been with us from the start, had concealed a chicken leg down her cleavage. It was only found because she bent down to pick up an apple, which she had concealed under her dress. God knows what else they had concealed in places where we could not search.

We replaced one of the waitresses because of thieving and took on a new one called Mavis. As Mavis was new, she was given the job of inspecting salads before they were sent out to the diners. It was only after numerous complaints that we realised that she was as blind as a bat and could not even see the host of caterpillars she had gaily passed on to the unsuspecting gourmets. We know for certain that at least one man ate the caterpillars he was given, either because his eyesight was as bad as Mavis's, or perhaps because he thought them to be some West Indian delicacy.

Half way through the month we ran out of water, the government had decided to mend the water pipes, but had not thought to tell anyone. This was obviously very much more serious than our previous burst pipe, and we had to struggle without water for almost a week.

The next thing that happened was that Alec caught our barman watering the Scotch whisky. Because there was no water, we had said that if anyone wanted water with their drinks, they would simply have to be told that we did not have any and offer soda instead. Pedro started to bring in his own water, and Alec became suspicious, catching him one evening filling a two-thirds full bottle of Bells with it.

We did not sack him, he was given a serious warning, but the fact that Alec had caught him, was to prove his undoing. Two days after getting our water back, Alec caught a man taking beef steaks out through a grill in the back door, which we had originally covered with metal gauze. The night watch and I made a citizen's arrest and found that the man was an

American yachtsman. As he had been a regular customer, we wondered how long he had been feeding from us free.

No wonder he only drank here said Liz afterwards.

We then discovered that he was Gregory's boyfriend. and that Gregory had been the person at the other side of the window, so we had to sack him, which annoyed Liz, because everyone had put a lot of training time into getting him up to a chef standard, and he was just starting to show real promise.

Because of the high unemployment in most of the Caribbean islands, anyone coming from abroad had to have a work permit. Because of the time taken to get this piece of paper, most people started work once the application was in, which was strictly illegal but was generally ignored by the authorities, unless it was specifically brought to their notice, when they had to act.

When Alec had arrived on the island, Archibald, Liz's business partner had assured her that he would deal with the formalities. He had completely forgotten to do so and when Pedro's little income on the side was blown by Alec, we suspected that he reported to the police that Alec had no permit to work. He probably did not know whether he had or not, but he reported him just the same, in the hope that he would be caused some hassle.

He did. One day when Liz was in town shopping, the police came and arrested poor Alec, taking him back to the main police station, and incarcerating him.

It happened to be a Friday, Alphonse's day off and we had not yet got a replacement for Gregory. Alec's unforeseen absence meant that the restaurant had no chef. When Liz returned, she was horrified to find what had happened and she went back down to Castries and sought an interview with the Police Commissioner, who eventually relented and let Alec out on parole, making Liz totally responsible for him. He was told he had to report daily to the police station until his permit came through. It took three months.

One of the stories Alec came back with was quite amusing. The jail was a place of sustenance for some of the inmates, and most would not consider leaving it.

Alec told us that they had been having a game of football

in the prison yard, and the ball had gone over the wall to the street outside. A long-term prisoner climbed over retrieved the ball, and then went back and knocked on the door to get back in again.

He was let in by a prison officer without comment. I had been getting concerned about our electricity bills, as they appeared to be going up alarmingly. I had the meter checked but was told it was okay. One day I turned off the power in the Captains Table and went to check the meter. The little disc was whizzing round at some speed. I then went back into the Captains Table and looked everywhere before satisfying myself that there was no electricity being used.

I called the electricity company again and they sent someone out to see me. As he looked at the spinning disc, he asked me if there was anything on at the house.

"House? What house?" I asked.

He then explained that Bessie, presumably as a tax dodge, had her house wired into the Captains Table electricity supply. I suddenly realised that during the six months we had lived there, I had not had a bill. I assumed that Bessie would at some stage charge us, and I had forgotten about it. Now some three years later, I realised that we had been footing the bill for the house during the whole of that time. The reason I had recently noticed the increase, was that the house had recently been let out to some Americans, who kept their air conditioners on all day.

The next shock I was to get was our telephone bill. Yes, you've guessed it, the house telephone was included on the same bill as the restaurant. This had been an arrangement with someone in the telephone company. The house number was simply not noted on the account, which is why I had not noticed it. Our American friends had been gaily calling their family in the states and elsewhere and had run up a huge account. Fortunately, in this case I was able to separate the past bills easily.

The last thing that was to concern us, was the matter of the police commissioner who had given parole to our chef. I will call him John Turner, although that was not his real name. John was a Saint Lucian, but because of his light colour, he clearly had some European genes. He was exceptionally

426

bright and although due for retirement, he was being considered for a senior Interpol position. He was also quite sweet on Elizabeth, which is no doubt how she managed to persuade him to help with the case of the chef.

Turner was walking along the beach with his daughter, when she was accosted by one of the young 'blue blood's' living on the island. This young man was particularly offensive and was told by Turner to get lost. The man continued to hassle his daughter, so Turner took told her to stay where she was, and he walked back to his car. Taking out his revolver he returned and shot the offensive individual between the eyes. It caused some consternation, as to how the island could charge their Chief of Police with murder. Eventually he was given five years, and the governor of the prison vacated his office suite to accommodate the ex-policeman, who was constantly let out to look after his estate in the south.

32 - THE FIRE

The end!

Four years had gone by extremely quickly. Perhaps because we were always so rushed, we did not notice the years clocking on. I had become more heavily involved in my own businesses, and we had, at the request of the government, moved into the area of data processing for the US market. Initially, we had gone into partnership with an American company, who had supplied a general manager to run it. The deal was that the American corporation would put in funding and look after the marketing in the States. Unfortunately, they did not do the latter, so we bought them out, returning their expensive general manager to them.

The French car dealership had closed due to the huge increase in the value of the franc, which made the cars uncompetitive on the island and I had recently sold my interest in the other restaurant and marina. The competition from new restaurants sprouting up was becoming intense, and the St Lucia tourist market was changing to all in deals with the hotels, which meant less business for those outside.

Liz and I discussed our future, and we decided that we had both had enough of the restaurant business, and in any case, I felt that I should go to the States to set up our own marketing operation for the computer company and this was necessary as we had been offered a contract there to carry out some sensitive work. We talked about what we should do over many weeks, and finally decided that we would find a manager to run the Captains Table and leave the island for the USA.

We eventually found a French chef and his wife who were prepared to take it on, and so preparations were made for us to leave. We would both be sad to go as St Lucia had been so much part of our life for the past six years, but at the same time, we were excited at the prospect of going to live in the USA.

We discussed what we should do to mark our send off from the island, while at the same time introducing the new chef/manager. Eventually, we hit on the idea of a fancy-dress party for all our friends and customers.

Alec Green had decided not to stay on with the new people, so he was to return to England after helping us with the party. We drew up our lists of invitees and were amazed at how many people there were. Even after pruning it considerably, we realised that we were going to have difficulty in fitting everyone in.

To simplify the food and drink, we decided on a buffet, with a choice of Rum Punch or orange juice which cut down our costs somewhat.

Liz had some trouble in getting the ingredients she required for the buffets, so we decided to go up to Martinique to buy some provisions up there. We chartered a St Lucia Airways plane for the trip, and it was during the flight that the captain told me that a pilot friend of ours had been killed while flying the C130 into Angola.

We had a good day in Martinique and as we knew we may not return for some years, we are had a good mooch around Fort de France, Liz buying some more substantial clothes for the colder American climate.

Our last flight on the now defunct airline was uneventful, and we managed to smuggle our cooked meats through the St Lucia customs. I had also bought some fireworks in Martinique, as Liz said she wanted to leave the island with a bang. I was later to find out that since the capital of Castries was almost burned down a few years ago, one needed

429

permission from the fire department to let them off. A fire engine had to be present also. The cost of arranging this was prohibitive, so rather than throw them away, I donated them to the government for them to let them off at the next Aqua Action function. (Aqua Action is a water sports week, which is held annually in St Lucia).

The planning and the work involved for our send-off went on at some pace, as we started to pack our personal effects ready for the big move. We hoped that the weather would stay fine for us.

Two days before the party, the water went off again. This time we discovered that the main had burst underground, and while it was known where the leak was, there was no new piping on the island, so it could not be repaired until the materials were imported from the USA. This caused us some problems, and we were sorry that the new chef/manager would have to deal with most of them. We were determined that it would not affect the party though. Little were we to know.

The great day came, and all concerned awaited the party scheduled for 8 p.m. with eager anticipation. We had laid on our usual musical trio, so we hoped the live music would quickly get everyone in the right mood.

The fancy dress was a huge success, and people had gone to enormous lengths to prepare their costumes, so much so that we decided to have a fancy-dress competition and give two bottles of champagne to the man and woman with the best and most innovative costumes. The male winner was a local man, who had created a Roman Centurion's outfit out of paper mâché, it looked outstanding. The woman who won had gone as Lady Godiva, and she had created a pink all in one costume that got a second look as she had even put black Velcro on the crutch area for realism.

By 10 p.m., the party was in full swing, and a great time was being had by all. It was then I noticed that we might have a problem.

When 'Lady Bertha' had ripped away our dock area, the supports, which effectively held up the Pub in which the main bar and Pub eating area were situated, had been weakened. We had got a carpenter to put pieces of timber underneath,

430

to shore the place up, and when we had the new dock built, these had been taken away, but without our knowledge. The carpenter concerned, obviously thought the nice expensive timber would serve him well elsewhere. The only problem was that the new dock had not been built as a composite part of the Pub as before, but I was to learn all this later in the evening when I inspected underneath the Pub bar.

There were a substantial number of people in the Pub area, certainly many more than normal, and during the evening I thought I heard a crack but as there was so much other noise going on at the time, I had ignored it.

At about 11 p.m. Liz came up to me with a St Lucian on her arm, and said she thought the Pub floor was sloping rather oddly. She then disappeared onto the dance floor, as I did with a young thing dressed as Nell Gwynn. I put Liz's comments about a sloping floor down to an excess of rum punch. Suddenly there was another much louder crack, and I could feel myself sliding towards the lagoon. I realised then that something had gone seriously wrong underneath the floor.

Fortunately, the whole thing did not collapse, otherwise there would almost certainly have been injuries. Those that fell on the now slanting wooden floor, took it all in good part. We moved everyone into the dining area, built very firmly on dry land. Going to the bar was quite good fun, as getting down the twenty-degree slope was no problem but getting back was hilarious, particularly if one was carrying more than one drink. With an engineering friend we had gone outside and inspected the underneath of the bar and had satisfied ourselves that providing we could keep excess weight off it, there was no need to move the actual bar itself, or to stop the odd person walking on the now inclined area.

While we were outside on the dock making this inspection, the new chef/manager approached me to find out what had gone wrong. I showed him the problem and suggested that as we were flying to the States the next day, that he got the same carpenter who rebuilt the dock, to replace the wooden supports. I felt that this could be easily accomplished by using ordinary industrial jacks, which I knew were on the island.

While we were chatting, I happened to mention the

fireworks I had brought from Martinique and said what a pity it was that we could not use them. He grinned and said that he had something much better, and he disappeared into his yacht which was moored to the dock.

I didn't think any more about this, until I was on the dance floor again scowling at Liz's rather too warm embrace with her partner. I was suddenly conscious of a few people out on the dock area. I then heard a swoosh and saw a delightful display through the window as a rocket burst in the heavens above. I excused myself from my partner and walked towards the dock, where I saw the new chef/manager with what looked like a small pole in his hand.

He turned to me and laughed, saying that he had found a couple of French distress rockets he had on his boat for some time, and he thought it appropriate, that he should let them off in honour of Liz and me. Someone was standing nearby with a lit match, and as he only had one more flare after the one, he was holding, I did not think it would create any problems. Just as the match was applied to the flare the whole Pub area shifted. It was not dangerous, but the noise alarmed some, in fact one of the parties fell into the lagoon, thinking the building was moving on top of him. The new chef/manager had turned around, to look at the source of the noise, and I saw he was pointing the bloody flare straight at me.

I ducked just in time as the missile winged across the top of my head, through the Pub windows, which were open and through the hatch into the kitchen area.

There were sudden yells, as the waitresses and kitchen staff poured out of the door leading to the kitchen, and suddenly I could see flames from behind them.

I rushed to the office for a fire extinguisher, but because the Pubs floor was sloping, I slipped on the way back and the extinguisher emptied itself uselessly on the floor. I knew the only other extinguishers were in the kitchen and the fire had now clearly caught hold and there was chance of anyone getting in there.

I yelled to Liz to get everyone out, and I rushed to the office to ring the fire brigade, it took a while to get through and when I did, the conversation went like this'.

"Hello, hello, we have a fire at Captain's Table in Rodney Bay..."

"Where is de fire?"

"AT CAPTAIN'S TABLE IN RODNEY BAY," I shouted.

"There's no need to shout man, I can hear you fine... Now, where did you say the fire was?" I took a deep breath; I could hear people moving out of the Pub area and cars being moved outside.

"There is a fire at Captain's Table, and it is catching hold fast..."

"At Captain's Table you say?"

"Yes, at Captain's Table," I almost yelped.

"Ah, isn't that the area that has a burst water pipe?"

I looked at the telephone receiver hardly believing what I was hearing.

"Yes" I said with all the patience I could muster.

"Ah. That's a problem, 'cause we do not carry enough water..."

"That's no problem," I said, as I heard the crackling of the fire moving ever closer. "We are right by the lagoon; you can pick your water up from there."

"Ah that's a problem."

"Why is it a fucking problem?" I snapped.

"'Cause de lagoon be salty water, an' our equipment doesn't like salty water..."

"What do you intend to do then, just let the bloody place burn down?"

"Is it bad?" Came back the answer.

I breathed out slowly, I could now feel the area getting warmer, and some smoke was starting to drift through. Someone was now banging on the external office door it was Liz, obviously concerned for my safety.

"Well, the kitchen was in flames when I left it, and I suspect..." I paused as I suddenly had an idea. "Trouble is, the Prime Minister's car is right in line of the fire, and we can't move it..." I lied.

"You mean the Prime Minister is there?"

"What do you think?" I answered.

"Hang on man we'll be down straight away," He rang off.

I put the phone on the hook, and went and opened the

door, Liz was standing there looking concerned.

"Did you get the money out of the safe...?" She brushed past me.

The smoke was getting quite thick now, and I knew we did not have much time. "And I thought it was me you were worried about," I said as Liz bent down to the floor safe and scooped up the takings, and then grabbed her handbag which was on the desk.

She gave me a kiss as she rushed past for the door, "Come on, there's nothing else we can do," she said, gasping for the cleaner air outside, as she dragged me out with her.

"What about the kitchen staff?" I asked.

"Everyone is out," said Liz.

"I've checked and some of the guys went to move the boats from the dock. Is the fire engine coming?" She asked.

I told her of my conversation with the fire chief.

"Well, it doesn't really matter" said Liz, now standing well back in the car park and surveying the burning inferno, "there is no way they can save it now."

Fortunately, there were no other buildings nearby, so it was unlikely that sparks would affect anything else. Just then the lead guitarist elbowed his way through the small crowd that was left and approached me.

"Say man, my equipment was all left in the fire, I'll give you a list for the insurance company in the morning..."

"Fine," I answered, suddenly realising the enormity of what had happened.

As he disappeared towards his van now parked outside on the road, a friend came up to me. "I heard what that guy said to you James, don't believe a word of it, I saw the bugger stashing his gear into the van long before the fire caught hold..."

I sighed as I thanked him.

The fire engine came eventually, but as there was no sign of the Prime Minister's car, and it was obvious they were too late anyway, they simply watched as the roof caved in, and disappeared among a huge cloud of sparks.

I turned to Liz who had tears in her eyes. "Well, you said you wanted to go with a bang..."

POSTSCRIPT

THE CHRISTINE KEELER AFFAIR

Some meetings can bring unforeseen

consequences

A TRUE STORY

I have already relayed a story told by John Golds about the Koo Stark affair. who we met in the West Indies when we lived there. He was the unofficial representative to the Royal family in the area, but his past was even more interesting. Marc had been the senior British Commissioner in Kenya during the Mau Mau crisis. He was responsible for the whole of northern Kenya, so not only did he have to contend with local unrest, but Kenya was at that time at war with Somalia in the north. His headquarters was in a sparsely inhabited area where he controlled all the security forces, including the army and police.

At the location where he was stationed, they had a yacht club called Wajir. This club was many miles from the sea and located in the middle of a dry and isolated dessert. Their main transport was a camel.

Every so often, the top brass from the UK would arrive at the small airport, which was part of the complex. This visit was headed by the then British War Minister, John Profumo, who was the Minister for war in the Macmillan government. After John had finished his private meeting with Profumo, they retired to the yacht club. After a few drinks, Profumo noticed a calendar on the wall with pictures of scantily clothed girls. He flipped through the various months and came to October. He wrote on it, 'this one is mine' and signed it. The picture was one of a Christine Keeler. The next month the world press arrived to assess the current situation regarding the Mau and the Somalian war. After a presentation, they were all entertained in the Wajir yacht club, and then boarded their aircraft, to fly back to Nairobi. Shortly after they had gone, John was informed that the calendar was missing from the yacht club wall. He immediately radioed the aircraft and told the pilot that he should ask his passengers to release it and for him to return it to the club on his next visit. The scandal over the Profumo affair was hotting up in the UK and Marc was determined that the press should not be allowed to steal what could be a compromising document, particularly so, as Profumo had made a statement to Parliament denying any involvement with Christine Keeler.

The co-pilot radioed John back, saying that he had made an announcement in the cabin, and all the members of the press swore that they had not seen the calendar.

Marc, who by then had consumed a fair amount of alcohol, and despite the furore he knew his next action would cause, ordered the pilot to return to Wajir. At first the pilot refused, and so John told him that his flight plan had been cancelled, and he would be arrested in Nairobi for disobeying a direct order, as the plane was still under his jurisdiction.

The threat of losing his air licence left the pilot with no choice, and he turned the aircraft around and landed back at Wajir. As it landed, John surrounded the plane with armed army personnel and then boarded it.

All the press were furious, but John told them that one of the members of the press had the calendar and unless it was given up, all would be arrested and searched, including the aircraft itself. He was pretty sure that it was the man from the Mirror but was extremely surprised when the senior journalist from the Times admitted that he had taken it for a joke. The fury from the press corps was then thankfully directed at the thief.

Once John had received the calendar, he allowed the plane to take off, and he returned to the yacht club, where he disposed of the evidence in a small fire, whilst drinking a large brandy.

The Leeward Islands:

This section just gives you an introduction to the Lower Antilles an area steeped with history.

The Leeward and Windward chain of islands are collectively part of the Lessor Antilles and are arguably one of the most beautiful areas of the world, with an average temperature of 31 degrees Celsius all the year round and with a wind speed of 18 knots, mostly easterly. This makes it a perfect area to sail as the islands run roughly north to south.

Originally the area was inhabited by the Arawak's', an Indian tribe that originated in South America. They were a peaceable people who lived mainly on a diet of fish and had few enemies. Subsequently they were invaded by the Caribs', also from South America, but this tribe was very different, in that they stole the land from the Arawak's' and exterminated them, so that by the time the Europeans arrived, there were very few Arawak's' remaining The Caribs gave their name to the Caribbean Sea and were very different from other indigenous Indians in that they have blue eyes.

Once the Europeans arrived on the scene, firstly the Spanish, then the French, British, Dutch, Swedes and Portuguese, the aggressive Caribs met much the same treatment as they had handed out to the Arawak's. There are a few left in Jamaica and Dominica, but probably less than 100 in each place.

The Spanish and Portuguese did not stay, preferring the land mass of South America where they already had colonies, and could defend their land, also stolen from the indigenous tribes, such as the Inca.

The islands became economically very important, as it was found that the climate was particularly favourable for growing sugar cane. Because of this they became hotly contested by the Europeans, many of the islands changing hands several times, usually connected to the European wars. For instance, Saint Lucia in the Windward Islands changed hands between the British and the French fourteen times. Indeed, in the eighteenth century, so important was this island to the British economy that the government of Great Britain forced General Cornwallis to send half his army to Saint Lucia to prevent the French invading it. This allowed General Washington to overcome his depleted force, which when blockaded by the French Navy, they could no longer receive replacement rations or ammunition.

The islands in the **Leeward** chain are as follows: North to South

Anguilla is a self-administered British overseas territory. It is the most northerly of the Leeward Islands, lying east of Puerto Rico and the Virgin Islands and directly north-west of Saint Martin. One Christmas we anchored in a beautiful bay there where we spent the whole holiday period. We never saw another human being, despite the bay being quite large. It was completely idyllic. Now Anguilla is the number one tourist spot for the northern Caribbean. The capital is called Valley.

Saba originally belonged to Sweden, subsequently ceded to the Dutch. It is a small mountainous island with two towns, you must travel to Top before you can go to Bottom. It has an air strip cut out of the side of a cliff called Hells Gate and it's well named. There is a video on U-tube which puts you in the co-pilots seat when landing on the island, not to be seen by those worried about flying.

Saint Martin a French possession share the island with the Dutch which is called

Sint Maarten. Rather than going to war over the territory, the story goes that a Dutchman and a Frenchman set off walking the perimeter of the island, one going west and the other east. When they met at the end of the walk a line was drawn from that point to the starting point, thus amicably separating the island into two parts. While the French have the larger part, the Dutch have the most important with the port of Philipsburg. It is a free port, so one can buy electrical goods, jewellery, and other expensive items free of tax. They also sport several large Casino's. The capital of the French side is called Marigot Bay, a quiet backwater with excellent restaurants.

Sint Eustatius is a Dutch island to the south west of Sint Maarten and is quite different in that the people living on the island still wear Dutch clothes and clogs that were worn by the Dutch in the 1800's. Most are white and the architecture is very Dutch. It is almost as though the island hasn't moved past the nineteenth century. Sint Eustatius was the first country to recognise the new country of the United States of America. This is no surprise, as they benefited hugely during the American War of Independence, by allowing weapons to be shipped from their country to the American rebels. At that stage of their history, they were by far the richest island in the Caribbean bar, none.

Saint Barthelemy (St Barts) this island is only a 10-minute speed boat ride south from Sint Maarten and its main port and town is called Gustavia, which reminds one of Gulliver's Travels. It has a beautiful beach on the north side, where a restaurant and hotel are owned by the parents of the son who married Pippa Middleton, the sister of Kate Middleton.

Going south, **Rotunda** is a small uninhabited island that has a solitary British pillar box on it. If you post a letter there, you will have a unique post mark on your envelope when it arrives. What stamp one uses has never been explained, but apparently letters are collected from time to time.

Antigua and Barbuda are two islands south east of St. Barts and Barbuda comes under the administration of Antigua. These were British islands until their independence in the early 1980's. Also, now members of the British Commonwealth. English harbour in the east, is a favourite for sailors because it is virtually surrounded by land with quite a narrow entrance, so it is a good place to anchor if the sea is rough. Unfortunately, they have the worst customs in the Caribbean as one must stay in one's yacht until they deign to come to you. Sometimes this takes a whole day. It is now very much a tourist island with prices higher than most. Nelson used to anchor in English Harbour, the gossip is that he had a mistress there. 'Harbour' is a bit of a misnomer as there is no actual harbour structure in the bay.

Barbuda administered by Antigua in the south can be reached only from Antigua, as one must clear customs there first. The whole of Barbuda was originally a sugar estate owned by the Boddington's who have a large estate just north of Bath. When we lived in Bath, I used to fly over their huge mansion before landing at the racecourse nearby where I sometimes kept my aircraft. It always brought back to me how they made their money, as Barbuda was the only area in the world that bred African slaves for the slave market. When we were sailing in the Caribbean, the island had been taken over by the mafia, no doubt as a staging post for drugs. A friend of ours who sailed there was met with several bullets which pierced his sails. He made a speedy retreat.

St Kitts and Nevis are a popular hideaway for the Royal family, particularly Prince Charles. Probably the strongest British fortress in the Leeward or Windward islands, is now a ruin but still a substantial military property. Originally occupied by the French and British, after much fighting the islands were ceded to the British in 1713 and it became the most profitable in the whole of the Antilles. It gained independence in 1983 and is part of the Commonwealth. In 1998 Hurricane Georges caused 458 million pounds worth of damage there.

Guadeloupe is a French Island south east of Antigua and is a Department of France along with small islands to the south of it, including Marie Galante and Ill des Saintes. This is where Christopher Columbus first found the Pineapple. It has one of the largest population's in the Leeward chain and the currency is the Euro.

Il Des Saintes are islands just south of Guadeloupe and administered by them. It is a delight to visit overnight as a sailor, as after checking in to the police station the next morning, one can buy hot chocolate croissants from the bakery next door. These islands have a notable history in that this is where the British and French fleet met in the Battle of the Saintes in 1782. The British thrashed the French capturing four of their main galleons including the flagship containing the French commander. This put an end to a joint French and Spanish threat to invade Jamaica. The importance of this battle, however, was that Admiral Rodney was credited with the tactic of 'breaking the line.' Subsequently this was used by Nelson in the Battle of Trafalgar and even later by

Admiral Jellico in the battle of Jutland. Rodney did not deserve the credit, as he was in fact in his cabin below with gout. It was due to his second in command, who was friendly with a man called Sir John Clerk who lived in Edinburgh. Clerk had never been to sea, but despite this he was very interested in naval tactics and over several dinners with various naval officers he proved his theory by war gaming on his small pool in his garden.

Montserrat this island is south west of Guadeloupe and is still British. It was well known for hosting various music groups in the 60's and seventies as they had first class facilities with a modern sound studio. This attracted the Beatles, Rolling Stones, and many others. Recently it suffered a cataclysmic volcanic eruption that destroyed part of the island, and the British Navy were called in to remove inhabitants from the area.

Dominica not to be confused with the Dominican Republic, is the southernmost island in the Leeward chain and was given their independence by Britain in 1976. It is a member of the commonwealth and possibly the most primitive of the islands having a large rain forest in the interior. It was ceded to Britain from the French after the seven year's war in 1713. It does not have good holding for yachts outside the capital of Roseau. Elizabeth and I anchored there once after a day's sail. The next morning, we found that we had drifted about a mile out to sea. Fortunately, there were no rocks in the area, or I wouldn't be telling you this story today.

THE WINDWARD ISLANDS

"As long as you miss the reefs, the rocks, other boats, Hurricanes, storms, thieves, and boat boys, you'll have a great time."

Martinique. Although held by the British at various times in history, Martinique is now definitely French. This is the island where Josephine, Emperor Napoleon's, wife was born. It is a Department of France, which means that they vote in the Presidential elections carried out on the mainland of France. It is by far the most sophisticated island in the Antilles. The island was traded by the British in 1815 and it has remained French since then.

Mont Pelée, the volcano in the north of the island erupted in 1902 and destroyed St. Pierre, a north eastern coastal town, killing over 30,000 people. The mayor of the town refused the inhabitants to flee Saint-Pierre, and all died except Auguste Cyparis, a prisoner in a thickly walled cell below ground, he was the only person the survive.

Diamond Rock is about an hour's sail due west from St. Anne. Shaped like the top of a bullet, it lifts sheer out of the sea to a height of about 500 feet. The distance between the south end of Martinique and the rock is only a few hundred yards, but the water between is deep enough to sail through safely.

While Silver Star was passing the rock to the port side, before turning south towards St. Lucia, I told the guests that some hundreds of British troops had captured the rock during the Napoleonic wars, and it had been a severe embarrassment to the French. The main reason for the capture was because some British military wag had decided that as there were no mosquitoes on the rock, it would be an ideal site for a hospital for sick troops based in St. Lucia. It was correct that there were no mosquitoes there, but the place was and still is apparently, infested with the deadly fer-de-lance snake. More British troops died from snake bites than they would have done from yellow fever.

Viewed from the sea it was difficult to imagine how they landed, never mind lived on the place and impossible to imagine them pulling heavy cannon up to the top, but they did. It was the only rock in the world at that time commissioned as a ship and it became HMS Diamond Rock. This annoyed Napoleon no end as his darling Josephine came from Martinique. To redress French honour Napoleon sent the French fleet under Admiral Villeneuve to remove the Brits.

Despite Nelson chasing him all the way there, he completed the job, and the occupation of Diamond Rock came to an inglorious end after only eighteen months of annexation.

Because Villeneuve had wisely chosen not to fight Nelson, Napoleon ordered him to return to France in disgrace. This stinging rebuke encouraged him to put to sea again rather earlier than he had contemplated and before the fleet was ready, the result was the Battle of Trafalgar.

The funnier story, which I enjoyed telling about the rock, came much later, however. In 1978, just before St Lucia became an independent country, some Brits and South Africans had been celebrating the New Year. The story of Diamond Rock had come up and for a dare, a dozen or so men set out from St. Lucia before first light in a fast motor boat. Their equipment included climbing gear and a huge Union Jack. By 10 in the morning, the British flag flew from the top of Diamond Rock for all to see.

Had that been all there was to it; a rather headstrong prank, it would have passed by without becoming an International incident. What the Brits and South Africans didn't know was that the senior admiral of the French navy had chosen that day to visit

445

Fort de France, the capital of Martinique, and was sailing in from the Atlantic just as the British flag was raised.

There are stories that the poor man almost had an apoplectic fit and he immediately ordered the marines to go in and remove the invaders. Unfortunately, the French marines had no climbing gear, so could only glower from the sea at the jeering throng on top, who were making unkind suggestions about the efficiency of the French Navy.

Now, of course, the whole thing had got out of hand, with a French cruiser and destroyer standing by at vast cost while twelve cold, hungry, and now worried Brits and South Africans stood their ground afraid to go down amongst the tough marines at whom they'd been hurling insults. In the end, the French sent in armed police paratroopers in helicopters. The offenders were slung in jail and subsequently deported. The French had the last laugh, because by the time the deported pranksters had bought their tickets to travel back to St. Lucia, the island had become independent, and they were denied entry into the new country.

SAINT LUCIA. The next island south is Saint Lucia, an island that changed hands fourteen times between the British and the French. It became so important that General Cornwallis in America, was ordered to send almost half his troops to Saint Lucia to defend it against the French. No doubt creating a situation that gave the American rebels under Washington a great opportunity, which they used to good effect. The capital Castries is still named after Admiral Castries, a French Governor. It is a pretty island and is now well known as a tourist spot. Most of the major hotels are on the north west of the island although the international airport is in the south. It has an open volcano near the town of Soufriere in the south west, and the well-known two Pitons which feature on the national flag, are just south of the town and over shadow it. The centre of the island is mountainous, as are most of the larger Caribbean islands, except for Barbados which is well to the east of the Windward Islands and is not generally included in the chain.

SAINT VINCENT & THE GRENADINES

St Vincent is about 38 sea miles from the bottom of St Lucia. It is best known for hosting many international banks which some have accused of dodgy practices. Like most of the Caribbean Islands, the country has been owned by the French and the English, finally ceded to Britain in 1783. Before then it was a haven for escaping slaves from Barbados and St Lucia. These mixed with the original owners, the Caribs, and created some problems for the British who eventually expelled them to a tiny island called Baliceaux just off the coast of Bequia. Subsequently they were moved to an island off the South American coast. At the time of writing, Baliceaux is for sale for thirty million dollars and is currently uninhabited. Saint Vincent has a large volcano in the north of the island that last erupted in 1979, causing huge damage to the area. There are a couple of stories about what happened on the island in my book 'Sailing on Silver'.

The first major island south is **Bequia**, an absolute delight particularly for sailors. Bequia has one of the largest natural harbours in the Antilles and because the bay is in the shape of a horseshoe facing west, it is an ideal anchorage. The people of Bequia are reputed to be the only people worldwide to be authorised by Greenpeace to catch whales. They usually only kill one a year and land it on a small island south of Bequia called Petit Nevis. There is much more of this story in 'Sailing on Silver'.

The Grenadines are several islands south of Saint Vincent and administered by them. The first major island is

Mustique, very well known for its inhabitants. Princess Margaret had a house there, as do the Rolling Stones and various other celebrities. The island was bought by Lord Glenconner, better known as Colin Tennant. Colin bought the island from a

447

Saint Vincent lawyer for £25,000 and turned it into one of the most exclusive places to live on the planet. I knew him well as I also knew the daughter of the lawyer who sold him the island. It has a small hotel there called the Cotton House and the place to eat is Basil's Bar in the bay on the west side of the island. There is an excellent book on Glenconnor's life, written by Nicholas Courtney and it is worth reading. I also knew the ex-chairman of the Mustique company which was owned by Colin Tennant, and it was run by one of the sons of Field Marshall Alexander. The last time I sailed there was in company of the man who put together the famous Indian temple in the garden of Colin Tennant's house. It is still there. If you are sailing in the Grenadines, Mustique is well worth a visit, but if you are anchoring opposite Basil's Bar, put out a rear anchor as it rolls during the night, often giving the impression that you have enjoyed yourself too much at Basil's Bar. There are a few stories about Mustique in Sailing on Silver.

There are some small uninhabited islands south of Mustique, but the next main one down is called

Canouan which is only about 3.5 miles long by 1.25 miles wide. It was sparsely inhabited when we were sailing there, but I understand that some progress has been made to make it attractive to tourists. It has a beautiful long bay with a sandy beach but was not good for yachts to moor.

Just south of Canouan is the island of

Mayreau which has a small, sheltered bay on its north end. It will only fit a few yachts in there, but it's great for swimming. There is also a small open-air restaurant that is open in the season.

The east of Mayreau are four small, inhabited islands which lead to **Tobago Cays**. This was a must to visit as it had a superb coral reef and very good holding for yachts. Unfortunately, last time we were there, the coral had died.

Union Island about 8 miles south west of Tobago Cays is where one can re-provision. The island is very French, although now under the auspices of St. Vincent. They have a small airport there which brings in day trippers. The airport is tucked under a hill, so aircraft must dive quite steeply to land, and if it goes too fast, you're in the sea.

Palm Island is situated to the east of Union and sports a small hotel and a few houses. It has arguably the nicest beach in the Antilles, it being pink in colour. One can moor there, but usually not for an overnight stay.

Petit St Vincent, is the last island in the Grenadine chain, belonging to St. Vincent. This island is completely taken over by a hotel. If you can afford to stay there, you are allocated a chalet and can order what you need by raising a flag outside your door. The restaurant is excellent. The last time we were there with our grandchildren we sat next to Daniel Craig with a partner, much to their excitement. The bay is enclosed by a reef at the eastern end with the island of Petit Martinique opposite, which is governed by the large Island of Grenada. The holding for yachts is very good and arguably one of the nicest anchorages in the Antilles.

Petit Martiniqe Despite the name, Petit Martinique is administered by Grenada. There used to be substantial smuggling between the islands north, but since the Communist government, defeated by the US forces, ensures the area is more settled. Sailing south one should book with the customs on the island, called

Jenny is just off the coast to the west, where there is an undersea volcano. The story is, should it erupt, it could wipe out most of the Antilles. I was informed that it is a similar size to the underground volcano at Yellowstone Park in the USA.

Carriacou where they have a customs post. There is also a hurricane hole there which one should head for if a hurricane is included in the weather forecast. There is also a pleasant bay there, called Tyrell Bay but most head straight for Grenada. Kick 'em

Grenada This island, named 'the spice island' is roughly the same size as St. Lucia or St. Vincent. We used to sail to the south of the island to a bay called Prickly Bay. It is many years since we sailed there, but we were warned not to anchor in Saint Georges, the capital. Since the US invasion, I am sure there have been many changes. The people are very welcoming and there are some first-class restaurants on the island.

They have a large airport there, which was built by the Cubans, and was the source of all the troubles.

My comments regarding the above island are based on the 1980's, and while we have sailed the Windward Islands in the late 90's and noted some changes there, we have not re visited the Leewards.

Barbados. Although part of the Lower Antilles it is about 180 miles east of Saint Lucia, and thus not normally considered part of the island chain. Barbados is outside the principal Atlantic hurricane belt. Its capital and largest city is Bridgetown. Inhabited by Kalinago people since the 13th century, and prior to that by other Amerindians, Barbados was visited by Spanish navigators in the late 15th century and claimed for the Spanish Crown. It first appeared in a Spanish map in 1511.The Portuguese Empire claimed the island between 1532 and 1536, but later abandoned it in 1620; with their only remnants being an introduction of wild boars for a good supply of meat whenever the island was visited, and to replenish their water supply. An English ship, the *Olive Blossom*, arrived in Barbados on 14 May 1625; its men took possession of it in the name of King James I. In 1627, the first permanent settlers arrived from England, and it became an English and later British colony. As a wealthy sugar colony, it became an English centre of the African slave trade until that trade was outlawed in 1807, with final emancipation of slaves in Barbados occurring over a period of years from 1833.

On 30 November 1966, Barbados became an independent state and Commonwealth realm with Elizabeth II as its queen. It has a population of 287,010 people, predominantly of African descent. Despite being classified as an Atlantic Island, Barbados is considered to be a part of the Caribbean, where it is ranked as a leading tourist destination. Of the tourists, 40% come from the UK, with the US and Canada making up the next large groups of visitors to the island. We have visited Barbados many times, but never sailed there.

The **Republic of Trinidad and Tobago** is the southernmost island country in the Caribbean. Consisting of the main islands Trinidad and Tobago, and numerous much smaller islands, it is situated 130 kilometres (81 miles) south of Grenada and 11 kilometres (6.8 miles) off the coast of northeastern Venezuela. It shares maritime boundaries with Barbados to the northeast, Grenada to the northwest, Guyana to the southeast, and Venezuela to the south and west.

The island of Trinidad was inhabited for centuries by native Amerindian peoples before becoming a colony in the Spanish Empire, following the arrival of Christopher Columbus in 1498. Spanish governor Don José María Chacón surrendered the island to a British fleet under the command of Sir Ralph Abercromby in 1797. During the same period, the island of Tobago changed hands among Spanish, British, French, Dutch and Courlander colonisers more times than any other island in the Caribbean. Trinidad and Tobago were ceded to Britain in 1802 under the Treaty of Amiens as separate states and unified in 1889. Trinidad and Tobago obtained independence in 1962, becoming a republic in 1976. Trinidad and Tobago have the third highest GDP per capita based on purchasing power parity (PPP) in the Americas after the United States and Canada. It is recognised by the World Bank as a

451

high-income economy Unlike most Caribbean nations and territories, which rely heavily on tourism, the Trinidadian economy is primarily industrial with an emphasis on petroleum and petrochemicals; much of the nation's wealth is derived from its large reserves of oil and natural gas.

We have never sailed to either Trinidad or Tobago but have visited to both islands. The Capitol of Tobago is called Scarborough.

Printed in Great Britain
by Amazon